Concise Applied Mathematics

Concise Applied Mathematics

Maureen Neal

Edward Arnold
A division of Hodder & Stoughton
LONDON NEW YORK MELBOURNE AUCKLAND

First published in Great Britain 1988

British Library Cataloguing in Publication Data

Neal, M.
Concise applied mathematics.
1. Applied mathematics
510

ISBN 0-7131-3650-2

Typeset in 10/11 pt Times by J. W. Arrowsmith Ltd. Printed and bound in Great Britain for Edward Arnold, the educational, academic and medical publishing division of Hodder and Stoughton Limited, 41 Bedford Square, London WC1B 3DQ, by J. W. Arrowsmith Ltd., Bristol.

Preface

The aim of this book is to present a concise but complete treatment of the content of the common core syllabus together with topics in applied mathematics for the majority of the A level examination boards.

The theory is covered briefly and illustrated by worked examples by the author and from the following examination boards:

AEB	Associated Examining Board
UL	University of London School Examination Board
JMB	Joint Matriculation Board

Some examples have been reproduced verbatim from the above boards: they accept no responsibility whatsoever for the accuracy or working in the answers given. The author is solely responsible for the solutions and they may not necessarily constitute the only solutions.

To prepare adequately for an A level examination in the subject students are advised to send for past papers from the board of their choice and work through them.

I am grateful to my husband and Mr Trevor Williams for their advice and their assistance in checking solutions during the preparation of this book and to the AEB, UL and JMB boards for their permission to reproduce questions from past examination papers.

Maureen Neal

Contents

Using this book

Objectives

The student should be able to:

(1) find any topic in applied mathematics plus a worked example to improve his or her understanding of that topic,
(2) demonstrate to himself or herself that improved understanding by solving a problem on that topic.

Structure of the book

This book is designed as a brief but complete guide to A level applied mathematics and covers topics required for a single or double A level in the subject.

Each chapter starts with a list of objectives and it is hoped that the student will be able to use these to identify the chapters he or she needs and discover at the end if he or she has reached those objectives. The theory is laid out briefly with simple worked examples. This is followed by worked examples from examining boards plus a few problems left for the student to attempt. The problems are given with an outline guide plus answers. The student could try them independently at first then use the guide if further assistance is required. Each chapter ends with a summary of its theoretical content.

Some examining boards now offer a core in applied mathematics plus options and others offer one or two complete applied mathematics papers. The exact content depends on the syllabus and also on whether mathematics is being offered as a single or double subject. The book is split into many small chapters, each covering one topic, so it is suitable for either type of syllabus and it should be easy for the student to determine which chapters he or she need cover.

First year undergraduate physics or engineering students may find the topics covered useful.

1 Basics

Newton's laws of motion

Newton's laws of motion are used to form a mathematical model of a physical situation, the study of which is called **mechanics**. Mechanics can be divided into:

dynamics—which is concerned with the physical causes of the motion,
statics—which is concerned with the condition under which no motion is apparent.

First law

A body continues in a state of rest or of uniform motion in a straight line unless acted upon by an external force.

This defines a **force** as that which tends to change the existing state of rest or uniform motion of a body. An external force acts from outside of a system, i.e. a collection of particles and/or bodies and the forces between them.

Second law

The rate of change of momentum of a body is proportional to the external force acting upon it and takes place along the line of action of the force.

Momentum is the product of mass and velocity. Therefore

$$\text{force } F = k\frac{\mathrm{d}}{\mathrm{d}t}(mv)$$

i.e. $$F = km\frac{\mathrm{d}v}{\mathrm{d}t}$$

where k is a constant of proportionality and is taken as 1 in the SI system of units used throughout this book (the basic units are mass in kilograms, length in metres and time in seconds). With $k = 1$ then 1 newton is the unit of force and is that magnitude of force needed to give a mass of 1 kg an acceleration of 1 m s^{-2}.

Third law

To every action there is an equal and opposite reaction.

In other words, when a body A exerts a force on a body B then B exerts an equal and opposite force on A.

Useful conventions and formulae

Conventions

Certain conventions are needed to simplify problems.

Friction force that occurs between two surfaces in contact and opposes potential or actual motion (see Fig. 1.1).

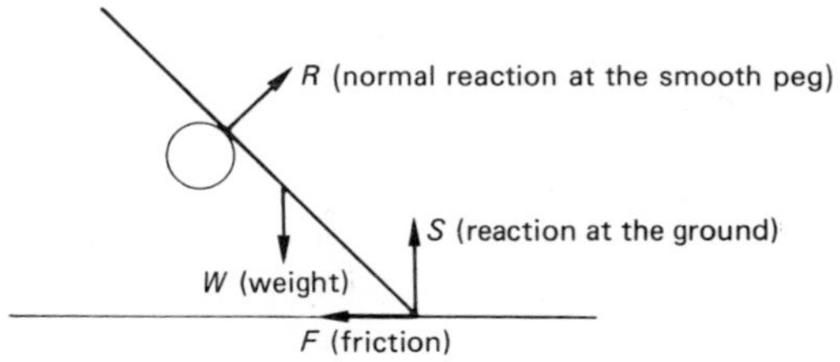

Figure 1.1

Hollow shell without thickness.

Lamina an object in two dimensions only, i.e. area.

Light a body is considered weightless.

Normal reaction always occurs between two bodies in contact and is perpendicular to the common tangent (see Fig. 1.1).

Particle a portion of matter represented by a point so its dimensions are neglected.

Rigid body one whose shape is unaltered by the forces acting upon it.

Smooth body without friction. N.B. air resistance is always ignored unless specifically stated.

Formulae

Some of the most commonly used formulae are given below. See Fig. 1.2.

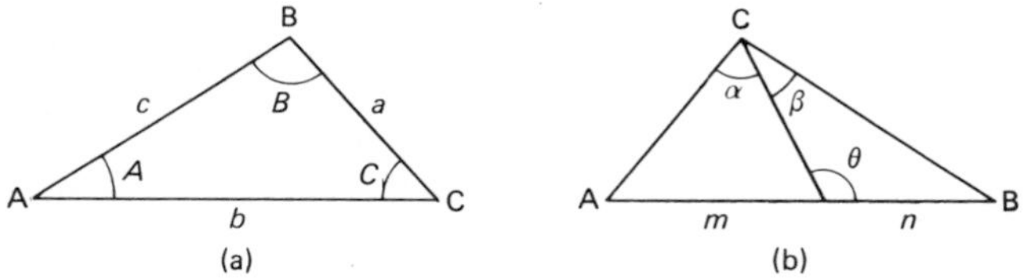

Figure 1.2

Sine rule

$$\frac{\sin A}{a} = \frac{\sin B}{b} = \frac{\sin C}{c}$$

Cosine rule

$$a^2 = b^2 + c^2 - 2bc \cos A$$

Cotangent rule

$$(m+n) \cot \theta = n \cot A - m \cot B = m \cot \alpha - n \cot \beta$$

Compound angle formulae

$$\sin(A \pm B) = \sin A \cos B \pm \cos A \sin B$$

$$\cos(A \pm B) = \cos A \cos B \pm \sin A \sin A$$

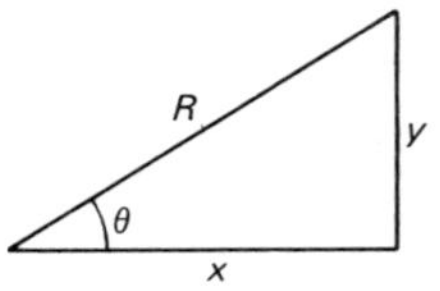

Figure 1.3

Identity

$$\sin^2 \theta + \cos^2 \theta = 1$$

In a right-angled triangle (Fig. 1.3),

$$R = \sqrt{(x^2 + y^2)}$$

$$\tan \theta = y/x$$

2
Introduction to vectors

Objectives

The student should be able to:

(1) define a scalar,
(2) define a vector,
(3) describe parallel, equal and opposite, and free and tied vectors,
(4) add, subtract and resolve a set of vectors,
(5) express a vector in cartesian vector notation,
(6) calculate the resultant or equilibriant of a set of vectors,
(7) find the position of the resultant of two vectors acting at a point,
(8) resolve a vector into two perpendicular components.

Scalar and vector quantities

A **scalar** quantity is specified by its magnitude only, e.g. a mass of 5 kg, a speed of 5 m s^{-1}, or a temperature of 80 °C.

A **vector** quantity is specified by its magnitude plus its direction, e.g. a velocity of 5 m s^{-1} due north or an acceleration of 10 m s^{-2} south east.

Vector notation

A vector is written $\underset{\sim}{a}$ or $\overrightarrow{AB}$ or $\underset{\sim}{A}$ or denoted by a bold faced letter $\boldsymbol{a}$ and is represented geometrically by a line segment drawn to scale in the direction of the vector with the direction indicated by an arrow (Fig. 2.1).

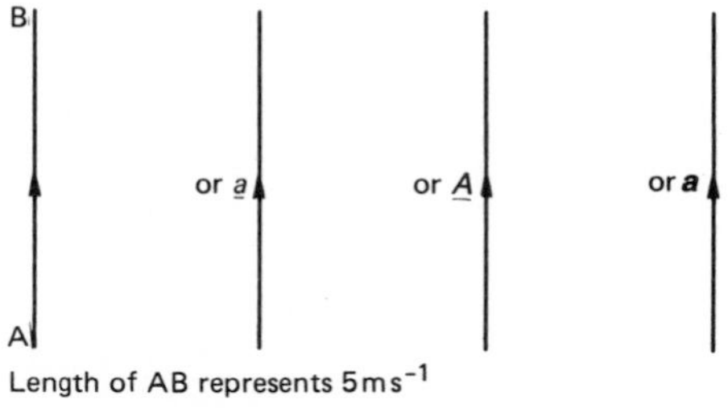

Figure 2.1

The modulus or magnitude of the vector of 5 m s^{-1} due N is 5 m s^{-1} and is written as

$$a = |\underset{\sim}{a}|$$

or $\quad AB = |\overrightarrow{AB}|$

or $\quad A = |\underset{\sim}{A}|$

or $\quad a = |\boldsymbol{a}|$

and the modulus is a scalar and is always positive.

Vector algebra

Parallel vectors

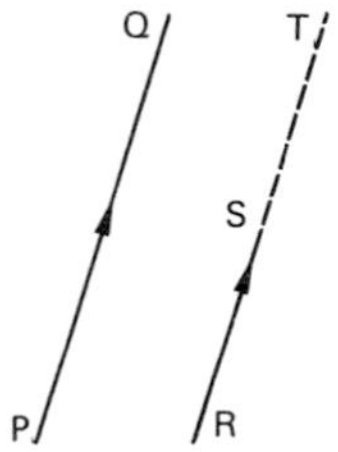

Figure 2.2

See Fig. 2.2. $\overrightarrow{PQ}$ is parallel to $\overrightarrow{RS}$ and the length of $\overrightarrow{PQ}$ is n times the length of $\overrightarrow{RS}$. If we produce RS to T then

$$PQ = RT$$

and $RT = nRS$

However, PQ and RT are identical in magnitude, direction and sense and therefore must represent equal vectors. Hence

$$\overrightarrow{PQ} = \overrightarrow{RT}$$

and $\overrightarrow{PQ} = n\overrightarrow{RS}$

Equal and opposite vectors

$\overrightarrow{PQ}$ is equal and opposite to $\overrightarrow{QP}$. Therefore

$$\overrightarrow{PQ} + \overrightarrow{QP} = \boldsymbol{0}$$

or $\quad \overrightarrow{PQ} = -\overrightarrow{QP}$

$\overrightarrow{PQ} + \overrightarrow{QP}$ is defined as the null or zero vector represented by $\boldsymbol{0}$. It has a magnitude of zero but its direction is not defined.

Free vectors

If the line of action of a vector is specified it is a **tied** vector, i.e. tied to that particular line; otherwise it is a **free** vector.

Addition of vectors

Consider a displacement vector $\overrightarrow{AB}$ due east followed by a displacement vector $\overrightarrow{BC}$ north east. The vector $\overrightarrow{AC}$ represents the resultant vector displacement as shown in Fig. 2.3. Therefore

$$\overrightarrow{AC} = \overrightarrow{AB} + \overrightarrow{BC}$$

$\overrightarrow{AC}$ is the resultant of $\overrightarrow{AB}$ plus $\overrightarrow{BC}$ or is equivalent to $\overrightarrow{AB} + \overrightarrow{BC}$.

If a third displacement vector is drawn from C to D then

$$\overrightarrow{AD} = \overrightarrow{AC} + \overrightarrow{CD} = \overrightarrow{AB} + \overrightarrow{BD}$$

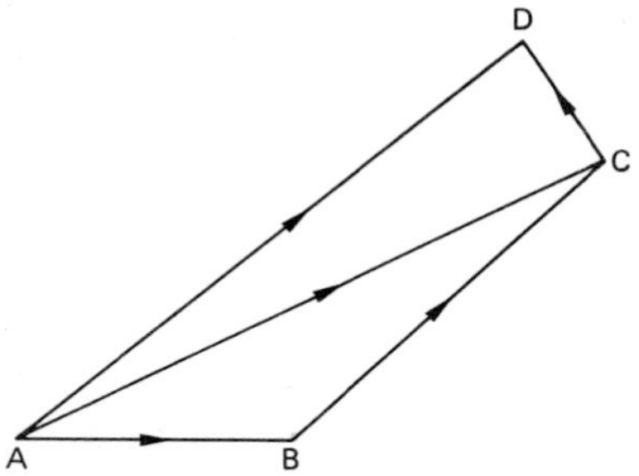

Figure 2.3

$$\overrightarrow{AC}+\overrightarrow{CD}=(\overrightarrow{AB}+\overrightarrow{BC})+\overrightarrow{CD}$$

$$\overrightarrow{AB}+\overrightarrow{BD}=\overrightarrow{AB}+(\overrightarrow{BC}+\overrightarrow{CD})$$

and is **associative**.

Consider the parallelogram ABCD (Fig. 2.4).

$$\overrightarrow{AC}=\overrightarrow{AB}+\overrightarrow{BC}$$

and $\overrightarrow{AC}=\overrightarrow{AD}+\overrightarrow{DC}$

but $\overrightarrow{AD}=\overrightarrow{BC}$ and $\overrightarrow{DC}=\overrightarrow{AB}$ because ABCD is a parallelogram. Therefore

$$\overrightarrow{AC}=\overrightarrow{BC}+\overrightarrow{AB}$$

and is **commutative**.

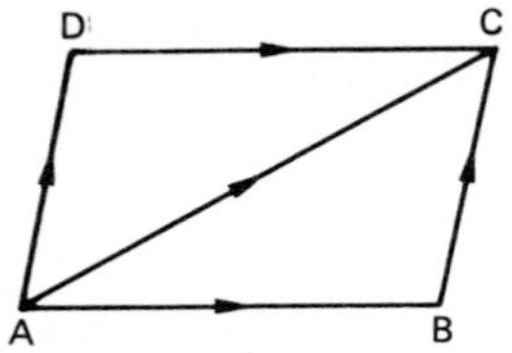

Figure 2.4

Subtraction of vectors

The vector $-\boldsymbol{b}$ is defined as a vector whose modulus is the same as that of $\boldsymbol{b}$ but acts in the opposite direction to $\boldsymbol{b}$ (Fig. 2.5). Then

$$\boldsymbol{a}-\boldsymbol{b}=\boldsymbol{a}+(-\boldsymbol{b})$$

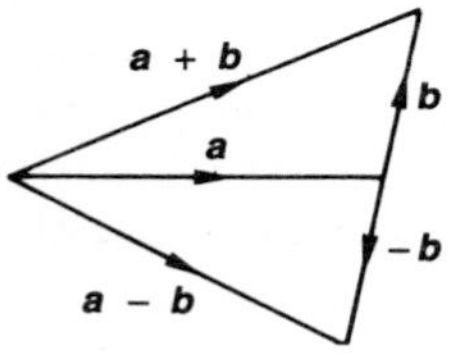

Figure 2.5

Example 2.1

What is the resultant of displacement vectors of 6 m north, 3 m east and 4 m south?

See Fig. 2.6.

$$\overrightarrow{AD}=\overrightarrow{AB}+\overrightarrow{BC}+\overrightarrow{CD}$$

In $\triangle$ADE, DE = 2 m and AE = 3 m. Therefore

$$AD^2=DE^2+AE^2=4+9$$

$$\underline{AD=\sqrt{13}\text{ m at N }\tan^{-1}(3/2)\text{ E}}$$

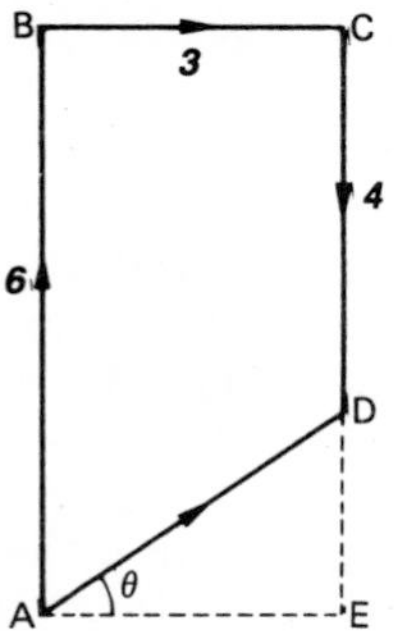

Figure 2.6

Example 2.2

ABCDEF is a regular hexagon in which $\overrightarrow{AB}$ represents a vector $\boldsymbol{a}$ and $\overrightarrow{BC}$ a vector $\boldsymbol{b}$ (Fig. 2.7). Express in terms of $\boldsymbol{a}$ and $\boldsymbol{b}$ the vectors $\overrightarrow{AD}$, $\overrightarrow{FE}$, $\overrightarrow{EF}$, $\overrightarrow{AF}$ and $\overrightarrow{BE}$.

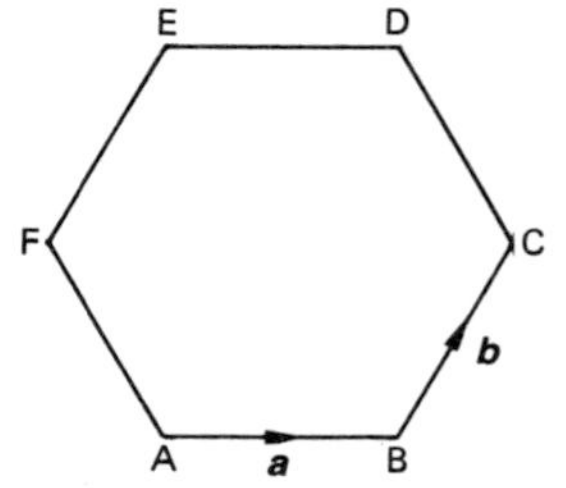

Figure 2.7

$\overrightarrow{FE}$ is equal and parallel to $\overrightarrow{BC}$, i.e.

$$\overrightarrow{FE} = \underline{\boldsymbol{b}}$$

$\overrightarrow{AD}$ is twice as long as $\overrightarrow{BC}$ and parallel to it, i.e.

$$\overrightarrow{AD} = \underline{2\boldsymbol{b}}$$

$\overrightarrow{EF}$ is equal and opposite to $\overrightarrow{FE}$, i.e.

$$\overrightarrow{EF} = \underline{-\boldsymbol{b}}$$

$$\overrightarrow{DC} = \overrightarrow{DA} + \overrightarrow{AB} + \overrightarrow{BC}$$

$$= -2\boldsymbol{b} + \boldsymbol{a} + \boldsymbol{b} = \boldsymbol{a} - \boldsymbol{b}$$

$$\overrightarrow{AF} = \overrightarrow{CD} = \underline{-\boldsymbol{a} + \boldsymbol{b}}$$

$$\overrightarrow{BE} = 2\overrightarrow{AF} = \underline{-2\boldsymbol{a} + 2\boldsymbol{b}}$$

Summary of the laws of vector algebra

Here $\boldsymbol{P}$, $\boldsymbol{Q}$ and $\boldsymbol{R}$ are vectors and r and s are scalars.

(1) $\boldsymbol{P} + \boldsymbol{Q} = \boldsymbol{Q} + \boldsymbol{P}$: Commutative law for addition.
(2) $\boldsymbol{P} + (\boldsymbol{Q} + \boldsymbol{R}) = (\boldsymbol{P} + \boldsymbol{Q}) + \boldsymbol{R}$: Associative law for addition.
(3) $r(s\boldsymbol{P}) = rs(\boldsymbol{P}) = r(s\boldsymbol{P})$: Associative law for multiplication.
(4) $(r+s)\boldsymbol{P} = r\boldsymbol{P} + s\boldsymbol{P}$: Distributive law.
(5) $r(\boldsymbol{P} + \boldsymbol{Q}) = r\boldsymbol{P} + r\boldsymbol{Q}$: Distributive law.

Cartesian vector notation

In this notation $\boldsymbol{i}$ is a vector of magnitude one unit in the direction $0x$, $\boldsymbol{j}$ is a vector of magnitude one unit in the direction $0y$, and $\boldsymbol{k}$ is a vector of magnitude one unit in the direction $0z$, where $0x$, $0y$ and $0z$ are the rectangular cartesian axes (Fig. 2.8).

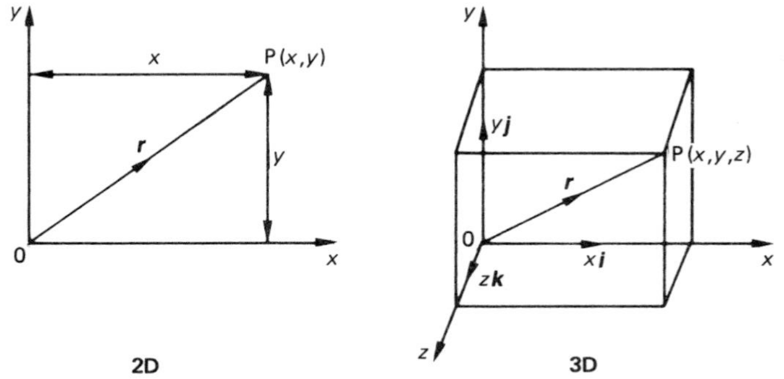

Figure 2.8

Example 2.3

Forces $\boldsymbol{A}$, $\boldsymbol{B}$, $\boldsymbol{C}$ and $\boldsymbol{D}$ of magnitude 3, 4, 5 and $3\sqrt{2}$ N respectively act as shown in Fig. 2.9. Express each vector in terms of $\boldsymbol{i}$ and $\boldsymbol{j}$.

$$\boldsymbol{A} = 3\cos 45^\circ\,\boldsymbol{i} + 3\cos 45^\circ\,\boldsymbol{j} = \underline{\frac{3}{\sqrt{2}}\boldsymbol{i} + \frac{3}{\sqrt{2}}\boldsymbol{j}}$$

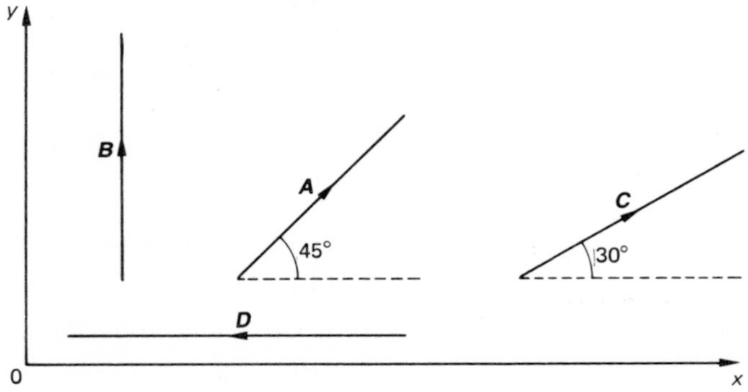

Figure 2.9

$\boldsymbol{B} = \underline{0\boldsymbol{i} + 4\boldsymbol{j}}$

$\boldsymbol{C} = -5 \cos 30° \, \boldsymbol{i} - 5 \sin 30° \, \boldsymbol{j} = \underline{-5 \frac{\sqrt{3}}{2} \boldsymbol{i} - \frac{5}{2} \boldsymbol{j}}$

$\boldsymbol{D} = \underline{-3\sqrt{2}\boldsymbol{i} + 0\boldsymbol{j}}$

Methods for determination of resultant vectors

A single vector $\boldsymbol{R}$ that is equivalent to a set of vectors is the resultant of those vectors.

Resultant of two perpendicular vectors of magnitudes P and Q

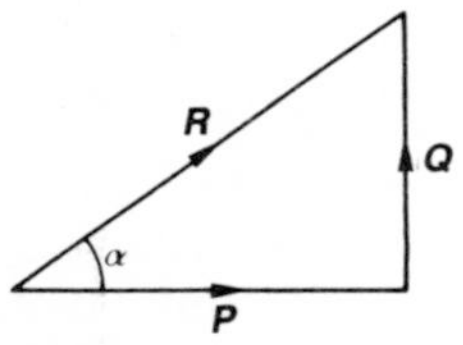

Figure 2.10

See Fig. 2.10. If R is the magnitude of the resultant then $R^2 = P^2 + Q^2$.

$R = \sqrt{(P^2 + Q^2)}$ and $\tan \alpha = Q/P$ between R and P.

Resultant of two vectors of magnitudes p and q inclined at an angle θ

See Fig. 2.11. If both vectors point inwards towards O or both point outwards from O then the angle between them is θ but if one vector points inwards and the other outwards then the angle between them is $180° - \theta$ and the resultant is different in magnitude for case (c) compared with cases (a) and (b).

The Triangle law governs the addition of these vectors: if the two vectors $\boldsymbol{p}$ and $\boldsymbol{q}$ are represented by the sides $\overrightarrow{PQ}$ and $\overrightarrow{QR}$

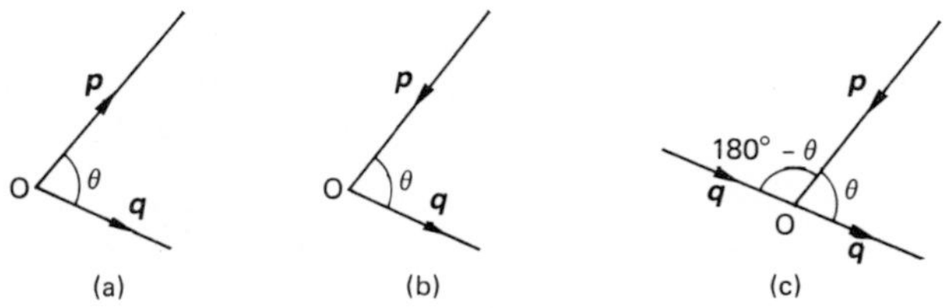

Figure 2.11

respectively of the triangle PQR then their resultant vector $\boldsymbol{r}$ is represented by the side $\overrightarrow{PR}$. Hence $\overrightarrow{PR}$ is equivalent to $\overrightarrow{PQ}+\overrightarrow{QR}$.

Figure 2.12(a), (b) and (c) show the resultant of the vectors drawn in Fig. 2.11(a), (b) and (c) respectively, $\boldsymbol{r}_1=-\boldsymbol{r}_2$ but $\boldsymbol{r}_1 \neq \boldsymbol{r}_3$ and $\boldsymbol{r}_2 \neq \boldsymbol{r}_3$.

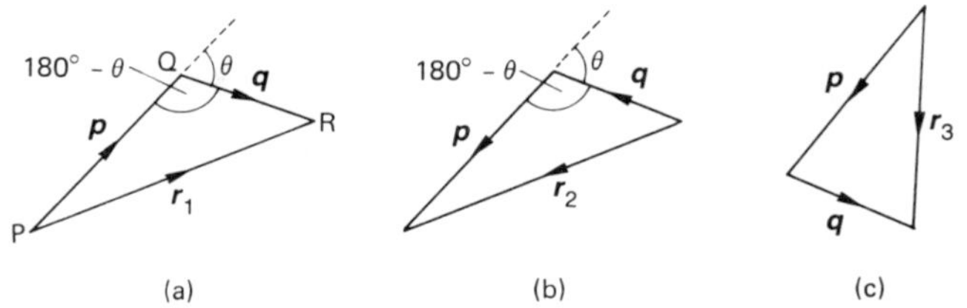

Figure 2.12

Where the angle between the vectors is θ then from the cosine formula

$$r^2=p^2+q^2-2pq\cos(180°-\theta)$$

and is the same for r_1 and r_2.

$$r^2=p^2+q^2+2pq\cos\theta$$

The direction of the resultant is given by

$$\frac{\sin(180°-\theta)}{r}=\frac{\sin\widehat{QPR}}{q}=\frac{\sin\widehat{QRP}}{p}$$

Resultant of more than two vectors

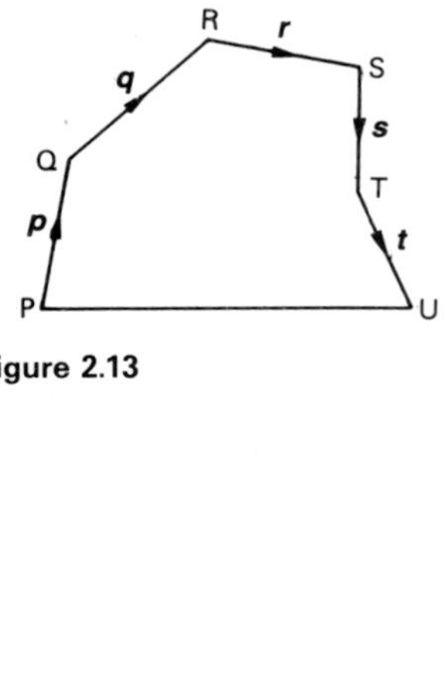

Figure 2.13

These will generalise to the polygon rule: if vectors $\boldsymbol{p}$, $\boldsymbol{q}$, $\boldsymbol{r}$, $\boldsymbol{s}$, $\boldsymbol{t}$, ... are represented completely by the sides $\overrightarrow{PQ}$, $\overrightarrow{QR}$, $\overrightarrow{RS}$, $\overrightarrow{ST}$, $\overrightarrow{TU}$, ... of the polygon PQRSTU ... (Fig. 2.13) then their resultant vector is represented completely by the side of the polygon needed to close it.

Drawing to scale gives a solution but more precise values are given by calculation. If $\boldsymbol{p}=x_p\boldsymbol{i}+y_p\boldsymbol{j}+z_p\boldsymbol{k}$

$$\begin{aligned}\text{resultant}=&(x_p+x_q+x_r+x_s+x_t)\boldsymbol{i}\\&+(y_p+y_q+y_r+y_s+y_t)\boldsymbol{j}\\&+(z_p+z_q+z_r+z_s+z_t)\boldsymbol{k}\end{aligned}$$

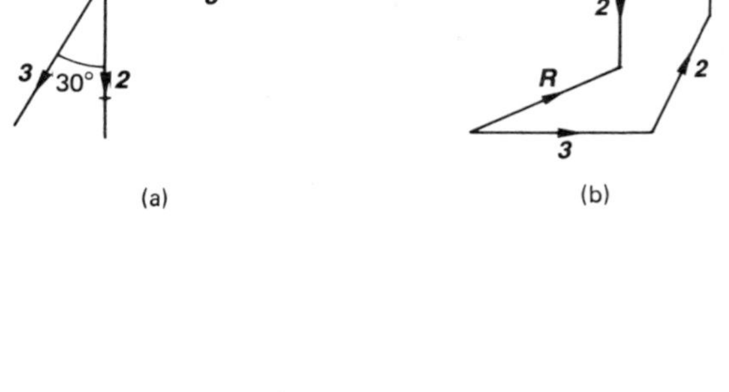

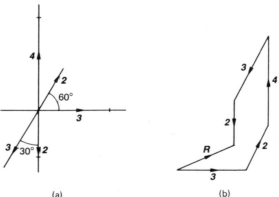

Figure 2.14

For example, consider the five vectors as shown in Fig. 2.14: 4 units N, 2 units 60° N of E, 3 units E, 2 units south and 3 units 30° W of S.

$$\boldsymbol{R} = 3\boldsymbol{i} + 2\cos 60°\,\boldsymbol{i} + 2\sin 60°\,\boldsymbol{j} + 4\boldsymbol{j} - 2\boldsymbol{j} - 3\cos 60°\,\boldsymbol{i} - 3\sin 60°\,\boldsymbol{j}$$

$$= 2.5\boldsymbol{i} + 1.13\boldsymbol{j}$$

Resolution of a vector

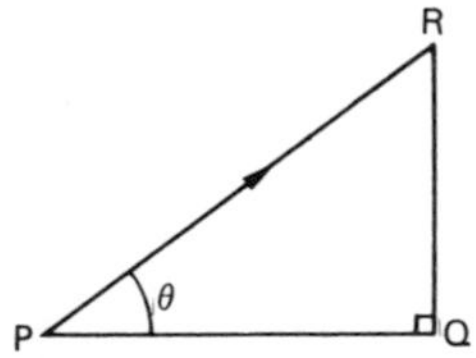

Figure 2.15

When a vector has been replaced by an equivalent set of components it has been resolved. See Fig. 2.15.

$$\overrightarrow{PQ} = \overrightarrow{PR}\cos\theta$$

$$\overrightarrow{QR} = \overrightarrow{PR}\sin\theta$$

Example 2.4

A weight of 20 N is supported by a light inextensible string. The weight is pulled aside by a horizontal force of 20 N until the string makes an angle of 30° with the downward vertical. Draw a diagram showing the forces acting on the weight and resolve each of these horizontally and vertically in the senses Ox and Oy as shown.

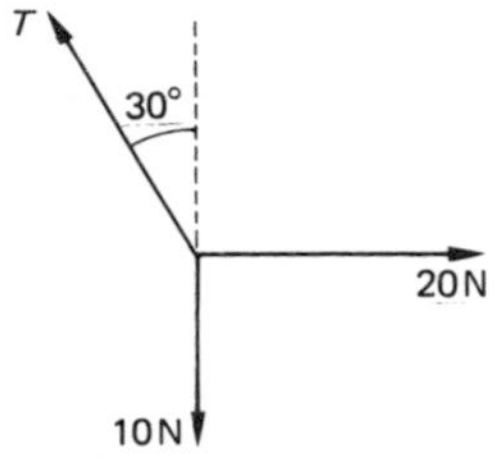

Figure 2.16

See Fig. 2.16. The components of the forces are tabulated below.

	Components	
Force	Parallel to Ox	Parallel to Oy
10 N	0 N	−10 N
20 N	20 N	0 N
T	$-T\sin 30°$	$T\cos 30°$

Unit vector

A unit vector $\hat{\boldsymbol{x}}$ in the direction of a vector $\boldsymbol{x}$ is defined as

$$\hat{\boldsymbol{x}} = \frac{1}{x}(\boldsymbol{x})$$

or $\boldsymbol{x} = x(\hat{\boldsymbol{x}})$

It has magnitude of one or unity.

In general, if $\boldsymbol{x} = a\boldsymbol{i} + b\boldsymbol{j} + c\boldsymbol{k}$ then

$$|\boldsymbol{x}| = \sqrt{(a^2+b^2+c^2)} = x$$

$$\hat{\boldsymbol{x}} = \frac{a}{\sqrt{(a^2+b^2+c^2)}}\boldsymbol{i} + \frac{b}{\sqrt{(a^2+b^2+c^2)}}\boldsymbol{j} + \frac{c}{\sqrt{(a^2+b^2+c^2)}}\boldsymbol{k}$$

For example, if $\boldsymbol{a} = 2\boldsymbol{i} + 3\boldsymbol{j} + \boldsymbol{k}$, then

$$\hat{\boldsymbol{a}} = \frac{2}{\sqrt{14}}\boldsymbol{i} + \frac{3}{\sqrt{14}}\boldsymbol{j} + \frac{1}{\sqrt{14}}\boldsymbol{k}.$$

A vector used to specify the direction of another vector is called a **direction** vector. The unit vector can be used in this way and is often very useful in problems.

Resultant vector theorem

Suppose that two vectors are represented by $p\overrightarrow{OA}$ and $q\overrightarrow{OB}$ in magnitude and direction as shown in Fig. 2.17. Their resultant passes through some point C along AB. Now

$$p\overrightarrow{OA} = p\overrightarrow{OC} + p\overrightarrow{CA}$$

and $q\overrightarrow{OB} = q\overrightarrow{OC} + q\overrightarrow{CB}$

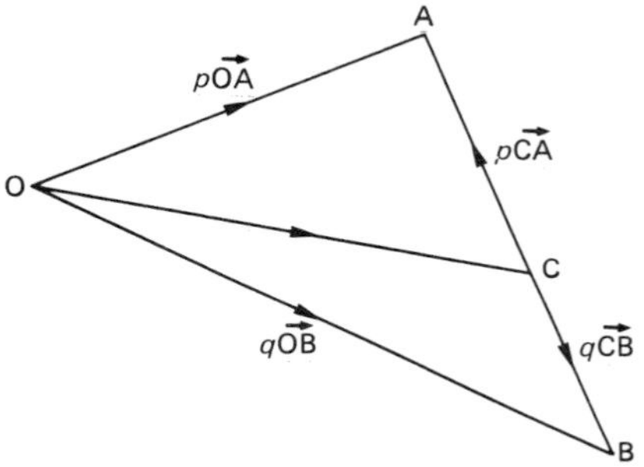

Figure 2.17

If OC is the line of action of the resultant so that it has no component along AB then

$$p\overrightarrow{CA} = q\overrightarrow{BC}$$

and CA : BC $= q : p$

Therefore

$$p\overrightarrow{OA} + q\overrightarrow{OB} = (p+q)\overrightarrow{OC} + p\overrightarrow{CA} + q\overrightarrow{CB}$$

so $p\overrightarrow{OA} + q\overrightarrow{OB} = (p+q)\overrightarrow{OC}$

Hence the resultant of forces represented completely by $p\overrightarrow{OA}$ and $q\overrightarrow{OB}$ is represented completely by $(p+q)\overrightarrow{OC}$, where C divides AB in the ratio $q:p$ so that AC : CB $= q:p$.

Example 2.5

At time $t=0$ two particles are set in motion in the (x, y) plane. Initially, P is at A $(1, 0)$ and Q is at B $(0, 8)$. The particle P moves with a constant speed of $5\ \mathrm{m\,s^{-1}}$ parallel to the line $3y=4x$ and Q moves with a constant speed of $4\ \mathrm{m\,s^{-1}}$ parallel to the line $y=-\lambda x$, the sense of motion of both P and Q being that in which x is increasing. Given that $\boldsymbol{i}$ and $\boldsymbol{j}$ are unit vectors in the direction of x increasing and y increasing respectively, show that the unit vectors in the directions of motion of P and Q are

$$\tfrac{3}{5}\boldsymbol{i} + \tfrac{4}{5}\boldsymbol{j}$$

and $\dfrac{1}{\sqrt{(1+\lambda^2)}}\boldsymbol{i} - \dfrac{\lambda}{\sqrt{(1+\lambda^2)}}\boldsymbol{j}$

respectively.

Determine in the form $a\boldsymbol{i}+b\boldsymbol{j}$

(a) the velocities of P and Q,
(b) the vectors $\overrightarrow{AP}$, $\overrightarrow{BQ}$ and $\overrightarrow{PQ}$ at time t.

Show that, if P and Q meet, λ must satisfy the equation

$$7\sqrt{(1+\lambda^2)}=8-\lambda$$

Verify that $\lambda=-3/4$ is a solution of this equation and for this value of λ find the time when P and Q meet. (AEB J82)

For P,

$$y=\tfrac{4}{3}x$$

$$\boldsymbol{V}_P=x\boldsymbol{i}+y\boldsymbol{j}=x\boldsymbol{i}+\tfrac{4}{3}x\boldsymbol{j}$$

so $$\hat{\boldsymbol{V}}_P=\frac{\boldsymbol{V}_P}{|\boldsymbol{V}_P|}=\left[\frac{x}{\sqrt{\left(x^2+\frac{16x^2}{9}\right)}}\right]\boldsymbol{i}+\frac{4}{3}\left[\frac{x}{\sqrt{\left(x^2+\frac{16x^2}{9}\right)}}\right]\boldsymbol{j}$$

$$\hat{\boldsymbol{V}}_P=\tfrac{3}{5}\boldsymbol{i}+\tfrac{4}{5}\boldsymbol{j}$$

For Q,

$$y=-\lambda x$$

$$\boldsymbol{V}_Q=x\boldsymbol{i}+y\boldsymbol{j}=x\boldsymbol{i}-\lambda x\boldsymbol{j}$$

so

$$\hat{\boldsymbol{V}}_Q=\frac{\boldsymbol{V}_Q}{|\boldsymbol{V}_Q|}=\left[\frac{x}{\sqrt{(x^2+\lambda^2x^2)}}\right]\boldsymbol{i}-\left[\frac{\lambda x}{\sqrt{(x^2+\lambda^2x^2)}}\right]\boldsymbol{j}$$

$$=\frac{1}{\sqrt{(1+\lambda^2)}}\boldsymbol{i}-\frac{\lambda}{\sqrt{(1+\lambda^2)}}\boldsymbol{j}$$

$$\boldsymbol{V}_P=|\boldsymbol{V}_P|\hat{\boldsymbol{V}}_P=\underline{3\boldsymbol{i}+4\boldsymbol{j}}$$

and $$\boldsymbol{V}_Q=|\boldsymbol{V}_Q|\hat{\boldsymbol{V}}_Q=\underline{\frac{4}{\sqrt{(1+\lambda^2)}}\boldsymbol{i}-\frac{4\lambda}{\sqrt{(1+\lambda^2)}}\boldsymbol{j}}$$

Now $\overrightarrow{OP}$ at time $t=\overrightarrow{OP}$ at time $0+\boldsymbol{V}_P t$, i.e.

$$\overrightarrow{OP}_t=(3t+1)\boldsymbol{i}+4t\boldsymbol{j} \qquad (1)$$

and $\overrightarrow{OQ}$ at time $t=\overrightarrow{OQ}$ at time $0+\boldsymbol{V}_Q t$, i.e.

$$\overrightarrow{OQ}_t=\frac{4t}{\sqrt{(1+\lambda^2)}}\boldsymbol{i}+\left[8-\frac{4\lambda t}{\sqrt{(1+\lambda^2)}}\right]\boldsymbol{j} \qquad (2)$$

If P and Q meet at some time t then $\overrightarrow{OP}_t=\overrightarrow{OQ}_t$. Comparing coefficients of $\boldsymbol{i}$ in equations (1) and (2),

$$3t+1=\frac{4t}{\sqrt{(1+\lambda^2)}}$$

Rearranging and multiplying by 8,

$$8=\frac{32t}{\sqrt{(1+\lambda^2)}}-24t$$

Comparing coefficients of $\boldsymbol{j}$ in equations (1) and (2),

$$8-\frac{4\lambda t}{\sqrt{(1+\lambda^2)}}=4t$$

Therefore

$$4t+\frac{4\lambda t}{\sqrt{(1+\lambda^2)}}=\frac{32t}{\sqrt{(1+\lambda^2)}}-24t$$

Multiplying by $\sqrt{(1+\lambda^2)}$ and collecting terms,

$$32-4\lambda=28\sqrt{(1+\lambda^2)}$$

so $\quad 8-\lambda=7\sqrt{(1+\lambda^2)}$

Squaring both sides,

$$48\lambda^2+16\lambda-15=0$$

Substituting $\lambda=-3/4$ gives $27-12-15=0$ so $\lambda=-3/4$ is a solution of this equation.

When P and Q meet the coefficients of $\boldsymbol{i}$ are equal so

$$\frac{4t}{\sqrt{(1+\lambda^2)}}=3t+1$$

Substituting $\lambda=-3/4$,

$$\frac{16t}{5}=3t+1$$

Therefore

$$t=5\text{ s}$$

i.e. P and Q meet after 5 seconds.

Example 2.6

The position vectors of A and C with respect to the origin O are $4\boldsymbol{i}+3\boldsymbol{j}$ and $3\boldsymbol{i}-4\boldsymbol{j}$ respectively. Show that $|\overrightarrow{OA}|=|\overrightarrow{OC}|$ and find the vector $\overrightarrow{OB}$, given that OABC is a square. Forces of magnitudes 10 N, $10\sqrt{2}$ N and 10 N act along $\overrightarrow{OA}$, $\overrightarrow{BO}$ and $\overrightarrow{CO}$ respectively. Express each of these forces as a vector in terms of $\boldsymbol{i}$ and $\boldsymbol{j}$. Hence calculate the magnitude of this resultant and show that it acts along CO.

It is always useful in vector problems to draw a diagram (Fig. 2.18).

$$|\overrightarrow{OA}|=\sqrt{(4^2+3^2)}=5$$

$$|\overrightarrow{OC}|=\sqrt{(3^2+4^2)}=5$$

Therefore

$$|\overrightarrow{OA}|=|\overrightarrow{OC}|$$

OABC is a square. Therefore

$$\overrightarrow{OA}=\overrightarrow{CB}$$

$$\overrightarrow{OB}=\overrightarrow{OC}+\overrightarrow{CB}=\overrightarrow{OC}+\overrightarrow{OA}$$

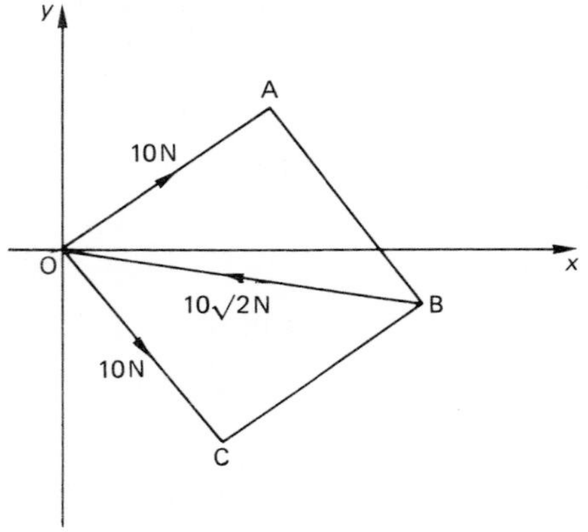

Figure 2.18

so $\overrightarrow{OB} = \underline{7\boldsymbol{i} - \boldsymbol{j}}$

$\widehat{OA} = \frac{4}{5}\boldsymbol{i} + \frac{3}{5}\boldsymbol{j}$

and $10\widehat{OA} = \underline{8\boldsymbol{i} + 6\boldsymbol{j}}$

$|\overrightarrow{OB}| = \sqrt{(7^2 + 1)} = \sqrt{50} = 5\sqrt{2}$

Similarly

$$\widehat{OB} = \frac{7}{10\sqrt{2}}\boldsymbol{i} - \frac{1}{10\sqrt{2}}\boldsymbol{j}$$

and $10\sqrt{2}\,\widehat{BO} = -14\boldsymbol{i} + 2\boldsymbol{j}$

Similarly

$\widehat{OC} = \frac{3}{5}\boldsymbol{i} - \frac{4}{5}\boldsymbol{j}$

$\widehat{CO} = -\frac{3}{5}\boldsymbol{i} + \frac{4}{5}\boldsymbol{j}$

and $10\widehat{CO} = \underline{-6 + 8\boldsymbol{j}}$

The resultant $\boldsymbol{R}$ is given by

$$\boldsymbol{R} = 10\widehat{OA} + 10\sqrt{2}\widehat{BO} + 10\widehat{CO}$$
$$= 8\boldsymbol{i} + 6\boldsymbol{j} - 14\boldsymbol{i} + 2\boldsymbol{j} - 6\boldsymbol{i} + 8\boldsymbol{j} = -12\boldsymbol{i} + 16\boldsymbol{j}$$

so $|\boldsymbol{R}| = \sqrt{(16^2 + 12^2)} = \underline{20}$

Now

$$\hat{\boldsymbol{R}} = -\tfrac{12}{20}\boldsymbol{i} + \tfrac{16}{20}\boldsymbol{j} = -\tfrac{3}{5}\boldsymbol{i} + \tfrac{4}{5}\boldsymbol{j} = \widehat{CO}$$

Hence $\boldsymbol{R}$ acts along CO as they both have the same unit vector.

Example 2.7

Referred to a fixed origin O and non-parallel vectors $\boldsymbol{a}$ and $\boldsymbol{b}$, six points A, B, C, D, E and F have position vectors $12\boldsymbol{a}$, $(8\boldsymbol{a} + 8\boldsymbol{b})$, $24\boldsymbol{b}$, $-4\boldsymbol{b}$, $(-8\boldsymbol{a} - 2\boldsymbol{b})$ and $-16\boldsymbol{a}$ respectively.

(a) Find in terms of $\boldsymbol{a}$ and $\boldsymbol{b}$ the vectors $\overrightarrow{AB}$ and $\overrightarrow{AC}$.
(b) Show that A, B and C are collinear and determine the ratio AB : AC.
(c) Show that D, E and F are collinear.

The point P is on AE such that $AP/AE = \lambda$ $(0 < \lambda < 1)$. Obtain expressions in terms of $\boldsymbol{a}$, $\boldsymbol{b}$ and λ for the vectors $\overrightarrow{AP}$ and $\overrightarrow{OP}$. Obtain similarly an expression involving $\boldsymbol{a}$, $\boldsymbol{b}$ and μ for the vector $\overrightarrow{OQ}$, where Q is on DB and $DQ/DB = \mu$ $(0 < \mu < 1)$. Hence determine the position vector of the point of intersection of DB and AE. (AEB N82)

It is helpful to draw a possible diagram (Fig. 2.19) giving $\boldsymbol{a}$ and $\boldsymbol{b}$ arbitrary magnitudes and directions.

(a) $\overrightarrow{OA} = 12\boldsymbol{a}$

$\overrightarrow{OB} = 8\boldsymbol{a} + 8\boldsymbol{b}$

$\overrightarrow{OC} = 24\boldsymbol{b}$

$\overrightarrow{AB} = \overrightarrow{OB} - \overrightarrow{OA} = 8\boldsymbol{a} + 8\boldsymbol{b} - 12\boldsymbol{a} = 8\boldsymbol{b} - 4\boldsymbol{a} = \underline{4(2\boldsymbol{b} - \boldsymbol{a})}$

$\overrightarrow{AC} = \overrightarrow{OC} - \overrightarrow{OA} = 24\boldsymbol{b} - 12\boldsymbol{a} = \underline{12(2\boldsymbol{b} - \boldsymbol{a})}$

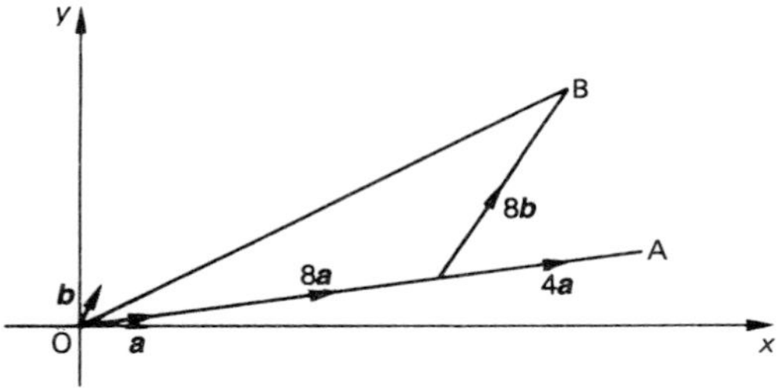

Figure 2.19

(b) $\overrightarrow{AB}$ and $\overrightarrow{AC}$ are multiples of the direction vector $2\boldsymbol{b} - \boldsymbol{a}$. Therefore A, B and C are collinear (they have a point A in common so are not parallel).

$$\frac{|\overrightarrow{AB}|}{|\overrightarrow{AC}|} = \frac{4|2\boldsymbol{b} - \boldsymbol{a}|}{12|2\boldsymbol{b} - \boldsymbol{a}|}$$

Therefore

$$\frac{AB}{AC} = \frac{1}{\underline{3}}$$

(c) $\overrightarrow{OD} = -4\boldsymbol{b}$ $\quad \overrightarrow{OE} = -8\boldsymbol{a} - 2\boldsymbol{b}$ $\quad \overrightarrow{OF} = -16\boldsymbol{a}$

$\overrightarrow{DE} = \overrightarrow{OE} = \overrightarrow{OD} = -8\boldsymbol{a} - 2\boldsymbol{b} + 4\boldsymbol{b} = -8\boldsymbol{a} + 2\boldsymbol{b} = 2(\boldsymbol{b} - 4\boldsymbol{a})$

$\overrightarrow{DF} = \overrightarrow{OF} - \overrightarrow{OD} = -16\boldsymbol{a} + 4\boldsymbol{b} = 4(\boldsymbol{b} - 4\boldsymbol{a})$

$\overrightarrow{DE}$ and $\overrightarrow{DF}$ are multiples of the direction vector $\boldsymbol{b} - 4\boldsymbol{a}$ and have a common point and therefore D, E and F are collinear.

$\overrightarrow{AE} = \overrightarrow{OE} - \overrightarrow{OA} = -8\boldsymbol{a} - 2\boldsymbol{b} - 12\boldsymbol{a} = -20\boldsymbol{a} - 2\boldsymbol{b}$

and $\overrightarrow{AP} = \lambda\overrightarrow{AE} = \underline{-20\lambda\boldsymbol{a} - 2\lambda\boldsymbol{b}}$

$\overrightarrow{OP} = \overrightarrow{OA} + \overrightarrow{AP} = 12\boldsymbol{a} - 20\lambda\boldsymbol{a} - 2\lambda\boldsymbol{b} = \underline{(12 - 20\lambda)\boldsymbol{a} - 2\lambda\boldsymbol{b}}$

Similarly

$\overrightarrow{DQ} = \mu\overrightarrow{DB}$

and $\overrightarrow{DB} = \overrightarrow{OB} - \overrightarrow{OD} = 8\boldsymbol{a} + 8\boldsymbol{b} + 4\boldsymbol{b} = 8\boldsymbol{a} + 12\boldsymbol{b}$

so $\overrightarrow{DQ} = 8\mu\boldsymbol{a} + 12\mu\boldsymbol{b}$

$$\overrightarrow{OQ} = \overrightarrow{OD} + \overrightarrow{DQ} = -4\boldsymbol{b} + 8\mu\boldsymbol{a} + 12\mu\boldsymbol{b} = \underline{8\mu\boldsymbol{a} + (12\mu - 4)\boldsymbol{b}}$$

If $\overrightarrow{OQ}$ and $\overrightarrow{OP}$ coincide then $\overrightarrow{AE}$ and $\overrightarrow{DB}$ intersect. Therefore

$$(12 - 20\lambda)\boldsymbol{a} - 2\lambda\boldsymbol{b} = 8\mu\boldsymbol{a} + (12\mu - 4)\boldsymbol{b}$$

Equating the coefficients of $\boldsymbol{a}$,

$$12 - 20\lambda = 8\mu$$

Equating the coefficients of $\boldsymbol{b}$,

$$-2\lambda = 12\mu - 4$$

Solving these gives

$$\mu = 1/4$$

Therefore

$$\overrightarrow{OP} = \overrightarrow{OQ} = \underline{2\boldsymbol{a} - \boldsymbol{b}}$$

and is the position vector of the point of intersection of DB and AE.

Problem 2.1

Two forces of magnitude $6\boldsymbol{i} + 5\boldsymbol{j}$ and $\mu\boldsymbol{i} + 15\boldsymbol{j}$ act at the origin O. The unit of the force is the newton. If the magnitude of the resultant of the two forces is 25 N calculate the two possible values of μ and show that the two possible directions of the line of action of the resultant are equally inclined to the y-axis.

(1) Add the two forces.
(2) Square the coefficients of $\boldsymbol{i}$ and $\boldsymbol{j}$ and set equal to 25^2.
(3) Solve the resulting quadratic equation for the two possible values of μ so the resultant $= (6 + \mu)\boldsymbol{i} + 20\boldsymbol{j}$, where $\mu = 9$ or -21.
(4) Insert the two values of μ so the two possible resultants are found to be $(15\boldsymbol{i} + 20\boldsymbol{j})$ and $(-15\boldsymbol{i} + 20\boldsymbol{j})$ so their lines of action are inclined at $\pm\tan^{-1}(20/15)$ to Ox and hence are equally inclined to Oy.
(5) Draw the resultants if you do not understand any part of the question and use the diagram to help.

Problem 2.2

The position vectors of P and R with respect to the origin O are $(12\boldsymbol{i} + 5\boldsymbol{j})$ and $(-5\boldsymbol{i} + 12\boldsymbol{j})$ respectively. Show that $|\overrightarrow{OP}| = |\overrightarrow{OR}|$. Given that OPQR is a square, find the vector $\overrightarrow{OQ}$. The midpoint of $\overrightarrow{OQ}$ is N and the midpoint of $\overrightarrow{RM}$ is L. Show that the position vector of L with respect to the origin is $(-3/4)\boldsymbol{i} + (41/4)\boldsymbol{j}$.

(1) Draw a diagram and label O, P, R and Q.
(2) Use $\overrightarrow{OP} = 12\boldsymbol{i} + 5\boldsymbol{j}$ and $\overrightarrow{OR} = -5\boldsymbol{i} + 12\boldsymbol{j}$ to show that $|\overrightarrow{OP}| = 13 = |\overrightarrow{OR}|$.
(3) Use $\overrightarrow{OR} = \overrightarrow{PQ}$ and $\overrightarrow{OQ} = \overrightarrow{OP} + \overrightarrow{PQ}$ to show that $\overrightarrow{OQ} = 7\boldsymbol{i} + 17\boldsymbol{j}$.
(4) Use $\overrightarrow{OM} = \frac{1}{2}\overrightarrow{OQ}$ to find $\overrightarrow{OM}$ and then use the resultant vector theorem. As L is the midpoint of CM, RL : LM = 1 : 1. Therefore $1(\overrightarrow{OR}) + 1(\overrightarrow{OM}) = 2\overrightarrow{OL}$ to show that $\overrightarrow{OL} = (-3/4)\boldsymbol{i} + (41/4)\boldsymbol{j}$.

Summary

(1) A vector has magnitude and direction; a scalar has magnitude only.

If the line of action of a vector is specified it is tied, e.g. a force or a position vector is tied to a fixed origin; otherwise it is free. A vector is represented by a line segment drawn to scale in the vector's direction.

(2) For parallel vectors $\overrightarrow{\mathrm{PQ}} = n\overrightarrow{\mathrm{RS}}$.

(3) For equal and opposite vectors $\overrightarrow{\mathrm{PQ}} = -\overrightarrow{\mathrm{QP}}$.

(4) For the addition of two vectors by the Triangle law: if two vectors $\boldsymbol{p}$ and $\boldsymbol{q}$ are represented by the sides $\overrightarrow{\mathrm{PQ}}$ and $\overrightarrow{\mathrm{QR}}$ respectively of the triangle PQR then their resultant vector $\boldsymbol{r}$ is represented by the side $\overrightarrow{\mathrm{PR}}$. If the angle between the vectors $\boldsymbol{p}$ and $\boldsymbol{q}$ is θ then

$$r^2 = p^2 + q^2 - 2pq \cos(180° - \theta)$$

(5) For the addition of more than two vectors by the Polygon rule: if vectors $\boldsymbol{p}, \boldsymbol{q}, \boldsymbol{r}, \boldsymbol{s}, \boldsymbol{t}, \ldots$ are represented completely by the sides $\overrightarrow{\mathrm{PQ}}, \overrightarrow{\mathrm{QR}}, \overrightarrow{\mathrm{RS}}, \overrightarrow{\mathrm{ST}}, \overrightarrow{\mathrm{TU}}, \ldots$ of the polygon PQRSTU . . . then their resultant vector is represented completely by the side of the polygon needed to close it, i.e. $\overrightarrow{\mathrm{PU}}$.

(6) The subtraction of vectors is defined as the addition of negative vectors.

(7) A unit vector $\hat{\boldsymbol{x}}$ in the direction of a vector $\boldsymbol{x}$ has magnitude one and is defined as

$$\hat{\boldsymbol{x}} = \frac{1}{|x|}\boldsymbol{x}$$

(8) A vector $\boldsymbol{R}$ may be resolved into two mutually perpendicular components $R \cos \theta$ and $R \sin \theta$.

(9) The vectors $\boldsymbol{i}$, $\boldsymbol{j}$ and $\boldsymbol{k}$ are mutually perpendicular unit vectors acting along the rectangular cartesian axes Ox, Oy and Oz. A vector $\boldsymbol{a}$ may be written in the cartesian form: $\boldsymbol{a} = x\boldsymbol{i} + y\boldsymbol{j} + z\boldsymbol{k}$.

(10) The resultant vector theorem states that if two vectors may be represented by $p\overrightarrow{\mathrm{OA}}$ and $q\overrightarrow{\mathrm{OB}}$ then their resultant is represented by $(p+q)\overrightarrow{\mathrm{OC}}$, where C divides AB such that AC : CB = $q : p$.

(11) When solving vector problems it is always useful to draw a diagram even if the scale is arbitrary. The solution then is often apparent to the student. The vector addition of $\overrightarrow{\mathrm{OA}} + \overrightarrow{\mathrm{AB}} = \overrightarrow{\mathrm{OB}}$ is used in most types of problems and must be thoroughly understood before more difficult problems can be solved. Resolution of a vector, particularly into $\boldsymbol{i}, \boldsymbol{j}, \boldsymbol{k}$ components, can lead to a simple solution with some problems and is always worth considering.

3
Equilibrium of forces. Friction

Objectives

The student should be able to:

(1) state the conditions of equilibrium for a set of concurrent forces acting on a particle,
(2) resolve a set of forces in two perpendicular directions,
(3) draw a closed vector polygon for a set of forces,
(4) use Lami's theorem,
(5) recognise and utilise the symmetry of a figure,
(6) draw the normal and frictional forces between two bodies in contact,
(7) state that the frictional force between two rough bodies is $\leqslant \mu R$, where μ is the coefficient of friction and R is the normal reaction,
(8) state that the angle of friction λ is defined by $\tan \lambda = \mu$,
(9) use the total reaction between two bodies to reduce a problem from one involving four forces to one involving three forces.

Equilibrium of forces

A set of forces acting on a body can be reduced:

(1) to a resultant turning effect which causes the body to rotate (this is discussed in the next chapter),
(2) to a single resultant force which causes the body to move in a straight line with non-zero acceleration,
(3) to equilibrium.

A body at rest or moving with uniform velocity and not rotating is said to be in equilibrium. The turning effect of concurrent forces is zero, so if their single resultant force is zero then concurrent forces are in equilibrium.

If a set of forces $\boldsymbol{F}_1$, $\boldsymbol{F}_2$, $\boldsymbol{F}_3, \ldots$, acts on a particle then the particle has zero linear acceleration if $\Sigma \boldsymbol{F} = 0$.

Each force $\boldsymbol{F}$ can be resolved into three non-coplanar directions determined by the unit vectors $\hat{\boldsymbol{a}}$, $\hat{\boldsymbol{b}}$ and $\hat{\boldsymbol{c}}$. Therefore

$$\sum \boldsymbol{F} = \sum F_a \hat{\boldsymbol{a}} + \sum F_b \hat{\boldsymbol{b}} + \sum F_c \hat{\boldsymbol{c}}$$

For equilibrium

$$0 = \sum F_a = \sum F_b = \sum F_c$$

where F_a is the component of $\boldsymbol{F}$ in the direction $\hat{\boldsymbol{a}}$, F_b is the component of $\boldsymbol{F}$ in the direction $\hat{\boldsymbol{b}}$, and F_c is the component of $\boldsymbol{F}$ in the direction $\hat{\boldsymbol{c}}$.

Therefore a particle is in translational equilibrium if the sum of the resolved parts of the forces in each of three non-coplanar directions is zero. For *coplanar forces* the sum in any two non-parallel directions must be zero as perpendicular to the plane the sum of the components of the forces is zero.

Methods of solution for coplanar forces

(1) The forces can be resolved and the sum of the components found in two perpendicular directions to be zero.
(2) A *closed* vector polygon may be drawn since the magnitude of their resultant is zero.
(3) Symmetry of a figure can often be used to provide a simple solution.

Example 3.1

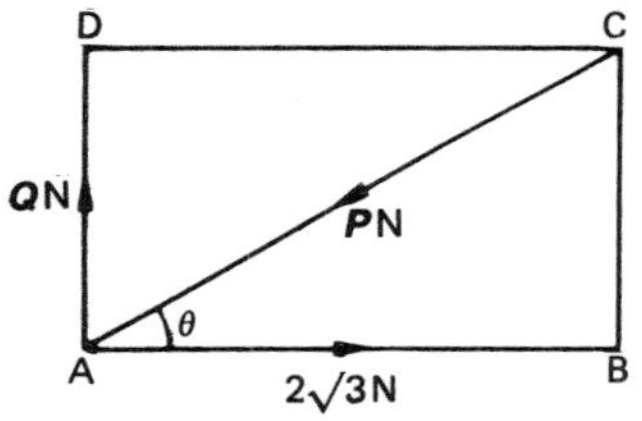

Figure 3.1

ABCD is a rectangle with side BC = 1 m and diagonal AC = 2 m (Fig. 3.1). If a force of $2\sqrt{3}$ N acts along $\overrightarrow{AB}$, $\boldsymbol{P}$ N acts along $\overrightarrow{CA}$ and $\boldsymbol{Q}$ N acts along $\overrightarrow{AD}$, find $\boldsymbol{P}$ and $\boldsymbol{Q}$ if the forces are in equilibrium.

$$\sin\theta = \frac{CB}{AC} = \frac{1}{2}$$

Therefore

$$\theta = 30°$$

The forces are in equilibrium so the sum of the components is zero horizontally and vertically. Resolving horizontally,

$$P\cos 30° = 2\sqrt{3}$$

Therefore

$$P\frac{\sqrt{3}}{2} = 2\sqrt{3}$$

$$\boldsymbol{P} = \underline{4\text{ N}}$$

Resolving vertically,

$$P\cos 60° = Q$$

$$\frac{P}{2} = Q$$

Therefore

$$\boldsymbol{Q} = \underline{2\text{ N}}$$

Example 3.2

A string is tied to two points at the same level and a smooth ring of weight 3 N which can slide freely along the string is pulled aside by a horizontal force of R newtons (Fig. 3.2). Find the values of the tensions in the string if they are inclined at 30° and 60° to the horizontal and also the magnitude of R.

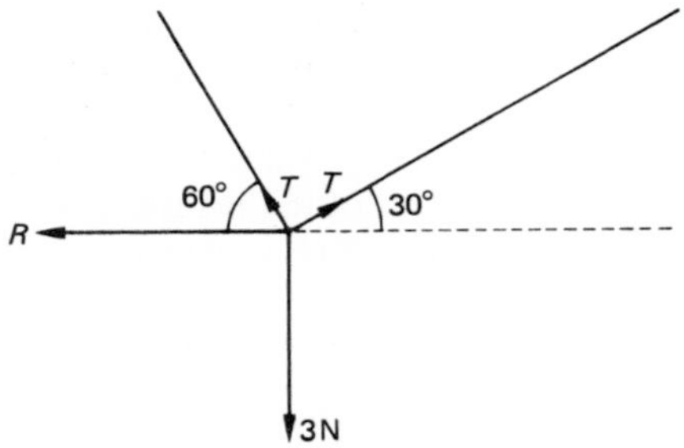

Figure 3.2

The ring is smooth so the two tensions are equal. Resolving horizontally,

$$R = T\cos 30° - T\cos 60° = 0.866T - 0.5T = 0.366T$$

Resolving vertically,

$$3 = T\sin 30° + T\sin 60° = 0.5T + 0.866T = 1.366T$$

Therefore

$$T = 3/1.366 = \underline{2.196\ \text{N}}$$

so $R = \underline{0.803\ \text{N}}$

Lami's theorem

If three concurrent forces are in equilibrium then the closed vector polygon is a triangle. Consider three forces ***P***, ***Q*** and ***R*** and the corresponding triangle of forces (Fig. 3.3).

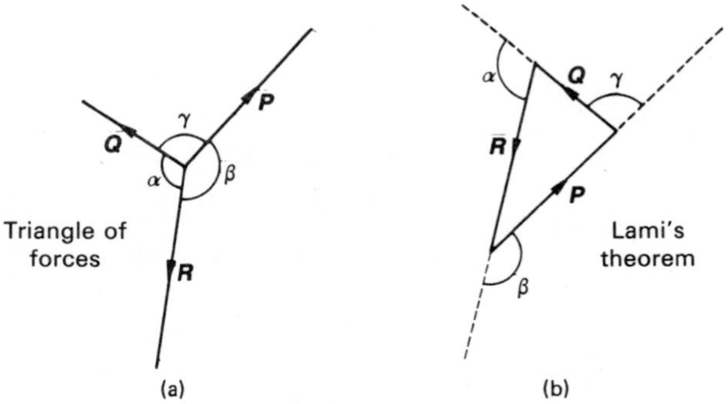

Figure 3.3

The triangle of force property states that if three concurrent forces may be represented by the sides of a triangle taken in order then the forces are in equilibrium.

Applying the sine rule to the vector triangle we have

$$\frac{P}{\sin(180° - \alpha)} = \frac{Q}{\sin(180° - \beta)} = \frac{R}{\sin(180° - \gamma)}$$

Therefore

$$\frac{P}{\sin\alpha}=\frac{Q}{\sin\beta}=\frac{R}{\sin\gamma}$$

This result is known as Lami's theorem: if three forces acting at a point are in equilibrium then the ratio of the magnitude of each force to the sine of the angle between the other two is constant.

This property can give a neat solution to many three forces problems as the three forces must be concurrent if they are to be in equilibrium and are non-parallel.

Example 3.3

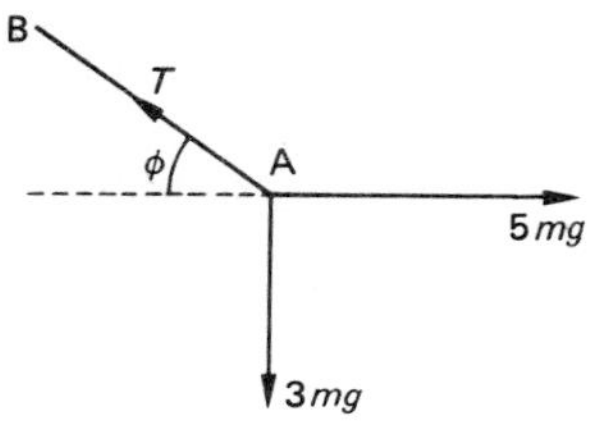

Figure 3.4

A particle of mass $3m$ is tied to the end A of a light inextensible string. The other end B is fixed and a horizontal force of $5mg$ is applied to the particle so the system hangs in equilibrium as shown in Fig. 3.4. Calculate:
(a) the inclination ϕ of AB to the horizontal,
(b) the tension in the string.

(a) The particle is in equilibrium under the action of three forces so using Lami's theorem:

$$\frac{T}{\sin 90°}=\frac{5mg}{\sin(90°+\phi)}=\frac{3mg}{\sin(180°-\phi)}$$

Therefore

$$5\sin\phi=3\cos\phi$$
$$\tan\phi=3/5$$
$$\phi=31°$$

i.e. the inclination ϕ of AB to the horizontal is 31°.

(b) $T=\dfrac{5mg}{\cos\phi}=\dfrac{5mg}{5/\sqrt{34}}=\sqrt{34}\,mg$

i.e. the tension in the string AB is $\sqrt{34}\,mg$ newtons.

Problem 3.1

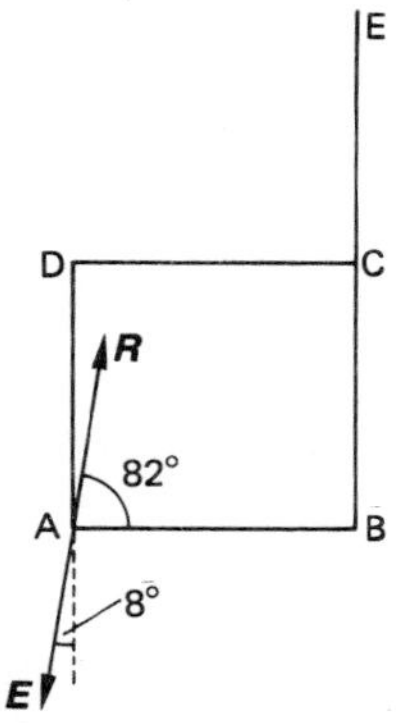

Figure 3.5

ABCD is a square with BC produced to E so CE = CB. A force of magnitude $3\sqrt{5}$ N acts along $\overrightarrow{AE}$, 2 N acts along $\overrightarrow{BA}$ and 1 N acts along $\overrightarrow{AD}$. Find the magnitude and direction of the force required to maintain equilibrium.

(1) Draw a diagram and mark in the forces (Fig. 3.5).
(2) Resolve horizontally to show that the total horizontal component $X=1$ N.
(3) Resolve vertically to show that the total vertical component $Y=7$ N.
(4) Find the resultant $R=\sqrt{(X^2+Y^2)}=\sqrt{50}$ N at $\tan^{-1} 7$ to AB.
(5) Thus find the equilibriant to be of magnitude $\sqrt{50}$ N at 88°.

Friction

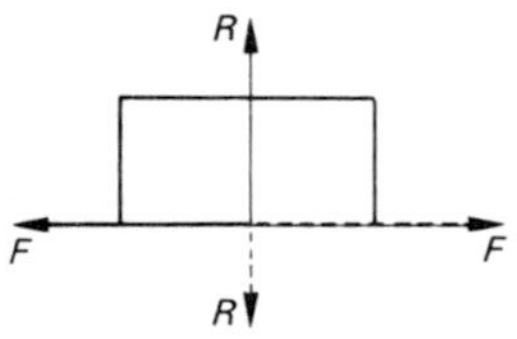

Figure 3.6

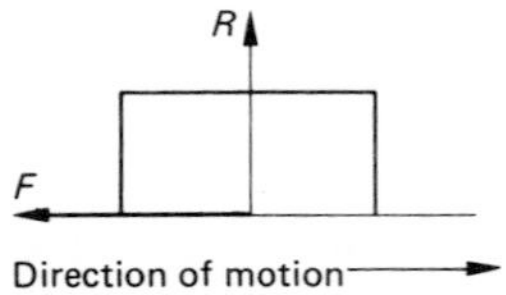

Figure 3.7

Two solid bodies exert equal and opposite forces on one another when they are in contact. There is always a normal reaction R which is perpendicular to the common tangent to the two surfaces in contact. If the bodies are smooth or if there is no tendency to move relative to one another then no frictional force exists. If the bodies are rough and do have a tendency to move relative to one another then frictional forces occur which act so as to oppose any potential motion. The normal reactions and frictional forces occur in equal and opposite pairs (Fig. 3.6) but as one set often acts upon the ground these two forces have no effect. Diagrams are usually drawn as shown in Fig. 3.7.

As the force applied to produce motion is increased so the frictional force increases accordingly and the two are equal and opposite up to a limiting value. The limiting value is related to the normal reaction R by the coefficient of friction which has a given value for each pair of surfaces.

The maximum frictional force $F = \mu R$ in limiting equilibrium. Motion begins when the applied force just exceeds μR. After motion has started the frictional force may be considered equal to μR no matter how much the applied force increases.

Angle of friction

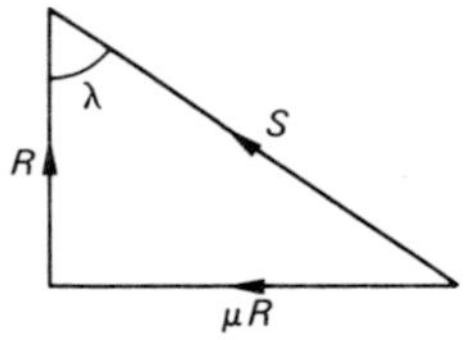

Figure 3.8

When two bodies are in rough contact and slipping is about to occur then friction is limiting and the two forces acting on the object are R and μR (Fig. 3.8)

$$\text{resultant reaction } S = \sqrt{(R^2 + \mu^2 R^2)} = R\sqrt{(1+\mu^2)}$$

The angle between the resultant reaction and the normal reaction of one surface on the other is called the angle of friction λ.

$$\tan \lambda = \frac{\mu R}{R} = \mu$$

i.e. the tangent of the angle of friction is the coefficient of friction.

Note Use of the resultant reaction S instead of R and μR can reduce a problem from four to three forces and sometimes help with the solution.

Example 3.4

Find the least force that will prevent a particle of weight W:

(a) Sliding down a plane inclined at an angle α to the horizontal, where the angle of friction between the particle and the plane is λ $(\lambda < \alpha)$,
(b) moving up the same plane.

(a) The total reaction S will act with the frictional component up the plane and at an angle λ to the normal to the plane as shown in Fig. 3.9(a).

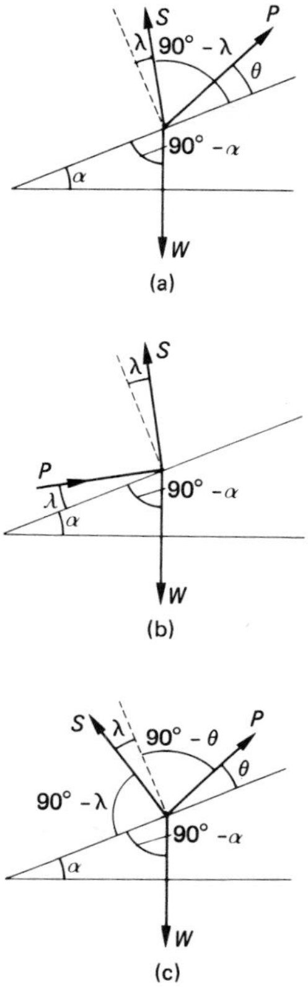

Figure 3.9

Let the force P act at angle θ to the plane as shown. P will be a minimum when the particle is about to slip so S makes an angle λ to the normal.

By Lami's theorem,

$$\frac{P}{\sin(90° - \alpha + 90° + \lambda)} = \frac{W}{\sin(90° - \lambda - \theta)}$$

$$\frac{P}{\sin(180° - (\alpha - \lambda))} = \frac{W}{\sin(90° - (\lambda + \theta))}$$

$$\frac{P}{\sin(\alpha - \lambda)} = \frac{W}{\cos(\lambda + \theta)}$$

Therefore

$$P = \frac{W \sin(\alpha - \lambda)}{\cos(\theta + \lambda)}$$

To find the minimum value of P for a given θ, $\cos(\theta + \lambda)$ must be a maximum, i.e. $\cos(\theta + \lambda) = 1$. Therefore

$$\theta = -\lambda$$

as shown in Fig. 3.9(b).

$$P = W \sin(\alpha - \lambda)$$

(b) When the particle is on the point of moving up the plane the total reaction S will act with the frictional component pointing down the plane so it makes an angle λ with the normal down the plane as shown in Fig. 3.9(c).

By Lami's theorem,

$$\frac{P}{\sin(90° - \lambda + 90° - \alpha)} = \frac{W}{\sin(90° - \theta + \lambda)}$$

$$\frac{P}{\sin(180° - (\alpha + \lambda))} = \frac{W}{\sin(90° - (\theta - \lambda)}$$

$$\frac{P}{\sin(\alpha + \lambda)} = \frac{W}{\cos(\theta - \lambda)}$$

Therefore

$$P = \frac{W \sin(\alpha + \lambda)}{\cos(\theta - \lambda)}$$

This time, minimising P to give the least force to cause sliding up the plane, i.e. $\cos(\theta - \lambda) = 1$. Therefore

$$\theta = \lambda$$

in the upward direction.

$$\underline{P = W \sin(\alpha + \lambda)}$$

(Both parts of this problem were simplified by using the total reaction S instead of R and F and by using $F = \mu R$ at limiting equilibrium.)

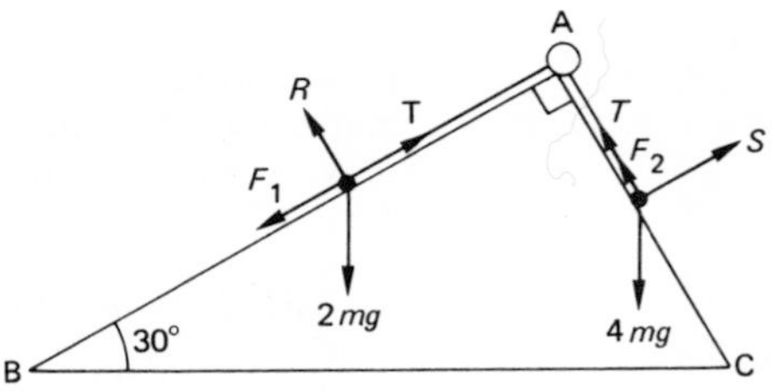

Figure 3.10

Problem 3.2

Figure 3.10 shows a fixed wedge with BC horizontal. An inextensible string carrying masses of $2m$ and $4m$ passes over a smooth frictionless pulley at A. The angle $\widehat{BAC} = 90°$ and the angle $\widehat{ABC} = 30°$. Find the range of values of μ such that the particles remain at rest.

(1) As the pulley is smooth, the tensions are equal in both parts of the string on either side of A. The system will tend to move along $\overrightarrow{AC}$ so the frictional force at the $4m$ mass acts towards A and at the $2m$ mass acts away from A.
(2) Mark in the frictional forces, normal reactions and tension.
(3) $F_1 \leqslant \mu R$ and $F_2 \leqslant \mu S$.
(4) Resolve perpendicular to AB and AC to show that $R = \sqrt{3}\, mg$ and $S = 2mg$.
(5) Resolve parallel to AC and AB respectively. The $4mg$ mass remains stationary if $4mg \cos 30° - T \leqslant \mu S$. The $2mg$ mass remains stationary if $T - 2mg \cos 60° \leqslant \mu R$. Substitute for R and S and add the equations to show that

$$4 \cos 30° - 2 \cos 60° \leqslant \mu(\sqrt{3} + 2)$$

i.e. $$\mu \geqslant \frac{2\sqrt{3} - 1}{2 + \sqrt{3}}$$

for the masses to remain stationary.

Example 3.5

A uniform rod AB of length $2l$ and weight 10 N is in equilibrium with the end A on a rough horizontal floor and the end B against a smooth vertical wall (Fig. 3.11). The rod makes an angle $\tan^{-1} 3$ with the horizontal and is in a vertical plane which is perpendicular to the wall. Find the least possible value of the coefficient of friction between the floor and the rod.

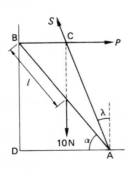

Figure 3.11

The frictional force is less than or equal to μR. The normal reaction is dependent on the weight and α so the minimum value of μ occurs when $F = \mu R$. The normal reaction and frictional force can be considered as one resultant reaction S making an angle λ with the vertical as shown. This reduces the problem to a three force problem.

$$\tan \lambda = \frac{AD/2}{BD} = \frac{l \cos \alpha}{2l \sin \alpha} = \frac{1}{2 \tan \alpha} = \frac{1}{6}$$

Therefore

$$\underline{\mu = \tan \lambda = \tfrac{1}{6} \text{ in limiting equilibrium}}$$

Summary

(1) A body acted on by a set of concurrent forces is in equilibrium if the sum of the resolved components of the forces in each of three non-coplanar directions is zero.

(2) For coplanar concurrent forces the sum of the components of the forces in two perpendicular directions is zero and this is the method often used for solution.

(3) A closed vector polygon may be drawn for a set of concurrent forces in equilibrium.

(4) Symmetry can be used to simplify a problem.

(5) Two bodies in contact exert equal and opposite normal reactions R perpendicular to the common tangent to the two surfaces of the bodies in contact.

(6) When two bodies are in rough contact then frictional forces occur which oppose any potential motion.

(7) When one of the bodies cannot move the pair of forces acting on it is usually not drawn.

(8) The frictional force F is $\leqslant \mu R$, where μ is the coefficient of friction and R is the normal reaction. When a body is about to slip $F = \mu R$.

(9) The angle of friction λ is the angle between the resultant reaction $S = \sqrt{(R^2 + \mu^2 R^2)}$ and the normal reaction. When the body is in limiting equilibrium $\tan \lambda = \mu$.

(10) Use of S can reduce a four force problem to a three force problem.

(11) If a body is in equilibrium under the action of three concurrent forces then Lami's theorem states that the ratio of the magnitude of each force to the sine of the angle between the other two is constant.

4
Moments, forces and equilibrium

Objectives

The student should be able to:

(1) define the moment of a force,
(2) use the graphical representation of a moment,
(3) calculate moments with forces and positions in $(\boldsymbol{i}, \boldsymbol{j})$ notation,
(4) use the principle of moments,
(5) use the three independent conditions for equilibrium of coplanar forces to produce three independent equations,
(6) find the resultant of parallel forces,
(7) state and use the characteristics of a couple,
(8) replace a force by a force plus a couple,
(9) determine equivalent systems of coplanar forces with $X = \Sigma F_x$, the sum of the x-components of the forces, $Y = \Sigma F_y$, the sum of the y-components of the forces, and $G = \Sigma(xF_y - yF_x)$, the resultant moment of the system and find the equation of the lines of action of the resultant in a plane,
(10) draw the forces acting at a joint.

Moment of a force

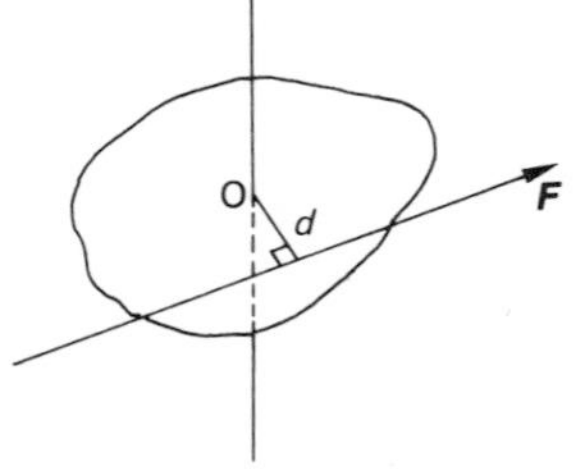

Figure 4.1

Consider a lamina free to rotate in its own plane about an axis through O, the axis being perpendicular to the plane of rotation (Fig. 4.1).

A force $\boldsymbol{F}$ whose line of action is in the plane of the lamina but that does not pass through O will cause the lamina to rotate about O.

The turning effect $\boldsymbol{G}$ of the force $\boldsymbol{F}$ about the axis O is calculated by multiplying the magnitude of the force with the perpendicular distance of the line of action of the force from the axis, i.e.

$$G = Fd$$

$\boldsymbol{G}$ is called the **moment of $\boldsymbol{F}$ about that axis** or the **torque about the axis**. It is measured in newton metres and is a vector quantity. Anticlockwise moments are taken as positive and clockwise as negative in the usual convention.

Graphical representation of a moment

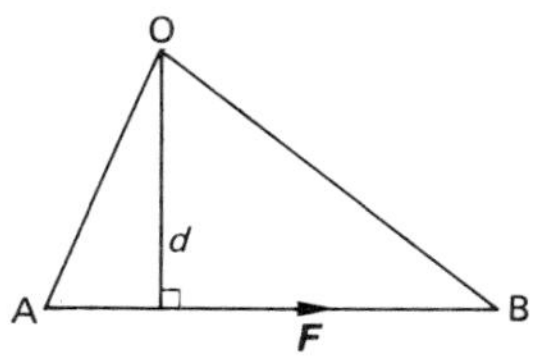

Figure 4.2

Let $\overrightarrow{AB}$ represent a force $\boldsymbol{F}$ in magnitude, direction and line of action (Fig. 4.2). The moment of the force about the axis O = Fd in magnitude.

$$\tfrac{1}{2} \times AB \times d = \text{area of the triangle OAB}$$

$$Fd = 2 \times \tfrac{1}{2} \times AB \times d$$

Therefore the magnitude of the moment about an axis through O of a force $\boldsymbol{F}$ completely represented by a line AB is represented by twice the area of the triangle OAB.

The moment is zero if the line of action of the force passes through the axis of rotation.

Position vector

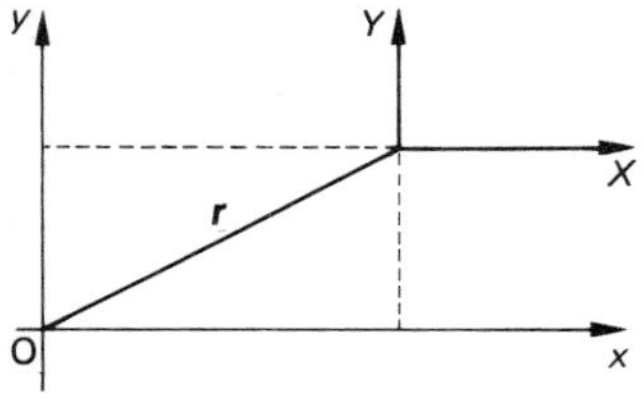

Figure 4.3

If $\boldsymbol{r}$ is the position vector of a force $\boldsymbol{F} = X\boldsymbol{i} + Y\boldsymbol{j}$, where $\boldsymbol{r} = x\boldsymbol{i} + y\boldsymbol{j}$ (Fig. 4.3), then

$$\text{moment of } \boldsymbol{F} \text{ about O} = xY - yX = G$$

Example 4.1

Calculate the moment of the force $\boldsymbol{F} = 6\boldsymbol{i} + 3\boldsymbol{j}$ acting through the point $\boldsymbol{i} + \boldsymbol{j}$ about an axis through O.

$$G = xY - yX = 1 \times 3 - 1 \times 6$$

i.e. $G = \underline{-3 \text{ N m}}$

where the minus sign indicates that the moment is clockwise.

Example 4.2.

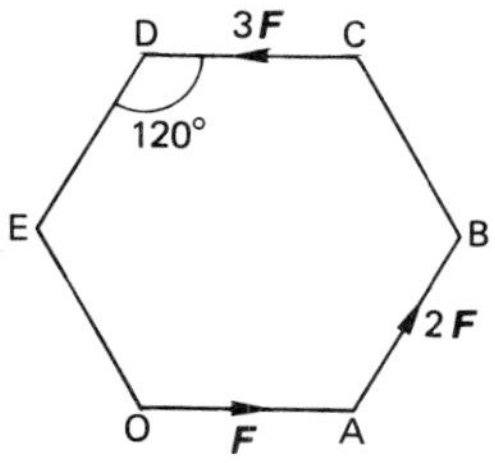

Figure 4.4

Calculate the anticlockwise torque of the forces shown in Fig. 4.4 about an axis perpendicular to the lamina through O, where OABCDE is a regular hexagon of side $2a$.

Taking moments about O,

$$\text{moment of } \boldsymbol{F} = 0$$

$$\text{moment of } 3\boldsymbol{F} = 3F \times 2a\sqrt{3} = 6Fa\sqrt{3}$$

$$\text{Moment of } 2\boldsymbol{F} = 2F \times 2a \cos 30° = 2Fa\sqrt{3}$$

Therefore total moment about O $= \underline{8Fa\sqrt{3} \text{ N m}}$

Resultant torque

The resultant torque of a set of forces about a given axis is the algebraic sum of their individual torques or moments about that axis, e.g. the resultant torque of the forces $\boldsymbol{F}_1$, $\boldsymbol{F}_2$ and $\boldsymbol{F}_3$ as shown about the axis A (Fig. 4.5) is

$$F_1 d_1 + F_2 d_2 - F_3 d_3$$

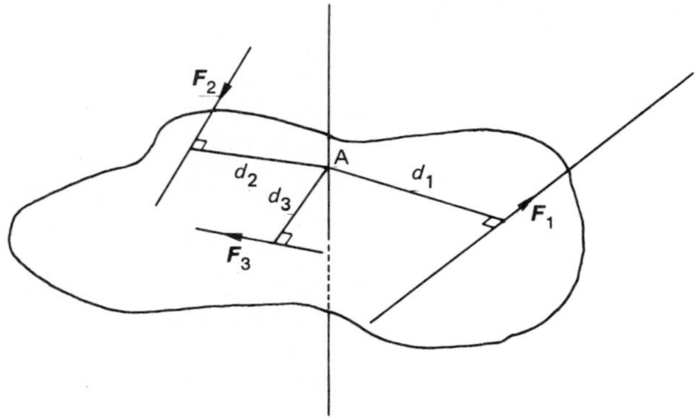

Figure 4.5

If the set of forces has a single resultant force (it may reduce to a couple as explained later) then the resultant moment of the set of forces is equal to the moment about the same axis of the resultant force: this is the **principle of moments**.

The corollary to this is that if a set of forces is in equilibrium so that the resultant force is zero then the algebraic sum of the moments of the forces about any axis is zero.

This can often be used to find unknown forces when an object is in equilibrium.

Coplanar forces in equilibrium

When an object is acted upon by a set of forces it has three possible independent modes of movement:

(1) parallel to the x-axis,
(2) parallel to the y-axis,
(3) rotation about an axis.

For the object to be in equilibrium the set of forces must therefore be such that

(1) the algebraic sum of the components parallel to the x-axis is zero, i.e. $\Sigma F_x = 0$,
(2) the algebraic sum of the components parallel to the y-axis is zero, i.e. $\Sigma F_y = 0$,
(3) the resultant moment of the forces about any specified axis is zero, i.e. $G = 0$.

These three conditions give three independent equations for a system of coplanar forces and can be used to find unknown forces, distances, etc., if the system is in equilibrium. An alternative set of conditions is that the resultant moments about three non-linear points are zero and this will also produce three independent equations corresponding to the three separate modes or degrees of freedom of the system. Three independent equations can also be produced by resolving in one direction and taking moments about two non-parallel axes. The first method is the most usual but careful study of a diagram in a given problem may show that the second or third technique is simpler in that case.

Example 4.3

Forces of $5\boldsymbol{F}$, $12\boldsymbol{F}$ and $13\boldsymbol{F}$ act along the sides of length 5 m, 12 m and 13 m respectively of a right-angled triangle in the same circular sense. Find the forces which acting at the ends of the side 13 m long and at right angles to it will maintain equilibrium.

Let the required forces be $\boldsymbol{P}$ and $\boldsymbol{Q}$ acting at A and C as shown in Fig. 4.6. Resolving vertically,

$$P \cos \theta - 5F + Q \cos \theta + 13F \sin \theta = 0$$

$$(P+Q)\cos \theta = 5F - 13F \times 5/13 = 0$$

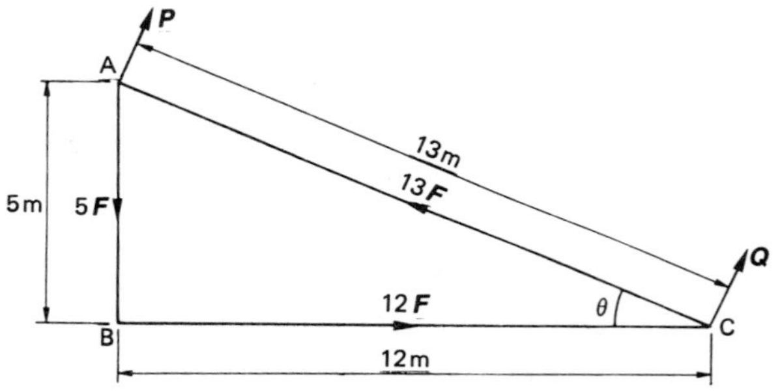

Figure 4.6

Therefore

$$P = -Q$$

To find P or Q we must take moments. Therefore taking moments about A,

$$Q \times 13 + 12F \times 5 = 0$$

so $$Q = -\frac{60F}{13}$$

and $$P = \frac{60F}{13}$$

Hence Q acts towards C and P acts away from A and the two forces required to maintain equilibrium are equal in magnitude and opposite in direction. They are known as a **couple**.

Resultant of parallel forces

Like parallel forces (i.e. forces in the same sense)

Consider two parallel forces P and Q acting at A and B, a distance d apart, as shown in Fig. 4.7. The resultant $R = P + Q$ and is parallel to P and Q. Its line of action is through C. It has no moment about this point so from the principle of moments:

$$P \times AC - Q \times CB = 0$$

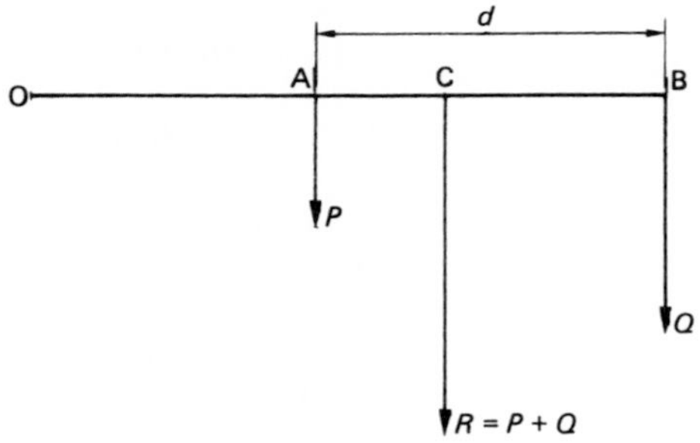

Figure 4.7

Therefore

$$\frac{P}{Q} = \frac{\text{CB}}{\text{AC}}$$

Hence the resultant of like parallel forces P and Q is parallel to P and Q, of magnitude $P+Q$ and its line of action divides AB (the distance between them) in the ratio $Q:P$.

Now

$$\text{moment of } R \text{ about O} = (P+Q)\times\text{OC}$$

and moment of P about O + moment of Q about O

$$= P\times\text{OA} + Q\times\text{OB} = P(\text{OC}-\text{AC}) + Q(\text{OC}+\text{OB})$$

$$= (P+Q)\text{OC} - P\times\text{AC} + Q\times\text{CB} = (P+Q)\times\text{OC}$$

Unlike parallel forces (i.e. forces in the opposite senses)

Consider two parallel unlike forces P and Q acting at A and B, a distance d apart, as shown in Fig. 4.8 and suppose that $Q > P$.

Resolving vertically,

$$R = Q - P$$

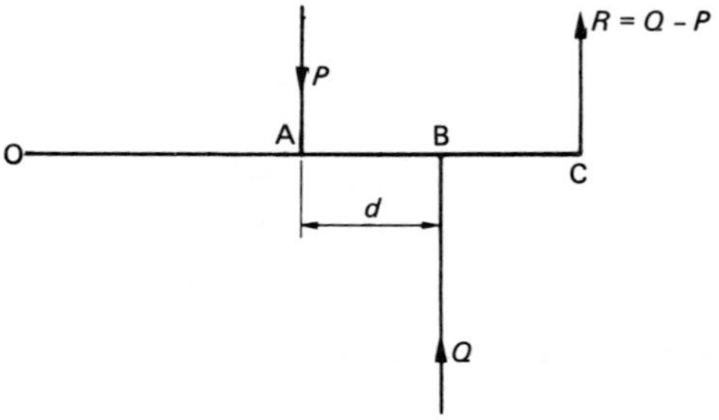

Figure 4.8

Let the resultant act at C. Then taking moments about A,

$$Q\times\text{AB} = R\times\text{AC} = (Q-P)\text{AC}$$

Therefore

$$\frac{\text{AC}}{\text{CB}} = \frac{Q}{-P}$$

showing that the resultant which has a magnitude of $Q-P$ divides AB externally in the ratio $Q:P$ as shown in Fig. 4.8.

Equal unlike parallel forces (i.e. a couple)

This is a special case when $Q=P$ but their lines of action are separated so the magnitude of the resultant, $Q-P$, is now zero but the turning effect is not zero (Fig. 4.9).

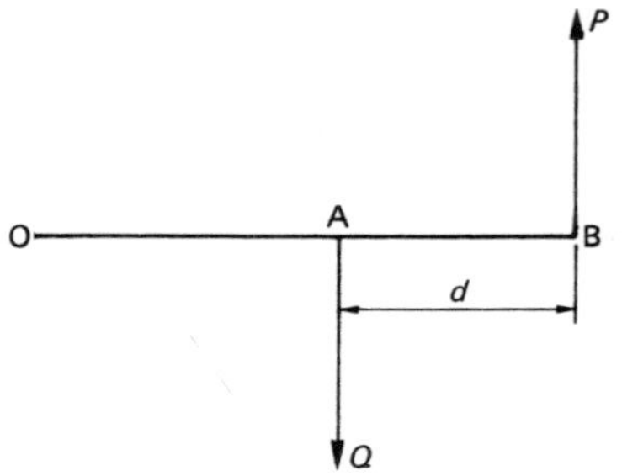

Figure 4.9

Taking moments about O,

$$G = P \times OB - P \times OA = P \times AB$$

i.e. $G = Pd$

This is independent of the position of O. Hence the *characteristics of a couple* are that its linear resultant in any direction in the plane is zero and it has a constant moment about any axis perpendicular to its plane equal to the product of the magnitude of one of the forces with the perpendicular distance between the forces.

Example 4.4

A uniform ladder of length l and weight W is held with its upper end resting against a smooth vertical wall and its lower end on a smooth horizontal surface (Fig. 4.10). A man of weight $W/2$ stands on the ladder at a distance $l/4$ from its lower end. If the ladder is kept from slipping by a couple, find its magnitude in terms of W, l and θ, where θ is the inclination of the ladder to the vertical.

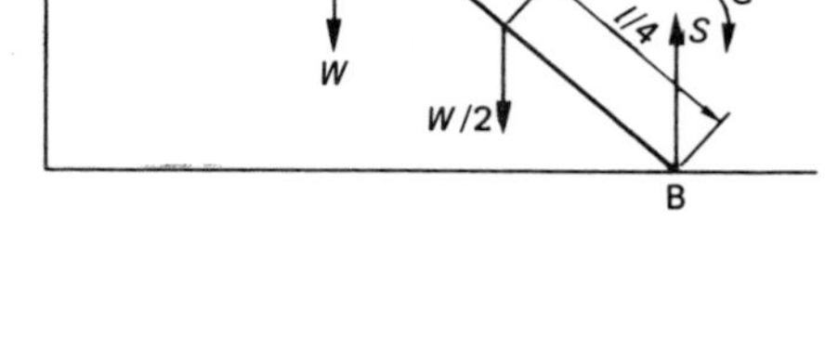

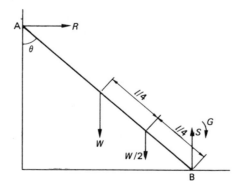

Figure 4.10

Resolving horizontally,

$R = 0$ (represented now by ↑)

Resolving vertically,

$S = 3W/2$ (represented now by →)

Taking moments about B,

$$G = W\frac{l}{2}\sin\theta + \frac{W}{2}\frac{l}{4}\sin\theta = \frac{5}{8}Wl\sin\theta$$

The magnitude of the couple required to maintain equilibrium is therefore $\frac{5}{8}Wl\sin\theta$.

Example 4.5

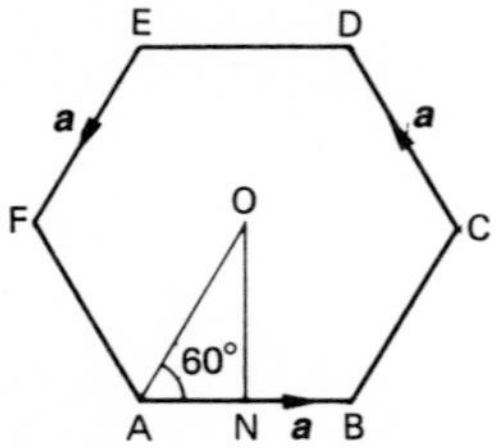

Figure 4.11

ABCDEF is a regular hexagon (Fig. 4.11). Show that forces represented in magnitude and direction by AB, CD and EF are equivalent to a couple of moments equal in magnitude to the area of the hexagon.

Let the hexagon be of side a, therefore each force is of magnitude a.

↑ $a\cos 30° - a\cos 30° = 0 = X$

→ $a - a\cos 60° - a\cos 60° = 0 = Y$

Therefore the resultant force is zero.

Taking moments about O, the centre of the hexagon,

$G = 3a \times \mathrm{ON} = 3a \times a\sqrt{3}/2 = 3a^2\sqrt{3}/2$ N m

area of the hexagon = 12 × area of the triangle AON

$$= 12 \times \left(\frac{1}{2}\frac{a}{2}\right) \times \left(a\frac{\sqrt{3}}{2}\right) = 3a^2\sqrt{3}/2\ \mathrm{m}^2$$

Hence the area of the hexagon is equal in magnitude to the moment of the couple.

Combination of a force and couple

Any force F acting at a point B on a rigid body is seen to be equivalent to a force F parallel to itself acting at a point A plus a couple, by introducing a couple whose moment is Fd, where d is the perpendicular distance of B from the line of action of F (Fig. 4.12). The couple acts so that it tends to turn the body about A in the same direction as F acting at B tends to move it. Hence a system of forces of resultant F may be replaced by

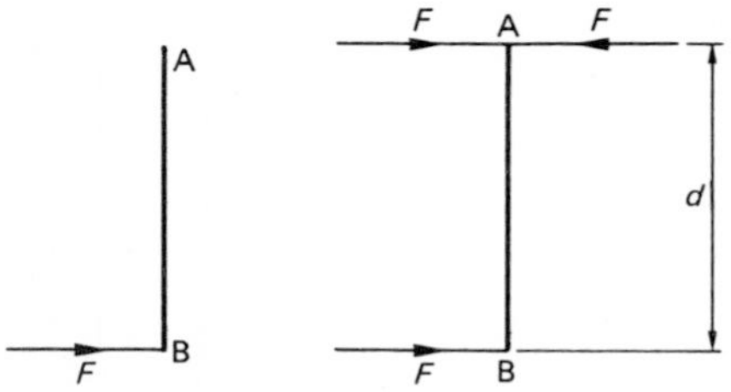

Figure 4.12

a single force F acting through a point together with a couple G and are equivalent to an equal force F displaced through G/F.

Equivalent systems of coplanar forces

Two sets of forces are equivalent if they have the same effect defined by the three independent relationships based on comparing components and/or torque.

Consider a force F acting at the point $A(x, y)$ as shown in Fig. 4.13. Let it have components F_x and F_y. Transfer F_x parallel to itself to act at O by introducing a couple of moment yF_x. Transfer F_y parallel to itself to act at O by introducing a couple of moment xF_y.

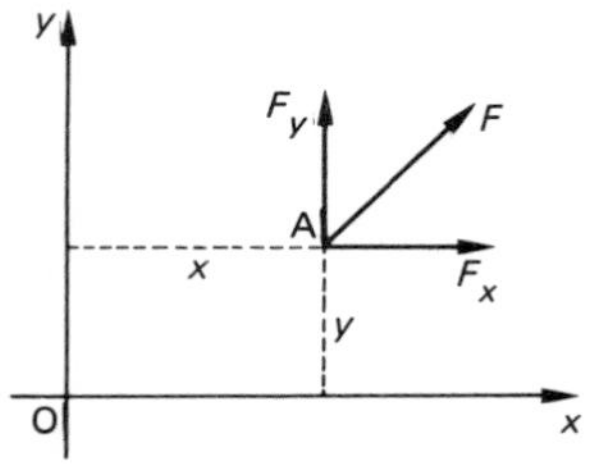

Figure 4.13

$$\text{sum of the moments of the two couples} = xF_y - yF_x$$

Now consider a set of forces $F_1, F_2, \ldots, F_n$ acting at $A_1, A_2, \ldots, A_n$. Resolving horizontally,

$$X = \sum_{i=1}^{i=n} F_x \qquad (=0 \text{ for equilibrium})$$

Resolving vertically,

$$Y = \sum_{i=1}^{i=n} F_y \qquad (=0 \text{ for equilibrium})$$

$$R = \sqrt{(X^2 + Y^2)} \qquad (\text{at } \tan^{-1}(Y/X) \text{ to O}x)$$

Taking moments about O,

$$G = \Sigma(xF_y - yF_x) \qquad (=0 \text{ for equilibrium})$$

If a system is *not* in equilibrium then it may reduce to a force R, a force R plus a couple G about a given axis or a couple G in the following cases:

(1) if $X \neq 0$ and $Y \neq 0$ but the resultant R passes through the origin,
(2) if $X = 0$ and $Y = 0$ then the system reduces to G,
(3) if $X \neq 0$ and $Y \neq 0$ let the resultant R cross Oy at $y = c$ (Fig. 4.14).

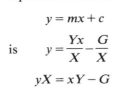

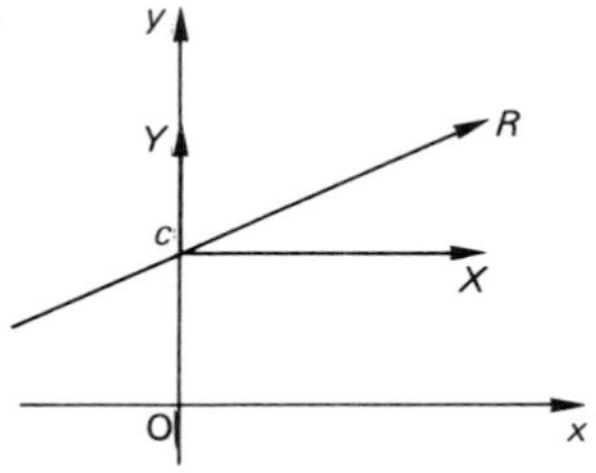

Figure 4.14

Taking moments about O,

$$G = -cX$$

Therefore

$$G/X = -c$$

where G is positive in the anticlockwise sense.

The gradient $m = Y/X$ for the line of action of R. So the equation of the line of action,

$$y = mx + c$$

is $$y = \frac{Yx}{X} - \frac{G}{X}$$

$$yX = xY - G$$

i.e. $G - xY + yX = 0$

is the equation of the line of action of the resultant in the (x, y) plane.

This system can be reduced to a force R only, displaced through G/R as in the previous theorem, so a system of coplanar forces is equivalent either to a single force or to a couple or is in equilibrium.

Jointed rods

If two bodies are connected by a smooth light hinge so that there is no resistance to motion they are **freely jointed**. If a system is in equilibrium then each part of the system is in equilibrium, hence the forces acting on the hinge are in equilibrium. If no external force acts on the joint the forces affecting it are the reactions of the two jointed bodies on one another. These hinge forces are often considered in their component form as their direction is not known, as shown in Fig. 4.15(b).

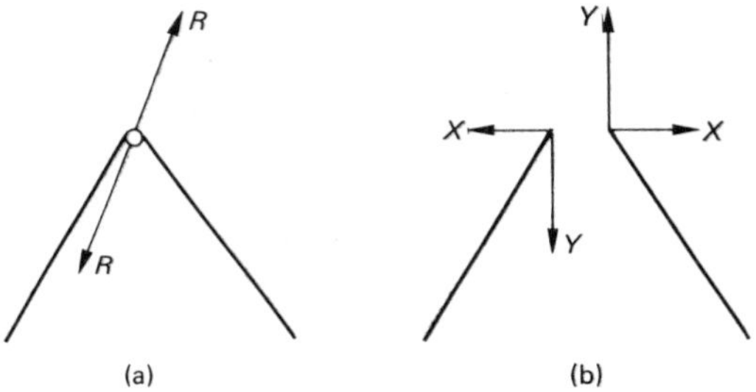

Figure 4.15

When there is an external force acting on the joint then the reactions will no longer be equal and opposite and the equilibrium of the hinge must be considered. It is usually possible by taking moments about the joint, or by considering the adjacent rod and hinge as one, to leave out the calculation of the reactions at the hinge.

Example 4.6

Forces of magnitudes $3\sqrt{2}p$, $5\sqrt{2}p$ and $9p$ act along the sides CA, BC and AB of a triangle ABC, where A is the origin, $\widehat{ACB} = 90°$ and AC = CB = a metres (Fig. 4.16). Find:

(a) the sum of the resolved parts of these forces parallel to AB,
(b) the sum of the resolved parts of these forces perpendicular to AB,

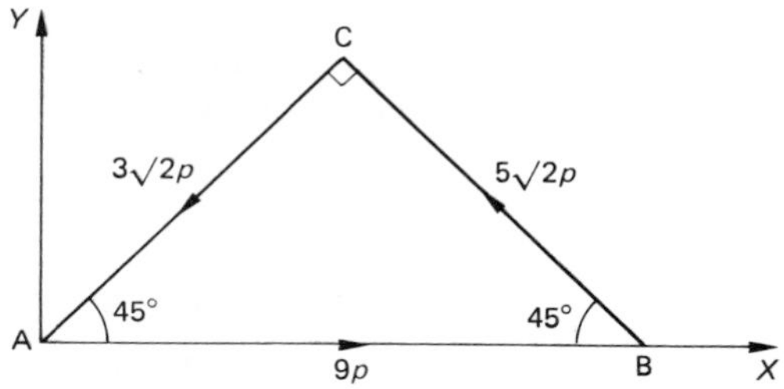

Figure 4.16

(c) the magnitude of the resultant of these forces,
(d) the acute angle made by the line of action of the resultant with AB,
(e) the distance from A where the line of action of the resultant cuts AB produced,
(f) the equation of the line of action of the resultant.

$AC = CB = a$ and $\widehat{CAB} = \widehat{CBA} = 45°$.
(a) Resolving $\parallel$ to AB,

$$X = -(3\sqrt{2}\cos 45° + 5\sqrt{2}\cos 45°)p + 9p = \underline{p}$$

(b) Resolving $\perp$ to AB,

$$Y = (5\sqrt{2}\cos 45° - 3\sqrt{2}\cos 45°)p = \underline{2p}$$

(c) $R = \sqrt{(X^2 + Y^2)} = \underline{\sqrt{5}p}$

(d) The resultant makes an angle $\tan^{-1} 2$ with AB, i.e. $\underline{63° \text{ with AB}}$.
(e) The moment of the system about $A = G = 5\sqrt{2}ap$. This must equal the moment of the resultant about $A = 2xp$, where x is the distance from A to where the line of action of the resultant cuts AB. Therefore

$$5\sqrt{2}ap = 2xp$$
$$x = 2.5\sqrt{2}a = 3.5a$$

as $AB = \sqrt{2}a$ then the resultant cuts AB produced a distance $\underline{3.5a \text{ from A}}$.
(f) The equation of the line of action of the resultant is given by $G - xY + yX = 0$. Therefore

$$5\sqrt{2}ap - x2p + yp = 0$$

and $\underline{5\sqrt{2}a - 2x + y = 0}$

is the equation required.

Example 4.7

Figure 4.17 shows two uniform rods AB and AC, each of weight $W/2$ and length $4a$, rigidly connected at A so that they are at right angles to each other. The rods are free to turn in a vertical plane about a horizontal axis at A. Two small rough rings P and Q, each of weight W, are threaded on AB and AC respectively and joined by a light inextensible string of length $2a$ and passing through a smooth ring at A. The coefficient of friction between the rings and the rod is μ, where $\mu < 1/2$. Given that AB is

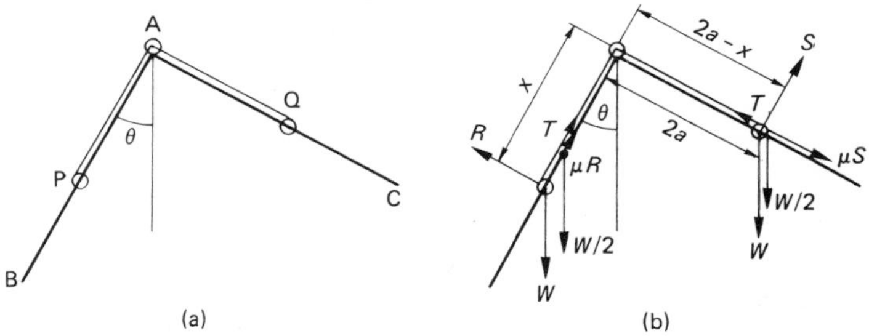

Figure 4.17

inclined at an angle θ to the vertical and P is just about to slip down AB, show that the tension T in the string is given by

$$T = W(\cos\theta - \mu\sin\theta)$$

By considering the equilibrium of Q when P is just about to slip down AB, obtain a second expression for T in terms of W, μ and θ. Hence express $\tan\theta$ in terms of μ.

Given that x denotes the distance of P from A when it is about to slip down AB, then by considering the equilibrium of the whole system show that

$$x = a + 2a\mu$$

Find also the distance of P from A when it on the point of moving up AB. (AEB N82)

The ring at A is smooth so the tensions are equal in AP and AQ. With P about to slip down AB, resolving ⊥ to AB,

$$R = W\sin\theta$$

and resolving ∥ to AB,

$$W\cos\theta = T + \mu R$$

Therefore

$$T = W\cos\theta - \mu W\sin\theta \qquad (1)$$

Similarly with Q when P is just about to slip down AB, the frictional force acts away from A. Resolving ⊥ to AC,

$$S = W\cos\theta$$

and resolving ∥ to AC,

$$T - \mu S = W\sin\theta$$

Therefore

$$\underline{T = \mu W\cos\theta + W\sin\theta} \qquad (2)$$

Subtracting equation (2) from equation (1) gives

$$0 = W\cos\theta - \mu W\sin\theta - \mu W\cos\theta - W\sin\theta$$

Dividing by $W\cos\theta$ gives

$$\underline{\tan\theta = \frac{1-\mu}{1+\mu}} \qquad (3)$$

Taking moments about A for the whole system, where AP $= x$ and so AQ $= 2a - x$,

$$Wx\sin\theta + \frac{W}{2}2a\sin\theta = W(2a-x)\cos\theta + \frac{W}{2}2a\cos\theta$$

Dividing by $W\cos\theta$ and substituting for $\tan\theta$ from equation (3) gives

$$x\frac{(1-\mu)}{(1+\mu)} = 3a - x \qquad (4)$$

i.e. $x = a + 2a\mu$

When P is on the point of moving up AB then μR and μS reverse directions. Therefore

$$\tan\theta = \frac{1+\mu}{1-\mu}$$

and equation (4) becomes

$$(x'+a)(1+\mu) = (1-\mu)(3a-x')$$

hence

$$\underline{x' = a - 2\mu a}$$

Example 4.8

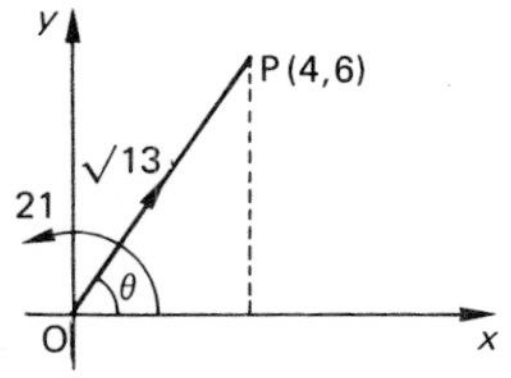

Figure 4.18

Ox and Oy are rectangular axes and P is the point whose coordinates are (4, 6) (Fig. 4.18). Find the line of action of the resultant of a force of $\sqrt{13}$ units along $\overrightarrow{\text{OP}}$ and an anticlockwise couple of moment 21 units.

The moment of the couple $G = 21$ units.

$$\rightarrow \quad X = \sqrt{13}\cos\theta = \sqrt{13}\times\frac{4}{2\sqrt{13}} = 2 \text{ units}$$

$$\uparrow \quad Y = \sqrt{13}\sin\theta = \sqrt{13}\times\frac{6}{2\sqrt{13}} = 3 \text{ units}$$

The equation of the line of action,

$$G = xY + yX = 0$$

is $\quad 21 - x\times 3 + y\times 2 = 0$

i.e. $\quad \underline{42 - 3x + 2y = 0}$

Problem 4.1

A square lamina ABCD of side a rests on a smooth horizontal plane and is acted on by a force of 6 N along $\overrightarrow{\text{BC}}$, $3\sqrt{2}$ N along $\overrightarrow{\text{AC}}$ and 2 N along $\overrightarrow{\text{AD}}$. Find the force at A and the couple which will keep the lamina at rest.

(1) Draw a diagram and label the forces.
(2) Resolve horizontally to show $X = 3$ N. Resolve vertically to show $Y = 11$ N. Hence find $R = \sqrt{130}$ N.
(3) The equilibriant is equal and opposite to the resultant and therefore has $X' = -3$ N and $Y' = -11$ N. It acts at $\tan^{-1}(11/3)$ to DA produced or $-164.7°$ to AB.
(4) Take moments about A, where the required couple for equilibrium, N + sum of moments of system about A = 0, to find $N = -6a$ units, i.e. clockwise.

Example 4.9

Figure 4.19(a) shows two uniform rods AB and BC which are smoothly jointed at B, with the ends A and C resting on a frictionless horizontal table. The rods are kept in equilibrium in a vertical plane by a light elastic string which is attached to the midpoints of AB and BC. The weights of AB and BC are $4W$ and $7W$ respectively; AB = BC = 2 m and the angle ABC = 90°. Find the reactions at A and C. Find the tension in the string and

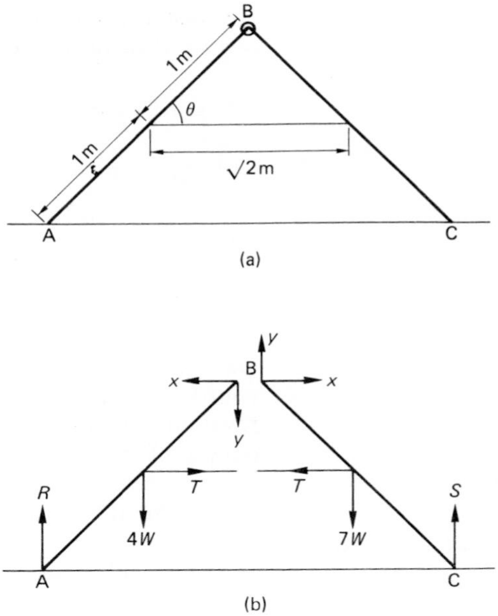

Figure 4.19

determine the vertical and horizontal components of the force acting on the rod AB at B.

There is no weight on the joint so the two reactions at B are equal and opposite as shown in Fig. 4.19(b).

$$AB = BC$$

Therefore

$$\widehat{BAC} = \widehat{BCA} = 45°$$

↑ for the system,

$$R + S = 11\,W \quad (1)$$

Taking moments about B for rod AB,

$$R \times 2\cos 45° - 4\,W \times \cos 45° - T\sin 45° = 0$$

Therefore

$$2R - 4\,W - T = 0 \quad (2)$$

Taking moments about B for BC, i.e. not including the reactions at the joint in either case,

$$7\,W\cos 45° + T\sin 45° - S(2\cos 45°) = 0$$

$$7\,W + T - 2S = 0 \quad (3)$$

Adding equations (2) and (3),

$$3\,W + 2R - 2S = 0 \quad (4)$$

Using $2R = 22\,W - 2S$ from equation (1) gives

$$3\,W + 22\,W - 2S - 2S = 0$$

Therefore

$$S = \underline{25W/4} \quad \text{and} \quad R = \underline{19W/4}$$

↑ for AB,

$$R - 4W = y$$

so $y = \underline{3W/4}$

Substituting in equation (2) for T,

$$T = 2R - 4W = 38W/4 - 22W = \underline{22W/4}$$

→ for AB,

$$x = T = \underline{22W/4}$$

Hence the horizontal component of the force acting on the rod AB at B is $22W/4$ along BA and the vertical component is $3W/4$ upwards.

Example 4.10

A uniform rod AB of length $2l$ and weight W has its end A in contact with a rough vertical wall and its end B connected by a string BC to a point C vertically above A with $AC = 2l$. The rod is in equilibrium in a vertical plane perpendicular to the wall with the angle $ACB = \alpha$, where $\alpha < 45°$. Show that the tension in the string is $W \cos \alpha$ and that the frictional force at A must act upwards. Show also that the least possible value of the coefficient of friction at A is $\tan \alpha$. Given that $\cos \alpha = 3/4$ and the string is an elastic one with modulus of elasticity $3W/2$, find the natural length of the string. (UL J83)

As $\alpha < 45°$, the diagram is as shown in Fig. 4.20.

$$AC = AB$$

Therefore

$$\widehat{ACB} = \widehat{CBA}$$

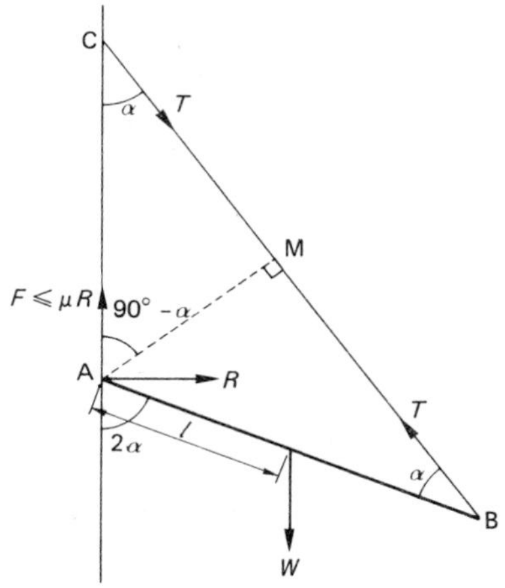

Figure 4.20

Let M be the midpoint of CB. Therefore

$$\widehat{CAM} = \widehat{MAB} = 90° - \alpha$$

Taking moments about A for AB,

$$Wl \cos(90° - 2\alpha) = T \times 2l \cos(90° - \alpha)$$

$$W \sin 2\alpha = 2T \sin \alpha$$

$$W \times 2 \sin \alpha \cos \alpha = 2T \sin \alpha$$

Therefore

$$T = W \cos \alpha$$

↑ for AB,

$$T \cos \alpha + F = W$$

taking F upwards. Therefore

$$W \cos^2 \alpha + F = W$$

$$F = W(1 - \cos^2 \alpha) \qquad (1)$$

$$0 \leqslant \cos^2 \alpha \leqslant 1$$

Therefore

$$1 - \cos^2 \alpha \geqslant 0$$

and F must act upwards.

$$F \leqslant \mu R$$

so the least value of μ needed is that for which $F = \mu R$ for the R occurring in this system.

$$\rightarrow \quad R = T \sin \alpha = W \sin \alpha \cos \alpha$$

$$F = W(1 - \cos^2 \alpha) \geqslant \mu R \geqslant \mu W \sin \alpha \cos \alpha$$

Therefore

$$\sin^2 \alpha \geqslant \mu \sin \alpha \cos \alpha$$

i.e. $\quad \mu \leqslant \tan \alpha$

Hookes law gives $T = \lambda x / L$ (see chapter 8), where T is the tension, x is the extension and L is the natural string length. Hence

$$BC = 4l \cos \alpha = 3l = L + x$$

Therefore

$$L = \frac{3W}{2} \frac{(3l - L)}{(3W/4)}$$

$$L = 6l - 2L$$

$$L = \underline{2l}$$

Problem 4.2

A light rod AB of length $2l$ is freely hinged to a vertical wall at A and the end B is connected to a vertical point C on the wall above A by a light inelastic string which is also of length $2l$.

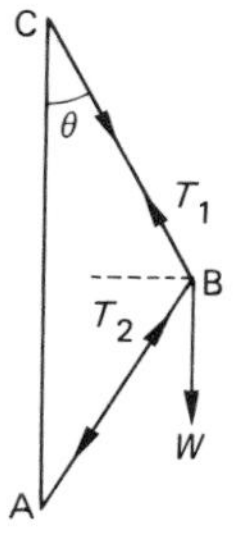

Figure 4.21

Find the tension in the string and the stress in the rod given that $\widehat{BCA} = \theta$ if a weight W hangs from B.

(1) Draw a diagram (Fig. 4.21). The rod is weightless but transmits stresses.
(2) $\widehat{BCA} = \widehat{CAB} = \theta$ because $CB = AB = 2l$.
(3) Resolve → to show that $T_1 = T_2 = T$, say.
(4) Resolve ↑ to show that $W = 2T \cos \theta$, i.e.

$$T = W/(2 \cos \theta)$$

The string is in tension; the rod AB is in compression.

Summary

(1) The moment of a force about an axis is the product of the magnitude of the force and the perpendicular distance from the line of action of the force to the axis. It is also called the torque about the axis and is measured in newton metres (N m). Anti-clockwise moments are usually taken as positive and clockwise as negative.

(2) The magnitude of the moment about an axis through the point O of a force F completely represented by a line AB is represented by twice the area of the triangle OAB.

(3) If $\boldsymbol{r} = x\boldsymbol{i} + y\boldsymbol{j}$ is the position vector of the force $\boldsymbol{F} = X\boldsymbol{i} + Y\boldsymbol{j}$ then the moment of $\boldsymbol{F}$ about the origin of the cartesian axes is $G = xY - yX$.

(4) The principle of moments states that the resultant moment of a set of forces is equal to the moment of the resultant force about the same axis (if the system reduces to a resultant force).

(5) A system may produce motion parallel to Ox, parallel to Oy and rotation about an axis perpendicular to a plane so it has three degrees of freedom and three independent equations may be found for a set of coplanar forces. They may be found:

(a) by resolving in two non-parallel directions to find the sum of the components and taking moments about one point in the plane,
(b) by taking moments about three non-colinear points in the plane,
(c) by resolving in one direction and taking moments about two non-colinear points in the plane.

(6) The resultant of two like parallel forces P and Q is parallel to them, of magnitude $P + Q$ and its line of action divides the distance between their lines of action in the ratio $Q : P$.

The resultant of two unlike parallel forces is of magnitude $Q - P$, and acts in the direction and sense of the larger magnitude. Its line of action divides the distance between the line of action of P and Q in the ratio $-Q : P$.

(7) A couple consists of two equal unlike parallel forces with separate lines of action. Its characteristics are that its linear

resultant is zero and it has a constant moment about any axis perpendicular to its plane equal to the product of the magnitude of one of the forces with the perpendicular distance between the line of action of the parallel forces. It is a turning effect only and is positive or negative if anticlockwise or clockwise respectively.

(8) A couple G together with a force F are equivalent to an equal force F displaced through G/F and vice versa.

(9) Two sets of forces are equivalent if they produce the same resultant linear and rotational motion. A system of forces $F_1, \ldots, F_n$ acting at $(x_1, y_1), \ldots, (x_n, y_n)$ can be reduced to $X = \Sigma F_x$, the sum of the x-components of the forces, $Y = \Sigma F_y$, the sum of the y-components of the forces, and $G = \Sigma(xF_y - yF_x)$, the resultant moment of the system. The resultant force $R = \sqrt{(X^2 + Y^2)}$ and acts at $\tan^{-1}(y/X)$ to Ox.

If the system is in equilibrium then $X = 0$, $Y = 0$ and $G = 0$.

If the system is not in equilibrium it may reduce to a single force R with $G = 0$, a single couple G with $R = 0$, or about a given axis to a force R plus a couple G. In the latter case the line of action of R is given by

$$G - xY + yX = 0$$

for the rectangular cartesian system of coordinates with $x = 0$ and $y = 0$ as the origin.

5

Velocity and acceleration in a straight line

Objectives

The student should be able to:

(1) define velocity, speed and acceleration,
(2) define average speed and average velocity,
(3) recognise a problem involving constant acceleration and apply the equations of motion,
(4) recognise a problem involving variable acceleration and

(a) plot appropriate graphs if data is given,
(b) use calculus to provide a solution if the acceleration is given as a function of time, velocity or displacement,

(5) recognise that particles connected to both ends of a light inextensible string passing over a smooth pulley are moving under constant forces and therefore accelerate when released.

Definitions

When a particle moves in a straight line its displacement, $\boldsymbol{s}$, velocity, $\boldsymbol{v}$, and acceleration, $\boldsymbol{a}$, can have one of two possible directions, one is taken as positive and the other as negative.

Speed and velocity

Speed is the rate of change of distance and is a scalar with units of $\mathrm{m\,s^{-1}}$.

Velocity is the rate of change of displacement, i.e

$$\boldsymbol{v} = \frac{\mathrm{d}s}{\mathrm{d}t}$$

It is a vector and has a direction.

Speed is the magnitude of velocity, i.e.

$$|\boldsymbol{v}| = v$$

In Fig. 5.1 curve A shows non-uniform motion, so to obtain the velocity at a point P the tangent must be constructed at that point then

$$\boldsymbol{v} = \frac{\Delta s}{\Delta t}$$

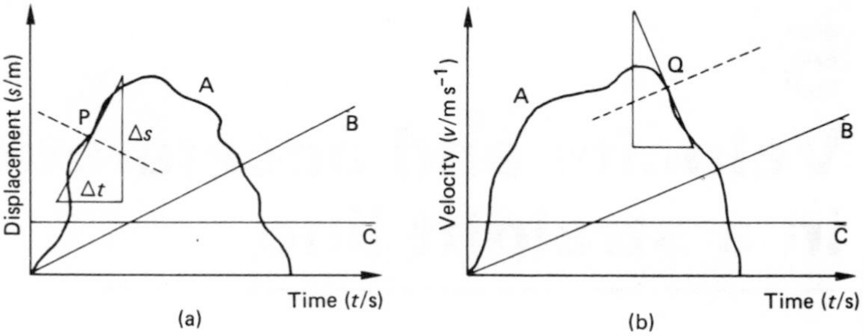

Figure 5.1

i.e. the gradient of the tangent. The straight line B shows uniform velocity, i.e. constant speed in a fixed direction, and the horizontal line C shows zero velocity.

Acceleration

Acceleration is the rate of change of velocity, i.e.

$$\boldsymbol{a} = \frac{\mathrm{d}\boldsymbol{v}}{\mathrm{d}t}$$

It is a vector and has units of m s^{-2}. In Fig. 5.1(b) curve A shows non-uniform acceleration, so to obtain the acceleration at a point Q the tangent must be constructed and its gradient found. The straight line B shows uniform acceleration, i.e. equal changes of velocity in equal successive time intervals, and the straight line C shows zero acceleration.

Average speed and average velocity

$$\text{average speed for a particle} = \frac{\text{total distance travelled}}{\text{time taken}}$$

$$\text{average velocity for a particle} = \frac{\text{increase in displacement}}{\text{time taken}}$$

For example, if a woman walks 100 m due N in 20 s, rests for 10 s and then walks 150 m due S in 50 s (Fig. 5.2), her average velocity $= -50/80$ m s^{-1}, i.e. the gradient of the chord AB, and her average speed $= 250/80$ m s^{-1} and are different.

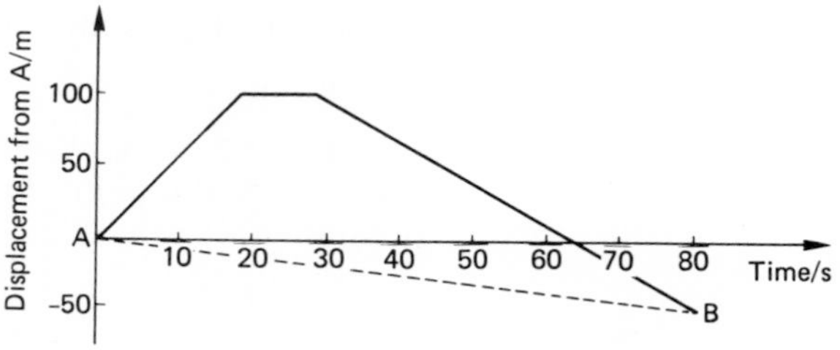

Figure 5.2

Constant acceleration

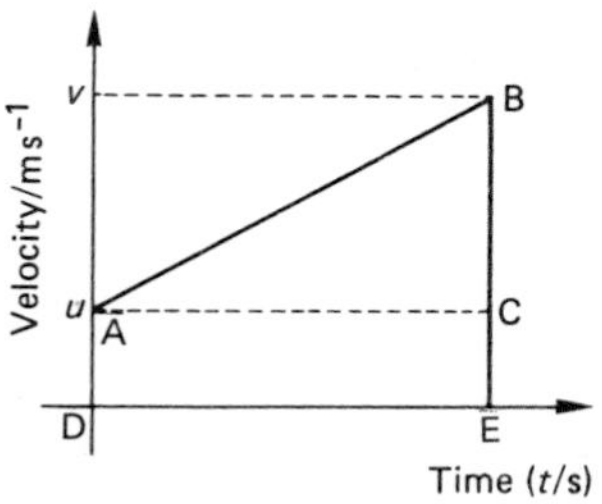

Figure 5.3

Consider a particle moving in a straight line with a constant acceleration a that has an initial velocity u and a final velocity v after a time interval t s (Fig. 5.3). Therefore

$$a = \frac{v-u}{t}$$

$$v = u + at \qquad (1)$$

i.e. the gradient of the line AB.

As $v = \mathrm{d}s/\mathrm{d}t$,

$$s = \int v\,\mathrm{d}t$$

i.e. displacement is the area under a velocity–time curve.

$$s = \text{area of } \triangle\text{ABC} + \text{area ADEC}$$

$$= ut + \tfrac{1}{2}(v-u)t = ut + \tfrac{1}{2}at^2 \qquad (2)$$

Substituting $t = (v-u)/a$ into this equation, gives

$$v^2 = u^2 + 2as \qquad (3)$$

Equations (1), (2) and (3) are the basic equations of motion in a straight line for a particle moving under constant acceleration. They are given in vector form in Chapter 6, dealing with further work on vectors.

Variable acceleration in a straight line

$$a = \frac{\mathrm{d}v}{\mathrm{d}t}$$

If experimental data is given then a graphical method can be used.

(1) If a graph of velocity against time is plotted then $a = \mathrm{d}v/\mathrm{d}t$ is the gradient of the graph and can be found from the gradient of the tangent at a point for any given instant in time as shown in Fig. 5.4. Also as

$$s = \int_{t_1}^{t_2} v\,\mathrm{d}t$$

the increase in displacement from time t_1 to t_2 is the area between the velocity–time graph, the time axis and the ordinates t_1 and t_2.

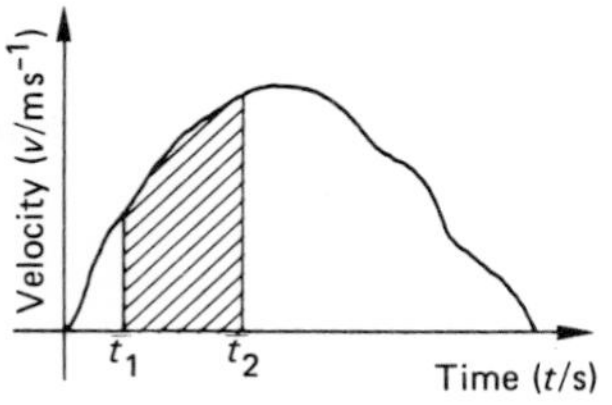

Figure 5.4

(2) $$a = \frac{\mathrm{d}v}{\mathrm{d}t} = \frac{\mathrm{d}v}{\mathrm{d}s}\frac{\mathrm{d}s}{\mathrm{d}t} = v\frac{\mathrm{d}v}{\mathrm{d}s} = \frac{\mathrm{d}}{\mathrm{d}s}(\tfrac{1}{2}v^2)$$

so if a graph of $\tfrac{1}{2}v^2$ is plotted against s then the gradient at any instant equals the instantaneous acceleration for that displacement.

$$(3) \quad v = \frac{ds}{dt}$$

$$\int dt = \int \frac{1}{v}\, ds$$

$$t = \int \frac{1}{v}\, ds$$

so
$$\int_{s_1}^{s_2} \frac{1}{v}\, ds$$

is the area between the curve of the $1/v$ against s graph, the displacement axis and the ordinates s_1 and s_2.

If acceleration is given as a function of displacement, time or velocity then calculus can be used to find velocity or distance.

Acceleration as a function of time: $a = f(t)$

For example,

$$a = \frac{dv}{dt}$$

Consider a particle moving from a fixed point with velocity $1\ \text{m s}^{-1}$ at time $t = 0$, with acceleration equal to $2t+1$.

$$\frac{dv}{dt} = 2t + 1$$

$$v = \int (2t+1)\, dt = t^2 + t + C_1$$

where C_1 is a constant. When $t = 0$, $v = 1$, therefore $1 = C_1$, and

$$v = t^2 + t + 1 = \frac{ds}{dt}$$

$$s = \int (t^2 + t + 1)\, dt = \frac{t^3}{3} + \frac{t^2}{2} + t + D$$

where D is a constant. Now, $s = 0$ when $t = 0$, therefore $D = 0$, and

$$s = \frac{t^2}{3} + \frac{t^2}{2} + t$$

Acceleration as a function of velocity: $a = f(v)$

$$a = v\frac{dv}{ds}$$

For example,

$$a = v^2$$

Therefore

$$v\frac{dv}{ds} = v^2$$

$$\int \frac{dv}{v} = \int ds$$

$$\ln v = s + C_2$$

giving a relationship between displacement and velocity. Also

$$\frac{dv}{dt} = v^2$$

$$\int v^{-2}\, dv = \int dt$$

$$-v^{-1} = t + C_3$$

giving a relationship between velocity and time.

Acceleration as a function of displacement: $a = f(s)$

For example,

$$a = s^2 + s$$

Therefore

$$v\frac{dv}{ds} = s^2 + s$$

$$\int v\, dv = \int (s^2 + s)\, ds$$

$$\frac{v^2}{2} = \frac{s^3}{3} + \frac{s^2}{2} + C_4$$

giving a relationship between velocity and displacement, where C_2, C_3 and C_4 are constant.

Motion of connected particles

Consider the motion of two particles connected by a light inextensible string passing over a smooth pulley. The tension in the string will be the same throughout its length and the motion is in a straight line up or down. To analyse the motion, $F = ma$ is applied to each particle in turn.

Consider masses m_1 and m_2 as shown in Fig. 5.5. When $m_1 > m_2$

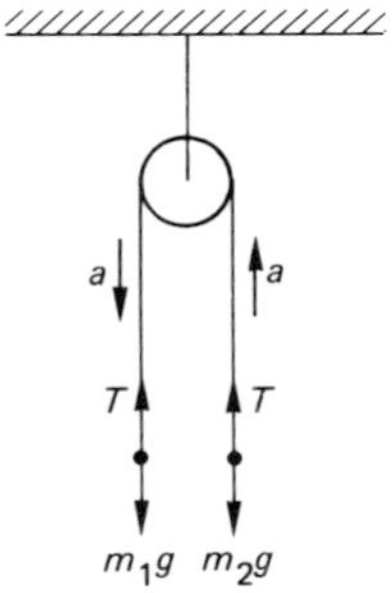

Figure 5.5

↑ $\quad m_1g - T = m_1a$

↓ $\quad T - m_2g = m_2a$

so $\quad a = \left(\frac{m_1 - m_2}{m_1 + m_2}\right)g$

and $\quad T = \frac{2m_1m_2g}{m_1 + m_2}$

Method of approach

The student must first decide if the problem involves uniform or variable acceleration in a straight line. If it is uniform then the equations of motion can be used. If the acceleration is variable and data is given then a graphical method can be used for solution. If the acceleration is non-uniform but it is given as a function of time, velocity or displacement then calculus can be used to find the required solution. Newton's law, $F = ma$, can be used to find the acceleration if information is given about the forces.

Example 5.1

A mass of 10 kg is connected by a light inextensible string over a smooth fixed pulley to a light scale pan carrying a mass of 5 kg. Find:

(a) the acceleration of the 10 kg mass,
(b) the tension in the string,
(c) the reaction between the 5 kg mass and the scale pan.

The pulley is smooth and the string light so the tension is transmitted throughout the string. The acceleration is uniform. Applying Newton's law,

$$\downarrow \quad -T + 10g = 10a \qquad (1)$$

$$\uparrow \quad -5g + T = 5a \qquad (2)$$

(a) Adding equations (1) and (2),

$$5g = 15a$$

so $\quad a = g/3 \text{ m s}^{-2}$

is the acceleration of the 10 kg mass downwards.
(b) In equation (2),

$$T = 5g + 5a = 20(g/3) \text{ N}$$

and is the tension in the string.
(c) The tension, the 10 kg weight and the 5 kg weight are external forces, taking the scale pan plus contents as the system. The reaction R between the scale pan and the 5 kg weight is an internal force and is dotted in Fig. 5.6 to distinguish this. From Newton's law

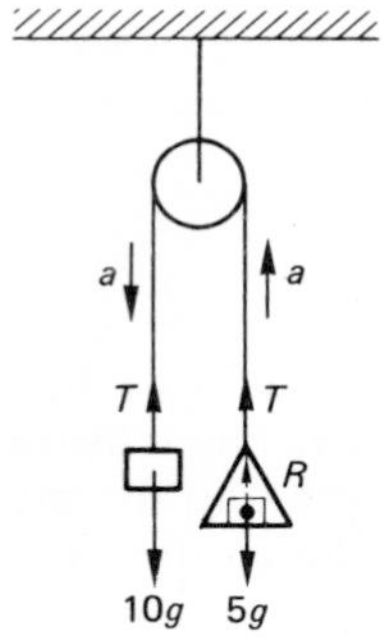

Figure 5.6

$$R = 5g + ma = \underline{20(g/3)\ N}$$

between the 5 kg mass and the scale pan.

Example 5.2

A car travelling along a straight road can accelerate at one-quarter of the rate at which it can decelerate. It travels a total distance of 1.5 km in two minutes accelerating uniformly to a fixed speed, maintaining that speed for 30 seconds and then decelerating to zero speed. Sketch a speed–time graph for the motion and find the magnitude of the acceleration and deceleration.

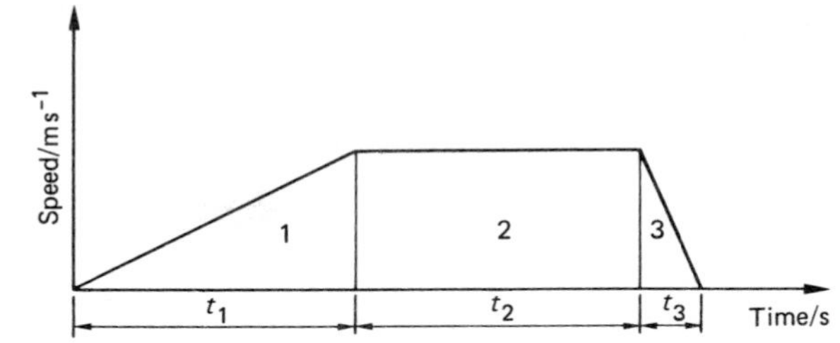

Figure 5.7

See Fig. 5.7. This is a uniform acceleration problem and so involves the equations of motion.

Let a_1 be the acceleration and a_3 the retardation. Let t_1, t_2 and t_3 be the times to accelerate, travel at constant speed and decelerate and let s_1, s_2 and s_3 be the distances travelled during those times. Let v be the maximum speed reached.

$$4a_1 = a_3$$

(given in the question) and using $v = u + at$,

$$v = a_1 t_1 = a_3 t_3$$

$$t_3 = t_1/4$$

The total time $= 120\text{ s} = t_1 + t_2 + t_3$ and $t_2 = 30$ s.

$$120 = t_1 + 30 + t_1/4$$

$$5t_1/4 = 90$$

Therefore

$$t_1 = 72\text{ s} \quad \text{and} \quad t_3 = 18\text{ s}$$

Also $s_1 + s_2 + s_3 = 1500$ m and using $s = ut + \frac{1}{2}at^2$,

$$s = \tfrac{1}{2}at^2 = \tfrac{1}{2}vt$$

for s_1 and s_2. Therefore

$$\tfrac{1}{2}vt_1 + vt_2 + \tfrac{1}{2}vt_3 = 1500$$

$$v\left(\frac{72}{2} + 30 + \frac{18}{2}\right) = 1500$$

i.e. $v = 20\text{ m s}^{-1}$

Hence

$$\text{magnitude of the acceleration} = \frac{v}{t_1} = \underline{\frac{20}{72}\text{ m s}^{-2}}$$

and

$$\text{magnitude of the deceleration} = \underline{\frac{80}{72}\text{ m s}^{-2}}$$

Example 5.3

A particle moving along a straight line with speed v experiences a retardation of magnitude $be^{v/u}$, where b and u are constants. Given that the particle is travelling with speed u at time $t = 0$, show that the time for the speed to decrease to $\frac{1}{2}u$ is given by

$$bt_1 = u(e^{-1/2} - e^{-1})$$

Find the further time t_2 for the particle to come to rest. Deduce that $t_2/t_1 = e^{1/2}$.

Find in terms of b and u an expression for the distance travelled in decelerating from speed u to rest. (UL J82)

The acceleration is non-uniform and negative. No data is given so calculus must be used.

$$a = -be^{v/u} = \frac{dv}{dt}$$

Velocity is required as a function of time so integrating with respect to time,

$$\int_u^{u/2} \frac{dv}{e^{v/u}} = -\int b\,dt$$

$$[-ue^{-v/u}]_u^{u/2} = -b[t]_0^{t_1} \qquad (1)$$

$$-ue^{-1/2} + ue^{-1} = -bt_1$$

i.e. $$bt_1 = u(e^{-1/2} - e^{-1})$$

Let t_3 be the time for the particle to come to rest; hence changing the limits on equation (1) to u and zero

$$[-ue^{-v/u}]_u^0 = -b[t]_0^{t_3}$$

$$-ue^0 + ue^{-1} = -bt_3$$

$$bt_3 = u(1 - e^{-1})$$

The further time t_2 after t_1 for the particle to come to rest is given by

$$t_2 = t_3 - t_1 = \underline{(u/b)(1 - e^{1/2})}$$

Hence

$$\frac{t_2}{t_1} = \frac{(u/b)}{(u/b)} \frac{(1 - e^{-1/2})}{(e^{-1/2} - e^{-1})}$$

Dividing the bottom line by $e^{-1/2}$,

$$\frac{t_2}{t_1} = \frac{1}{(e^{-1/2})} \frac{(1 - e^{-1/2})}{(1 - e^{-1/2})} = e^{1/2}$$

To find the distance X travelled in decelerating from speed u to rest, acceleration is expressed as a function of distance, i.e.

$$a = v\frac{dv}{ds} = -be^{v/u}$$

Therefore

$$\int ve^{-v/u}\,dv = -\int b\,ds$$

Using $\int u\frac{dv}{dx}\,dx = uv - \int v\frac{du}{dx}\,dx$,

$$-b\,[s]_0^x = v\int e^{-v/u}\,dv - \int -ue^{-v/u}\,dv$$

$$-b\,[s]_0^x = [uve^{-u/v} - u^2e^{-v/u}]_u^0$$

$$-bx = -u^2e^0 - (-u^2e^{-1} - u^2e^{-1})$$

$$x = \underline{(u^2/b)(1-2e^{-1})}$$

Example 5.4

A particle moves along a straight line from a fixed point 0. Corresponding values of time and displacement are given in the table below. By drawing a suitable graph, find the values of:

(a) the average velocity in the time $t=1$ to $t=4$ s,
(b) the distance covered in the time $t=1$ to $t=4$ s,
(c) the average speed in the time $t=0$ to $t=4$ s,
(d) the time at which the velocity is zero,
(e) the velocity at time $t=5$ s.

t(s)	*s*(m)
0	12
1	0
2	−6
3	−8
4	−6
5	0
6	6

As data has been given, the problem is dealt with by plotting a graph of displacement against time (Fig. 5.8).

(a) $\text{velocity} = \frac{\text{change in displacement}}{\text{change in time}} = \frac{\text{chord AB}}{3} = \underline{\frac{-6}{3}\ \text{m s}^{-1}}$

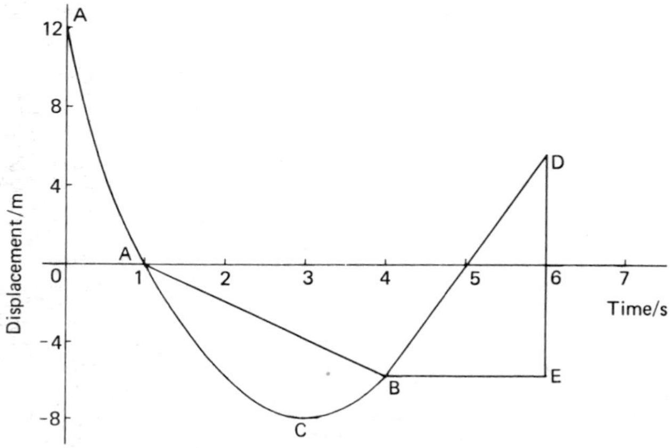

Figure 5.8

(b) From 1 to 3 s the distance travelled = 8 m. From 3 to 4 s the distance travelled = 2 m. The distances are travelled in opposite directions but distance is a scalar so the total distance travelled = 10 m.
(c) average speed in time 0 to 4 s

$$= \frac{\text{total distance travelled}}{\text{time taken}} = \frac{10}{3}\,\text{m s}^{-1}$$

and is different from the velocity in part (a).
(d) The velocity is zero when the gradient of the tangent to the curve is zero, i.e. at the point C when $t = 3$ s.
(e) The velocity at $t = 5$ s = gradient of the tangent to the curve at $t = 5$ s = DE/BE. Therefore

velocity at $t = 5$ s = 12/2 = 6 m s^{-1}

Problem 5.1

A particle is moving in a straight line along a smooth horizontal surface with an acceleration which is proportional to the cube of the speed V for $t \leqslant 5$ s. For $t \geqslant 5$ s the acceleration is zero. It passes through a fixed point 0 at time $t = 0$ with acceleration = 1/50 m s^{-2} and $V = 1$ m s^{-1}. Find the velocity at $t = 5$ s and the distance travelled after 6 s.

(1) Let $a = kV^3$. Calculus must be used to obtain the answers. Substitute the initial conditions for a and V to find $k = 1/50$.
(2) Express acceleration as a function of time: $\mathrm{d}V/\mathrm{d}t = V^3/50$. Separate the variables and integrate to find $V^2 = \sqrt{1.25}$, i.e. $V =$ 1.12 m s^{-1} at $t = 5$ s using the positive value.
(3) Now to find the distance, split the problem into two parts.

(a) From $t = 5$ to $t = 6$ s, using $s = ut + \frac{1}{2}at^2$ with $a = 0$,

$$s_{5\to 6} = 1.12 \times 1 = 1.12 \text{ m}$$

(b) From $t = 0$ to $t = 5$ s, using $V\,\mathrm{d}V/\mathrm{d}s = V^3/50$, i.e. acceleration as a function of distance, and integrating to find $s = 50(1 - 1/\sqrt{1.25})$,

$$s_{0\to 5} = 5.28 \text{ m}$$

Therefore the total distance travelled = 6.4 m.

Problem 5.2

A ball is thrown vertically upwards with a velocity of 20 m s^{-1}. Three seconds later a second ball is dropped from the same spot. Neglecting air resistance, find the height of the spot above the ground if the balls meet one metre above the ground.

(1) Let T be the time for the first ball and $T - 3$ the time for the second ball when they meet.
(2) Let $-d$ be the displacement from the spot when the balls meet, taking up as positive.
(3) Using $s = ut + \frac{1}{2}at^2$, substitute values for both balls to find

$$-d = 20T - 5T^2 = -5(T-3)^2$$

Hence $T = 4.5$ s, $d = 11.25$ m and the height of the spot above the ground = 12.25 m.

Summary

(1) speed is a scalar and equal to $\dfrac{ds}{dt}$

velocity is a vector and equal to $\dfrac{d\mathbf{s}}{dt}$

acceleration is a vector and equal to $\dfrac{d\mathbf{v}}{dt}$

(2) average speed $= \dfrac{\text{total distance travelled}}{\text{time taken}}$

average velocity $= \dfrac{\text{increase in displacement}}{\text{time taken}}$

(3) For constant acceleration the equations of motion

$s = ut + \frac{1}{2}at^2$

$v = u + at$

$v^2 = u^2 + 2as$

may be used in solving problems.

(4) For variable acceleration, given as *data*:

(a) a is the gradient of a v against t graph because

$$a = \frac{d\mathbf{v}}{dt} \quad \text{and} \quad s = \int v\,dt$$

so is the area under a v against t graph,

(b) $a = \dfrac{d}{ds}(\frac{1}{2}v^2)$

so is the gradient of a $\frac{1}{2}v^2$ against s graph,

(c) $t = \displaystyle\int \frac{1}{v}\,ds$

so is the area under a $1/v$ against s graph.

(5) For variable acceleration, given as a *function*:

(a) of time, $dv/dt = f(t)$,

$$\int dv = \int f(t)\,dt \quad \text{to find } v \text{ or } t$$

(b) of displacement, $v\,dv/ds = f(s)$,

$$\int v\,dv = \int f(s)\,ds \quad \text{to find } v \text{ or } s$$

(c) $v\,dv/ds = f(v)$,

$$\int \frac{v\,dv}{f(v)} = \int ds \quad \text{to find } s \text{ or } v$$

or $\mathrm{d}v/\mathrm{d}t = f(v)$

$$\int \frac{\mathrm{d}v}{f(v)} = \int \mathrm{d}t \quad \text{to find } t \text{ or } v$$

(6) Apply Newton's law and the equation of motion to particles connected to both ends of a light inextensible string, passing over a smooth pulley, when released.

6
Further vector analysis

Objectives

The student should be able to:

(1) use the direction ratios, direction cosines and the unit vector $\hat{\boldsymbol{r}}$ of a given vector $\boldsymbol{r} = a\boldsymbol{i} + b\boldsymbol{j} + c\boldsymbol{k}$,
(2) find the distance between two points A and B with position vectors $\boldsymbol{a}$ and $\boldsymbol{b}$,
(3) find the position vector $\boldsymbol{c}$ of a point C dividing the line AB in a given ratio,
(4) define and use the scalar product of two vectors,
(5) define and use the vector product of two vectors,
(6) use the equation of a straight line in vector, parametric and cartesian forms,
(7) state the conditions for two lines $\boldsymbol{r} = \boldsymbol{a}_1 + \lambda\boldsymbol{b}_1$ and $\boldsymbol{r} = \boldsymbol{a}_2 + \lambda\boldsymbol{b}_2$ to be parallel, intersect or to be skew and find the shortest distance between a pair of skew links,
(8) find the distance of a point from a line,
(9) find the angle between two lines,
(10) use the equation of a plane in its vector, cartesian and parametric forms,
(11) find the angle between two planes,
(12) find the angle between a line and a plane,
(13) find the distance of a point from a plane,
(14) differentiate and integrate a vector with respect to a scalar variable.

Direction ratios and direction cosines

A vector $\boldsymbol{r}$ represents the line $\overrightarrow{OP}$, where P has coordinates (a, b, c) so the components parallel to Ox, Oy and Oz are of magnitudes a, b and c respectively.

Figure 6.1 shows two right-handed systems of reference directions and both are correct, but for preference Fig. 6.1(b) will be used in this book.

$$\boldsymbol{r} = a\boldsymbol{i} + b\boldsymbol{j} + c\boldsymbol{k}$$

and the modulus of $\boldsymbol{r}$,

$$|\boldsymbol{r}| = \sqrt{(a^2 + b^2 + c^2)} = r$$

and is always positive.

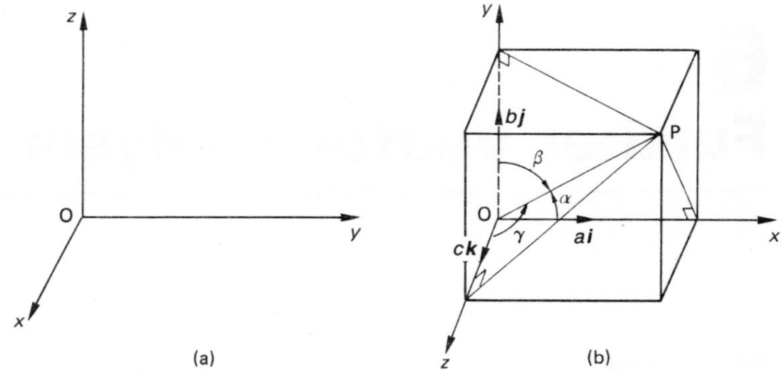

Figure 6.1

The ratios $a:b:c$ are the ratios of the components of $\boldsymbol{r}$ parallel to Ox, Oy and Oz and are called the **direction ratios** of $\boldsymbol{r}$.

A vector parallel to $\boldsymbol{r}$ would have the same direction ratios even if it acted in the opposite sense. If $\overrightarrow{\mathrm{OP}}$ makes angles α, β and γ with Ox, Oy and Oz respectively, then the direction cosines are:

$$\cos\alpha = \frac{a}{r} = l \quad \cos\beta = \frac{b}{r} = m \quad \cos\gamma = \frac{c}{r} = n$$

The direction cosines are given the letters l, m and n and are unique for like parallel vectors. Unlike parallel vectors have direction cosines equal in magnitude but opposite in sign. The unit vector $\hat{\boldsymbol{r}} = l\boldsymbol{i} + m\boldsymbol{j} + n\boldsymbol{k}$ acts along $\overrightarrow{\mathrm{OP}}$ and $l^2 + m^2 + n^2 = (a^2 + b^2 + c^2)/r^2 = 1$. Thus the sum of the squares of the direction cosines of any vector is unity.

Example 6.1

Find the modulus and direction cosines of the vector $\boldsymbol{P} = 3\boldsymbol{i} - 2\boldsymbol{j} + 6\boldsymbol{k}$.

$$|\boldsymbol{P}| = \sqrt{(3^2 + (-2)^2 + 6^2)} = \underline{7}$$

$\boldsymbol{P}$ has direction ratios $3:-2:6$. Hence $\boldsymbol{P}$ has direction cosines $\underline{\frac{3}{7}, -\frac{2}{7}, \frac{6}{7}}$.

Example 6.2

Find the modulus and direction cosines of the line joining the points A and B with position vectors $3\boldsymbol{i} + 4\boldsymbol{j} - \boldsymbol{k}$ and $2\boldsymbol{i} + \boldsymbol{j} + \boldsymbol{k}$ respectively.

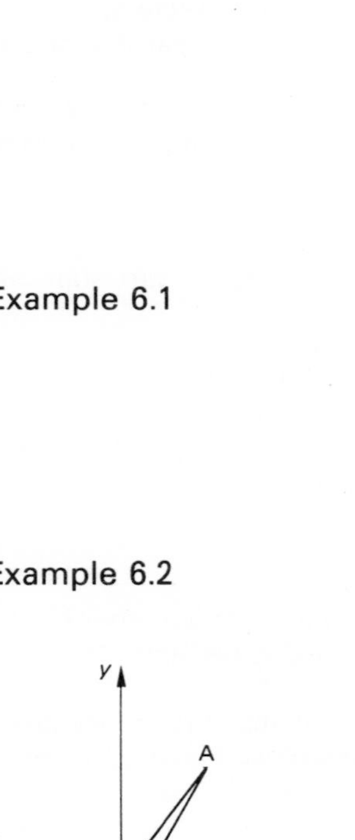

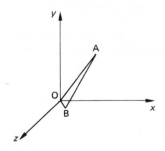

Figure 6.2

See Fig. 6.2.

$$\overrightarrow{\mathrm{AB}} = \overrightarrow{\mathrm{OB}} - \overrightarrow{\mathrm{OA}} = (2\boldsymbol{i} + \boldsymbol{j} + \boldsymbol{k}) - (3\boldsymbol{i} + 4\boldsymbol{j} - \boldsymbol{k})$$
$$= -\boldsymbol{i} - 3\boldsymbol{j} + 2\boldsymbol{k}$$

Therefore

$$|\overrightarrow{\mathrm{AB}}| = \sqrt{(1 + 9 + 4)} = \underline{\sqrt{14}}$$

and the direction cosines of $\overrightarrow{\mathrm{AB}}$ are $\underline{\frac{-1}{\sqrt{14}}, \frac{-3}{\sqrt{14}}, \frac{2}{\sqrt{14}}}$.

Distance between two points

If two points A and B have coordinates (x_1, y_1, z_1) and (x_2, y_2, z_2) (Fig. 6.3) then

$$\overrightarrow{AB} = (x_2 - x_1)\boldsymbol{i} + (y_2 - y_1)\boldsymbol{j} + (z_2 - z_1)\boldsymbol{k}$$

and $|\overrightarrow{AB}| = \sqrt{[(x_2 - x_1)^2 + (y_2 - y_1)^2 + (z_2 - z_1)^2]}$

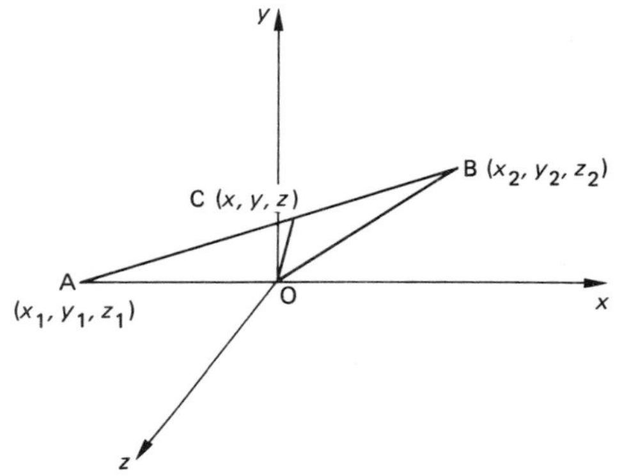

Figure 6.3

Point dividing a line in a given ratio

Let C divide AB internally in the ratio $\lambda : \mu$. Then

$$\overrightarrow{OC} = \overrightarrow{OA} + \overrightarrow{AC} = \overrightarrow{OA} + \left(\frac{\lambda}{\lambda + \mu}\right)\overrightarrow{AB}$$

$$= \boldsymbol{a} + \left(\frac{\lambda}{\lambda + \mu}\right)(\boldsymbol{b} - \boldsymbol{a})$$

Therefore

$$\overrightarrow{OC} = \frac{\lambda \boldsymbol{b} + \mu \boldsymbol{a}}{\lambda + \mu}$$

$$= \tfrac{1}{2}(\boldsymbol{a} + \boldsymbol{b}) \text{ (for the midpoint)}$$

In cartesian form

$$\overrightarrow{OC} = \frac{\lambda(x_2\boldsymbol{i} + y_2\boldsymbol{j} + z_2\boldsymbol{k}) + \mu(x_1\boldsymbol{i} + y_1\boldsymbol{j} + z_1\boldsymbol{k})}{\lambda + \mu}$$

Thus

$$x = \frac{\lambda x_2 + \mu x_1}{\lambda + \mu} \quad y = \frac{\lambda y_2 + \mu y_1}{\lambda + \mu} \quad z = \frac{\lambda z_2 + \mu z_1}{\lambda + \mu}$$

Note For external division the ratio is used in the form $\lambda : -\mu$.

Example 6.3

Find the position vector of the point C in the line AB if C divides AB internally in the ratio 2:1 and the position vectors of A and B are $\boldsymbol{i} + 3\boldsymbol{j} + 2\boldsymbol{k}$ and $4\boldsymbol{i} - 2\boldsymbol{j} + \boldsymbol{k}$ respectively.

For C

$$x = \frac{(2\times 4)+1}{3} \qquad y = \frac{(-2\times 2)+3}{3} \qquad z = \frac{(2\times 1)+2}{3}$$

$$x = 3 \qquad y = -\tfrac{1}{3} \qquad z = \tfrac{4}{3}$$

Therefore

$$\overrightarrow{OC} = \underline{3\boldsymbol{i} - \tfrac{1}{3}\boldsymbol{j} + \tfrac{4}{3}\boldsymbol{k}}$$

Products of vectors

There are two operations applied to vectors, both of which are called products. The first operation results in a scalar quantity and is known as the scalar product. The second operation results in a vector quantity and so is known as the vector product.

For two vectors $\boldsymbol{a}$ and $\boldsymbol{b}$ the scalar product is written $\boldsymbol{a}\cdot\boldsymbol{b}$ and the vector product $\boldsymbol{a}\times\boldsymbol{b}$. It is better then to represent multiplication of two real numbers by brackets to avoid confusion with the very different operation of vector products.

Scalar product (or 'dot' product) of two vectors

The scalar product $\boldsymbol{a}\cdot\boldsymbol{b}$ of two vectors $\boldsymbol{a}$ and $\boldsymbol{b}$ inclined at an angle θ to each other (Fig. 6.4(a)) is defined as

$$\boldsymbol{a}\cdot\boldsymbol{b} = |\boldsymbol{a}|\,|\boldsymbol{b}|\cos\theta = (\text{OA})(\text{OB})\cos\theta$$

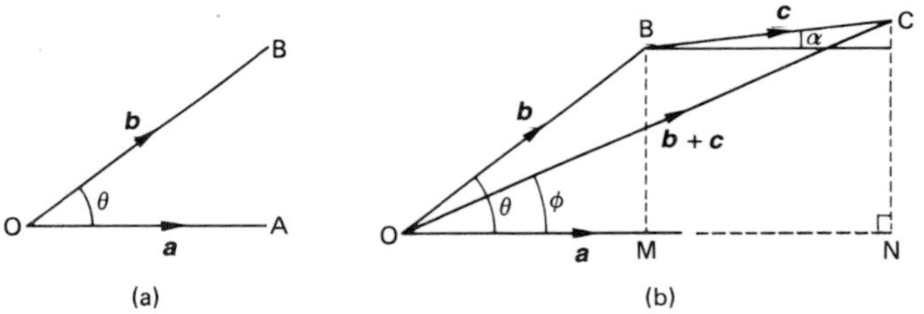

Figure 6.4

Now

$$\boldsymbol{b}\cdot\boldsymbol{a} = |\boldsymbol{b}|\,|\boldsymbol{a}|\cos\theta = ab\cos\theta$$

Therefore

$$\boldsymbol{a}\cdot\boldsymbol{b} = \boldsymbol{b}\cdot\boldsymbol{a}$$

and is commutative.

From Fig. 6.4(b)

$$\begin{aligned}\boldsymbol{a}\cdot(\boldsymbol{b}+\boldsymbol{c}) &= (\text{OA})(\text{OC})\cos\Phi\\ &= (\text{OA})(\text{ON}) = (\text{OA})(\text{OM}+\text{MN})\\ &= (\text{OA})(\text{OB}\cos\theta) + (\text{OA})(\text{BC}\cos\theta)\end{aligned}$$

i.e. $\boldsymbol{a}\cdot(\boldsymbol{b}+\boldsymbol{c}) = \boldsymbol{a}\cdot\boldsymbol{b} + \boldsymbol{a}\cdot\boldsymbol{c}$

hence the scalar product is distributive over addition.

(If two vectors are *parallel* their scalar product is $|\boldsymbol{a}|\,|\boldsymbol{b}|$ since

$$\boldsymbol{a}\cdot\boldsymbol{b} = |\boldsymbol{a}|\,|\boldsymbol{b}|\cos 0° = |\boldsymbol{a}|\,|\boldsymbol{b}|$$

The scalar product of a vector with itself

$$\boldsymbol{a} \cdot \boldsymbol{a} = |\boldsymbol{a}|^2 = a^2$$

In particular,

$$\boldsymbol{i} \cdot \boldsymbol{i} = \boldsymbol{j} \cdot \boldsymbol{j} = \boldsymbol{k} \cdot \boldsymbol{k} = 1$$

If two vectors are *perpendicular* their scalar product is zero since

$$\boldsymbol{a} \cdot \boldsymbol{b} = |\boldsymbol{a}|\,|\boldsymbol{b}| \cos 90° = 0$$

In particular,

$$\boldsymbol{i} \cdot \boldsymbol{j} = \boldsymbol{j} \cdot \boldsymbol{k} = \boldsymbol{k} \cdot \boldsymbol{i} = 0$$

Calculation of the scalar product

Let $\boldsymbol{p} = a_1\boldsymbol{i} + a_2\boldsymbol{j} + a_3\boldsymbol{k}$ and let $\boldsymbol{q} = b_1\boldsymbol{i} + b_2\boldsymbol{j} + b_3\boldsymbol{k}$ be inclined to each other at an angle θ. Then

$$\begin{aligned}\boldsymbol{p} \cdot \boldsymbol{q} &= (a_1\boldsymbol{i} + a_2\boldsymbol{j} + a_3\boldsymbol{k}) \cdot (b_1\boldsymbol{i} + b_2\boldsymbol{j} + b_3\boldsymbol{k}) \\ &= a_1 b_1 \boldsymbol{i} \cdot \boldsymbol{i} + a_2 b_2 \boldsymbol{j} \cdot \boldsymbol{j} + a_3 b_3 \boldsymbol{k} \cdot \boldsymbol{k} \\ &\quad + (a_1 b_2 \boldsymbol{i} \cdot \boldsymbol{j} + a_1 b_3 \boldsymbol{i} \cdot \boldsymbol{k}) + (a_2 b_1 \boldsymbol{j} \cdot \boldsymbol{i} + a_2 b_3 \boldsymbol{j} \cdot \boldsymbol{k}) \\ &\quad + (a_3 b_1 \boldsymbol{k} \cdot \boldsymbol{i} + a_3 b_2 \boldsymbol{k} \cdot \boldsymbol{j})\end{aligned}$$

i.e. $\boldsymbol{p} \cdot \boldsymbol{q} = a_1 b_1 + a_2 b_2 + a_3 b_3 + (0) + (0) + (0)$

Now

$\boldsymbol{p} \cdot \boldsymbol{q} = |\boldsymbol{p}|\,|\boldsymbol{q}| \cos \theta$. Therefore

$$\cos \theta = \frac{a_1 b_1 + a_2 b_2 + a_3 b_3}{|\boldsymbol{p}|\,|\boldsymbol{q}|}$$

but $\dfrac{a_1}{|\boldsymbol{p}|} = l_1 \quad \dfrac{a_2}{|\boldsymbol{p}|} = m_1 \quad \dfrac{a_3}{|\boldsymbol{p}|} = n_1$ (for $\boldsymbol{p}$)

and $\dfrac{b_1}{|\boldsymbol{q}|} = l_2 \quad \dfrac{b_2}{|\boldsymbol{q}|} = m_2 \quad \dfrac{b_3}{|\boldsymbol{q}|} = n_2$ (for $\boldsymbol{q}$)

so $\cos \theta = l_1 l_2 + m_1 m_2 + n_1 n_2$

and is the scalar product of the unit vectors $\hat{\boldsymbol{p}}$ and $\hat{\boldsymbol{q}}$ in the directions $\boldsymbol{p}$ and $\boldsymbol{q}$. Hence

$$\hat{\boldsymbol{p}} \cdot \hat{\boldsymbol{q}} \cos \theta = l_1 l_2 + m_1 m_2 + n_1 n_2$$

Example 6.4

Find the angle between the directions of the vectors:

(a) $2\boldsymbol{i} + 3\boldsymbol{j} + \boldsymbol{k}$ and $4\boldsymbol{i} + 5\boldsymbol{j} + \boldsymbol{k}$,
(b) $2\boldsymbol{i} + 3\boldsymbol{j}$ and $4\boldsymbol{i} + 6\boldsymbol{j}$.

(a) $(2\boldsymbol{i} + 3\boldsymbol{j} + \boldsymbol{k}) \cdot (4\boldsymbol{i} + 5\boldsymbol{j} + \boldsymbol{k}) = (8 + 15 + 1) \cos \theta = 24 \cos \theta$

$|2\boldsymbol{i} + 3\boldsymbol{j} + \boldsymbol{k}| = \sqrt{14}$

$|4\boldsymbol{i} + 5\boldsymbol{j} + \boldsymbol{k}| = \sqrt{42}$

so $\cos\theta = 24/\sqrt{(14\times 42)}$

i.e. $\theta = \underline{8.2°}$

$$(2\boldsymbol{i}+3\boldsymbol{j})\cdot(4\boldsymbol{i}+6\boldsymbol{j}) = 26\cos\theta$$

$$|2\boldsymbol{i}+3\boldsymbol{j}| = \sqrt{13}$$

$$|4\boldsymbol{i}+6\boldsymbol{j}| = \sqrt{52}$$

so $\cos\theta = 26/\sqrt{(13\times 52)} = 1$

$\theta = \underline{0°}$

hence the vectors are parallel.

Example 6.5

Find the angle between the vectors $a\boldsymbol{i}+b\boldsymbol{j}$ and $b\boldsymbol{i}-a\boldsymbol{j}$.

$$(a\boldsymbol{i}+b\boldsymbol{j})\cdot(b\boldsymbol{i}-a\boldsymbol{j}) = (ab-ba)\cos\theta = 0$$

$$\theta = \underline{90°}$$

Therefore the vectors are perpendicular since their scalar product is zero. This can be a useful form to remember.

Resolving a vector in a specified direction

If a vector $\boldsymbol{a}$ is inclined at an angle θ to a vector $\boldsymbol{b}$ then the component of $\boldsymbol{a}$ in the direction of $\boldsymbol{b}$ is of magnitude $|\boldsymbol{a}|\cos\theta$, but

$$\boldsymbol{a}\cdot\boldsymbol{b} = |\boldsymbol{a}|\,|\boldsymbol{b}|\cos\theta$$

Therefore

$$|\boldsymbol{a}|\cos\theta = \frac{\boldsymbol{a}\cdot\boldsymbol{b}}{|\boldsymbol{b}|} = \boldsymbol{a}\cdot\hat{\boldsymbol{b}}$$

Vector product (or 'cross' product) of two vectors

The vector product of two vectors $\boldsymbol{a}$ and $\boldsymbol{b}$ which are inclined at an angle θ is written $\boldsymbol{a}\times\boldsymbol{b}$ (or $\boldsymbol{a}\wedge\boldsymbol{b}$) and is defined as a vector of magnitude $ab\sin\theta$ in a direction perpendicular to the plane containing $\boldsymbol{a}$ and $\boldsymbol{b}$ in the sense of a right-handed screw from $\boldsymbol{a}$ to $\boldsymbol{b}$.

$$a\times b = ab\sin\theta\,\hat{\boldsymbol{n}}$$

From this definition

$$\boldsymbol{a}\times\boldsymbol{b} = -\boldsymbol{b}\times\boldsymbol{a}$$

so it is *not* commutative (Fig. 6.5).

If two vectors are *parallel*

$$\boldsymbol{a}\times\boldsymbol{b} = |\boldsymbol{a}|\,|\boldsymbol{b}|\sin 0°\,\hat{\boldsymbol{n}} = 0$$

Therefore

$$\boldsymbol{i}\times\boldsymbol{i} = \boldsymbol{j}\times\boldsymbol{j} = \boldsymbol{k}\times\boldsymbol{k} = 0$$

If two vectors are *perpendicular*

$$\boldsymbol{a}\times\boldsymbol{b} = ab\sin 90° = ab$$

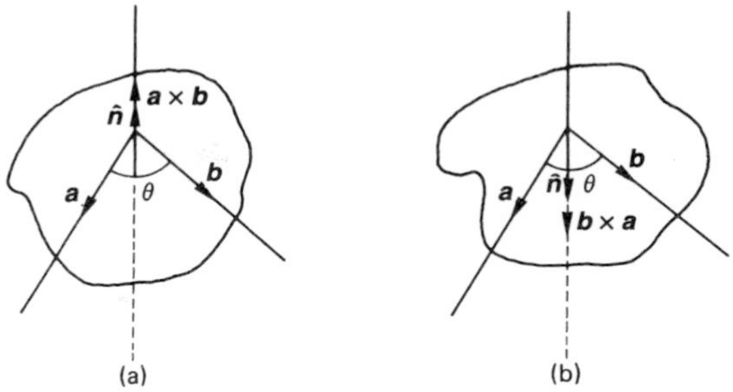

Figure 6.5

Therefore

$$\boldsymbol{i}\times\boldsymbol{j}=\boldsymbol{k} \quad \boldsymbol{j}\times\boldsymbol{k}=\boldsymbol{i} \quad \boldsymbol{k}\times\boldsymbol{i}=\boldsymbol{j}$$

$$\boldsymbol{j}\times\boldsymbol{i}=-\boldsymbol{k} \quad \boldsymbol{k}\times\boldsymbol{j}=-\boldsymbol{i} \quad \boldsymbol{i}\times\boldsymbol{k}=-\boldsymbol{j}$$

Vector product of vectors in cartesian component form

The vector product is distributive, i.e.

$$\boldsymbol{a}\times(\boldsymbol{b}+\boldsymbol{c})=\boldsymbol{a}\times\boldsymbol{b}+\boldsymbol{a}\times\boldsymbol{c}$$

Consider two vectors $\boldsymbol{p}=a_1\boldsymbol{i}+b_1\boldsymbol{j}+c_1\boldsymbol{k}$ and $\boldsymbol{q}=a_2\boldsymbol{i}+b_2\boldsymbol{j}+c_2\boldsymbol{k}$.

$$\begin{aligned}\boldsymbol{p}\times\boldsymbol{q}&=(a_1\boldsymbol{i}+b_1\boldsymbol{j}+c_1\boldsymbol{k})\times(a_2\boldsymbol{i}+b_2\boldsymbol{j}+c_2\boldsymbol{k})\\&=a_1a_2\boldsymbol{i}\times\boldsymbol{i}+a_1b_2\boldsymbol{i}\times\boldsymbol{j}+a_1c_2\boldsymbol{i}\times\boldsymbol{k}\\&\quad+b_1a_2\boldsymbol{j}\times\boldsymbol{i}+b_1b_2\boldsymbol{j}\times\boldsymbol{j}+b_1c_2\boldsymbol{j}\times\boldsymbol{k}\\&\quad+c_1a_2\boldsymbol{k}\times\boldsymbol{i}+c_1b_2\boldsymbol{k}\times\boldsymbol{j}+c_1c_2\boldsymbol{k}\times\boldsymbol{k}\end{aligned}$$

i.e. $\boldsymbol{p}\times\boldsymbol{q}=a_1b_2\boldsymbol{k}-b_1a_2\boldsymbol{k}-a_1c_2\boldsymbol{j}+c_1a_2\boldsymbol{j}+b_1c_2\boldsymbol{i}-c_1b_2\boldsymbol{i}$

$$=(b_1c_2-c_1b_2)\boldsymbol{i}-(a_1c_2-c_1a_2)\boldsymbol{j}+(a_1b_2-b_1a_2)\boldsymbol{k}$$

This result is the expansion of the determinant

$$\begin{vmatrix}\boldsymbol{i} & \boldsymbol{j} & \boldsymbol{k}\\ a_1 & b_1 & c_1\\ a_2 & b_2 & c_2\end{vmatrix}.$$

Application of the vector product

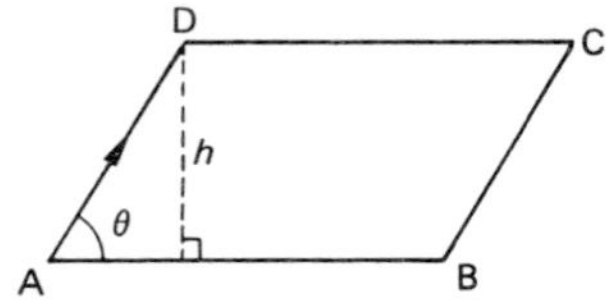

Figure 6.6

Area of a parallelogram
See Fig. 6.6.

$$\begin{aligned}\text{area of parallelogram ABCD}&=\text{base}\times\text{height}\\&=(\text{AB})(h)\\&=(\text{AB})(\text{AD}\sin\theta)\\&=|\overrightarrow{\text{AB}}\times\overrightarrow{\text{AD}}|\end{aligned}$$

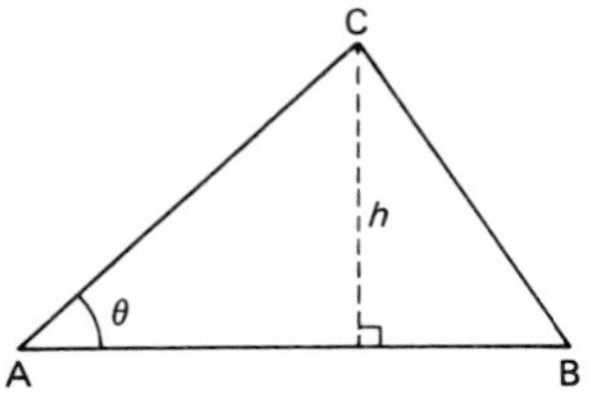

Figure 6.7

Area of a triangle
See Fig. 6.7.

$$\begin{aligned}\text{area of }\triangle\text{BAC}&=\tfrac{1}{2}(\text{base}\times\text{height})\\&=\tfrac{1}{2}|\overrightarrow{\text{AB}}\times\overrightarrow{\text{AC}}|\end{aligned}$$

Example 6.6

Find the angle between $\overrightarrow{BA}$ and $\overrightarrow{BC}$, where A, B and C are the points (1, 2, 2), (2, 0, 1) and (3, −1, 1) respectively.

$$\overrightarrow{OA} = \boldsymbol{i} + 2\boldsymbol{j} + 2\boldsymbol{k}$$
$$\overrightarrow{OB} = 2\boldsymbol{i} + \boldsymbol{k}$$
$$\overrightarrow{OC} = 3\boldsymbol{i} - \boldsymbol{j} + \boldsymbol{k}$$

Therefore

$$\overrightarrow{BA} = \overrightarrow{OA} - \overrightarrow{OB} = -\boldsymbol{i} + 2\boldsymbol{j} + \boldsymbol{k} \quad \text{and} \quad |\overrightarrow{BA}| = \sqrt{6}$$
$$\overrightarrow{BC} = \overrightarrow{OC} - \overrightarrow{OB} = \boldsymbol{i} - \boldsymbol{j} \quad \text{and} \quad |\overrightarrow{BC}| = \sqrt{2}$$
$$\sin\theta = \frac{|\overrightarrow{BA} \times \overrightarrow{BC}|}{(\text{BA})(\text{BC})}$$
$$\overrightarrow{BA} \times \overrightarrow{BC} = \begin{vmatrix} \boldsymbol{i} & \boldsymbol{j} & \boldsymbol{k} \\ -1 & 2 & 1 \\ 1 & -1 & 0 \end{vmatrix} = \boldsymbol{i}(0+1) - \boldsymbol{j}(0-1) + \boldsymbol{k}(1-2)$$
$$= \boldsymbol{i} + \boldsymbol{j} - \boldsymbol{k}$$

and $|\overrightarrow{BA} \times \overrightarrow{BC}| = \sqrt{3}$

Therefore

$$\sin\theta = \sqrt{3}/\sqrt{12} = 1/2$$

i.e. $\qquad \underline{\theta = 30°}$

Vector, parametric and cartesian equations of a straight line

Let P be any point on the line and let it have position vector $\boldsymbol{r}$. Consider a line in a specified direction parallel to a vector $\boldsymbol{b}$ and with position vector $\boldsymbol{a}$ from a fixed origin as shown in Fig. 6.8(a), then

$$\boldsymbol{r} = \boldsymbol{a} + \lambda\boldsymbol{b}$$

where λ is a scalar, will be the position vector of the point P and this is called the **vector equation** of the line.

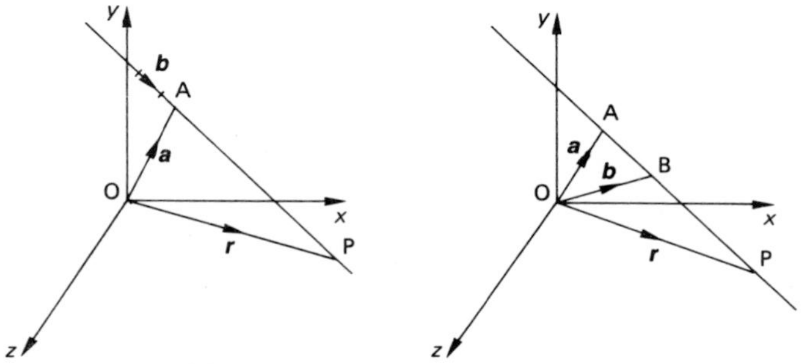

Figure 6.8 (a) (b)

(If two points on the line, A and B, with position vectors $\boldsymbol{a}$ and $\boldsymbol{b}$ are known (Fig. 6.8(b)) then

$$\boldsymbol{r} = \boldsymbol{a} + \lambda(\boldsymbol{b} - \boldsymbol{a})$$

is another form of the vector equation of the line.)

Each value of the parameter λ corresponds to one position of P.

If $\boldsymbol{a} = x_1\boldsymbol{i} + y_1\boldsymbol{j} + z_1\boldsymbol{k}$, $\boldsymbol{b} = x_2\boldsymbol{i} + y_2\boldsymbol{j} + z_2\boldsymbol{k}$ and $\boldsymbol{r} = x\boldsymbol{i} + y\boldsymbol{j} + z\boldsymbol{k}$ then

$$\boldsymbol{r} = x_1\boldsymbol{i} + y_1\boldsymbol{j} + z_1\boldsymbol{k} + \lambda(x_2\boldsymbol{i} + y_2\boldsymbol{j} + z_2\boldsymbol{k})$$

Comparing coefficients of $\boldsymbol{i}, \boldsymbol{j}$ and $\boldsymbol{k}$,

$$x = x_1 + \lambda x_2 \quad y = y_1 + \lambda y_2 \quad z = z_1 + \lambda z_2$$

These are the **parametric equations** of the line. Rearranging gives

$$\lambda = \frac{x - x_1}{x_2} = \frac{y - y_1}{y_2} = \frac{z - z_1}{z_2}$$

which are the **cartesian equations** of the line.

Note The direction ratios $x_2 : y_2 : z_2$ for the line are the coefficients of λ in the parametric equations and the denominators in the cartesian equations.

Pairs of lines

Two lines,

$$\boldsymbol{r}_1 = x_1\boldsymbol{i} + y_1\boldsymbol{j} + z_1\boldsymbol{k} + \lambda(a_1\boldsymbol{i} + b_1\boldsymbol{j} + c_1\boldsymbol{k})$$

and $\boldsymbol{r}_2 = x_2\boldsymbol{i} + y_2\boldsymbol{j} + z_2\boldsymbol{k} + \mu(a_2\boldsymbol{i} + b_2\boldsymbol{j} + c_2\boldsymbol{k})$

with direction ratios $a_1 : b_1 : c_1$ and $a_2 : b_2 : c_2$ may be:

(1) parallel, in which case they have equal direction ratios so $a_1/a_2 = b_1/b_2 = c_1/c_2$,

(2) non-parallel but intersect at a point P (Fig. 6.9), in which case there are unique values of λ and μ which satisfy $\boldsymbol{r}_1 = \boldsymbol{r}_2$, so

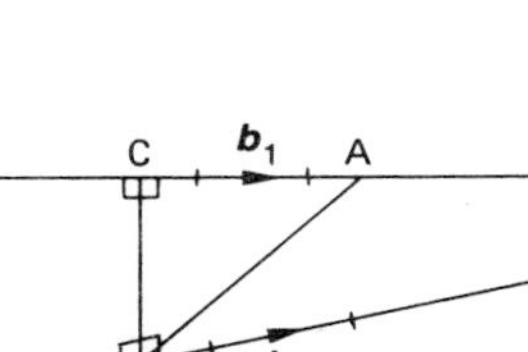

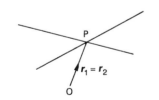

Figure 6.9

$$x_1\boldsymbol{i} + y_1\boldsymbol{j} + z_1\boldsymbol{k} + \lambda(a_1\boldsymbol{i} + b_1\boldsymbol{j} + c_1\boldsymbol{k})$$
$$= x_2\boldsymbol{i} + y_2\boldsymbol{j} + c_2\boldsymbol{k} + \mu(a_2\boldsymbol{i} + b_2\boldsymbol{j} + c_2\boldsymbol{k})$$

(3) non-parallel and do not intersect, in which case they are said to be **skew**.

If l_1 and l_2 are two skew lines and C is the point on l_1 which is nearest to l_2 then if CB is perpendicular to both l_1 and l_2 it will be the **shortest** distance between the two lines (Fig. 6.10).

Figure 6.10

If $\overrightarrow{OA} = \boldsymbol{a}_1$ and $\overrightarrow{OB} = \boldsymbol{a}_2$ and $\boldsymbol{b}_1$ and $\boldsymbol{b}_2$ are direction vectors for the lines l_1 and l_2 then the equations of l_1 and l_2 are $\boldsymbol{a}_1 + \lambda\boldsymbol{b}_1$ and $\boldsymbol{a}_2 + \mu\boldsymbol{b}_2$ respectively and

$$\overrightarrow{BA} = \boldsymbol{a}_1 - \boldsymbol{a}_2$$

$$\overrightarrow{BC} = \overrightarrow{BA}\cos\theta = (\boldsymbol{a}_1 - \boldsymbol{a}_2)\cdot\hat{\boldsymbol{n}}$$

where $\hat{\boldsymbol{n}}$ is the unit vector in the direction perpendicular to both lines so is along BC. Therefore

$$\hat{\boldsymbol{n}} = \frac{\boldsymbol{b}_1 \times \boldsymbol{b}_2}{|\boldsymbol{b}_1 \times \boldsymbol{b}_2|}$$

and a second condition for intersection is thus

$$(\boldsymbol{a}_1 - \boldsymbol{a}_2) \times (\boldsymbol{b}_1 \times \boldsymbol{b}_2) = 0$$

i.e. BC $= 0$

Angle between two lines

If two lines have direction cosines l_1, m_1, n_1 and l_2, m_2, n_2 then the angle between the lines is given by

$$\cos\theta = l_1 l_2 + m_1 m_2 + n_1 n_2$$

as before, where $\boldsymbol{r}_1 = \boldsymbol{a}_1 + \lambda \boldsymbol{b}_1$ and $\boldsymbol{r}_2 = \boldsymbol{a}_2 + \mu \boldsymbol{b}_2$ are the equations of the lines and $\hat{\boldsymbol{b}}_1 = l_1 \boldsymbol{i} + m_1 \boldsymbol{j} + n_1 \boldsymbol{k}$ and $\hat{\boldsymbol{b}}_2 = l_2 \boldsymbol{i} + m_2 \boldsymbol{j} + n_2 \boldsymbol{k}$, or by

$$\cos\theta = \frac{\boldsymbol{b}_1 \cdot \boldsymbol{b}_2}{|\boldsymbol{b}_1|\,|\boldsymbol{b}_2|}$$

where $\boldsymbol{b}_1$ and $\boldsymbol{b}_2$ are the direction vectors of the line.

Distance of a point from a line

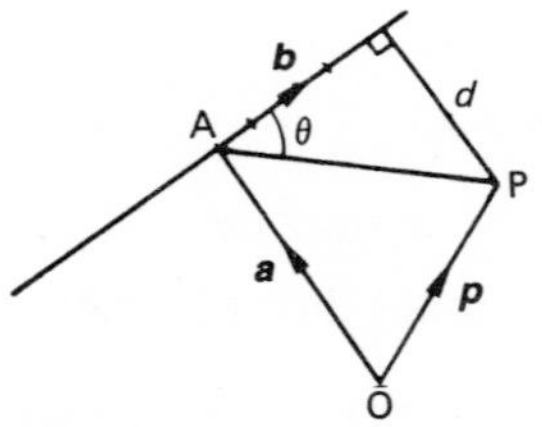

Figure 6.11

Consider a line whose equation is $\boldsymbol{a} + \lambda \boldsymbol{b}$ and the point P with position vector $\boldsymbol{p}$ a distance d from the line (Fig. 6.11). If A is a point on the line with position vector $\overrightarrow{OP}$ then $\overrightarrow{AP} = \boldsymbol{p} - \boldsymbol{a}$. Now $d = \text{AP} \sin\theta$, where θ is the angle between the line and $\overrightarrow{AP}$. Therefore

$$d = \frac{|\boldsymbol{b} \times \overrightarrow{AP}|}{|\boldsymbol{b}|} = \frac{|\boldsymbol{b} \times (\boldsymbol{p} - \boldsymbol{a})|}{|\boldsymbol{b}|}$$

Thus, for example, the distance of the point (1, 1, 1) from the line $\boldsymbol{r} = \boldsymbol{i} + \boldsymbol{j} - \boldsymbol{k} + \lambda(\boldsymbol{i} - \boldsymbol{j})$ is given by

$$d_{(1,1,1)} = \frac{|\boldsymbol{b} \times (-2\boldsymbol{k})|}{\sqrt{2}} = \frac{|2\boldsymbol{i} + 2\boldsymbol{j}|}{\sqrt{2}} = \frac{\sqrt{8}}{\sqrt{2}} = 2$$

Example 6.7

Show that the following three forces are in equilibrium and find the position vector of their point of concurrence.

$\boldsymbol{F}_1 = 3\boldsymbol{i} + \boldsymbol{j} + 2\boldsymbol{k}$ acting through the point with position vector $6\boldsymbol{i} + 2\boldsymbol{j}$

$\boldsymbol{F}_2 = 6\boldsymbol{i} - \boldsymbol{j} - 2\boldsymbol{k}$ acting through the point with position vector $3\boldsymbol{i} + 2\boldsymbol{j}$

$\boldsymbol{F}_3 = -9\boldsymbol{i}$ acting through the point with position vector $14\boldsymbol{i} + (5/3)\boldsymbol{j} - (2/3)\boldsymbol{k}$

Find the angle between the lines of action of $\boldsymbol{F}_1$ and $\boldsymbol{F}_2$.

$$\begin{aligned}\boldsymbol{F} &= \boldsymbol{F}_1 + \boldsymbol{F}_2 + \boldsymbol{F}_3 \\ &= (3+6-9)\boldsymbol{i} + (1-1)\boldsymbol{j} + (2-2)\boldsymbol{k}\end{aligned}$$

The three forces have zero resultant and will be in equilibrium if their lines of action are concurrent.

The equations of the lines of action of $\boldsymbol{F}_1$ and $\boldsymbol{F}_2$ are given by

$$\boldsymbol{r}_1 = 6\boldsymbol{i} + 2\boldsymbol{j} + \lambda(3\boldsymbol{i} + \boldsymbol{j} + 2\boldsymbol{k})$$

$$\boldsymbol{r}_2 = 3\boldsymbol{i} + 2\boldsymbol{j} + \mu(6\boldsymbol{i} - \boldsymbol{j} - 2\boldsymbol{k})$$

Comparing coefficients of $\boldsymbol{i}$,

$$6 + 3\lambda = 3 + 6\mu \qquad (1)$$

and $\boldsymbol{j}$,

$$2 + \lambda = 2 - \mu \qquad (2)$$

Multiplying equation (2) by 6 and adding it to equation (1) gives

$$\lambda = -1/3$$

so $\quad 5 = 3 + 6\mu$

and $\mu = 1/3$

Then for $\boldsymbol{k}$

$$2\lambda = -2\mu$$

so the third equation is satisfied and the lines intersect at the point with position vector given by $\underline{5\boldsymbol{i} + (5/3)\boldsymbol{j} - (2/3)\boldsymbol{k}}$.

The line of action of the third force is given by

$$\boldsymbol{r} = 14\boldsymbol{i} + (5/3)\boldsymbol{j} - (2/3)\boldsymbol{k} + s(-9\boldsymbol{i})$$

If $s = 1$ then

$$\boldsymbol{r} = 5\boldsymbol{i} + (5/3)\boldsymbol{j} - (2/3)\boldsymbol{k}$$

All three forces are concurrent at the point defined by this position vector so they are in equilibrium.

The angle between the lines of action $\boldsymbol{F}_1$ and $\boldsymbol{F}_2$ depends on their direction cosines: $\boldsymbol{F}_1$ has direction cosines $3/\sqrt{14}$, $1/\sqrt{14}$, $2/\sqrt{14}$ and $\boldsymbol{F}_2$ has direction cosines $6/\sqrt{41}$, $-1/\sqrt{41}$, $-2/\sqrt{41}$.

$$\cos\theta = l_1 l_2 + m_1 m_2 + n_1 n_2 = (18 - 1 - 4)/\sqrt{(14 \times 41)}$$

so $\quad \theta = \underline{57.1°}$

Vector equation of a plane

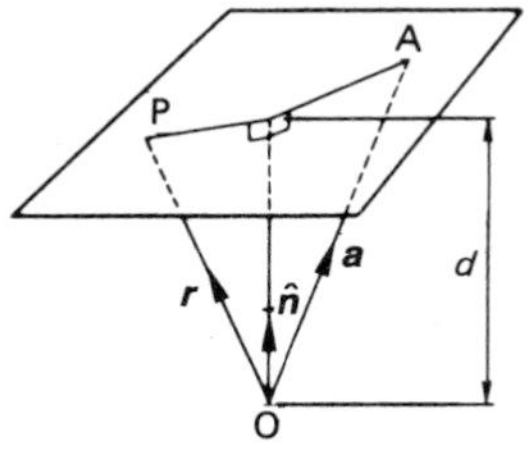

Figure 6.12

A plane can be defined in many ways. The most usual way is to consider a plane at a distance d from the origin and perpendicular to the unit vector $\hat{\boldsymbol{n}}$, $\hat{\boldsymbol{n}}$ being directed away from O (Fig. 6.12). If $\boldsymbol{r}$ is the position vector of a general point P on the plane then

$$\boldsymbol{r} \cdot \hat{\boldsymbol{n}} = d$$

is the **vector equation** of the plane.

If instead of being given d we are given the position vector of a point A on the plane, where $\overrightarrow{OA} = \boldsymbol{a}$, then

$$\boldsymbol{a} \cdot \hat{\boldsymbol{n}} = d$$

Therefore

$$\boldsymbol{r} \cdot \hat{\boldsymbol{n}} = \boldsymbol{a} \cdot \hat{\boldsymbol{n}}$$

is also a vector equation of the plane. The more general form of the equation of the plane is

$$\boldsymbol{r} \cdot \boldsymbol{n} = D$$

where $\boldsymbol{n}$ is the normal to the plane. Therefore $\boldsymbol{r} \cdot \hat{\boldsymbol{n}} = D/|\boldsymbol{n}|$, where $D/|\boldsymbol{n}|$ is the distance from the origin, d.

Cartesian equation of a plane

If $P(x, y, z)$ is any point on the plane and (l, m, n) are the direction cosines of the normal to the plane then

$$(x\boldsymbol{i} + y\boldsymbol{j} + z\boldsymbol{k}) \cdot (l\boldsymbol{i} + m\boldsymbol{j} + n\boldsymbol{k}) = d$$

so $\quad lx + my + nz = d$

is the **cartesian equation** of the plane or

$$Lx + My + Nz = D$$

where (L, M, N) are the direction ratios of the normal to the plane.

Parametric equation of a plane

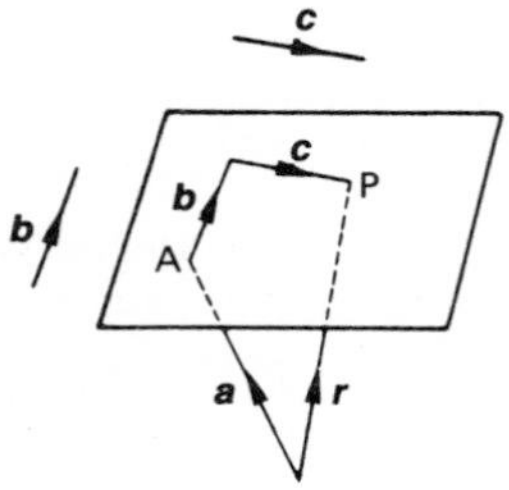

Figure 6.13

The **parametric equation** of a plane is

$$\boldsymbol{r} = \boldsymbol{a} + s\boldsymbol{b} + t\boldsymbol{c}$$

where $\boldsymbol{a}$ is the position vector of a point on the plane and $\boldsymbol{b}$ and $\boldsymbol{c}$ are two non-parallel vectors parallel to the plane and s and t are constants (Fig. 6.13).

Angle between two planes

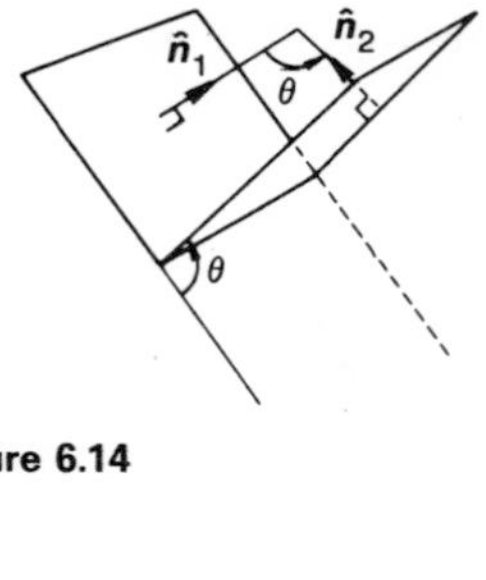

Figure 6.14

Consider the planes π_1 and π_2 whose equations are $\boldsymbol{r}_1 \cdot \hat{\boldsymbol{n}}_1 = d_1$ and $\boldsymbol{r}_2 \cdot \hat{\boldsymbol{n}}_2 = d_2$. The angle between the two planes, θ, equals the angle between the normals $\hat{\boldsymbol{n}}_1$ and $\hat{\boldsymbol{n}}_2$ to the two planes (Fig. 6.14). Therefore

$$\cos\theta = \hat{\boldsymbol{n}}_1 \cdot \hat{\boldsymbol{n}}_2$$

and the two planes are parallel if

$$\cos\theta = 1$$

and perpendicular if

$$\cos\theta = 0$$

Angle between a line and a plane

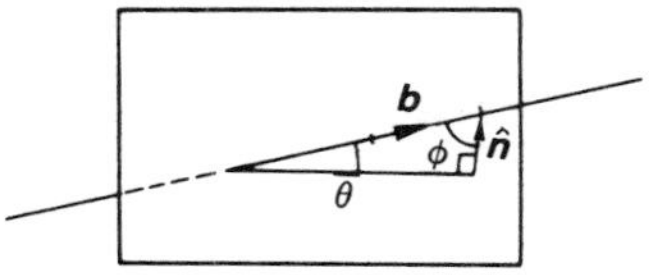

Figure 6.15

Consider the plane $\boldsymbol{r}\cdot\hat{\boldsymbol{n}}=d$ and the line $\boldsymbol{r}=\boldsymbol{a}+t\boldsymbol{b}$,

$$\boldsymbol{b}\cdot\hat{\boldsymbol{n}}=|\boldsymbol{b}|\cos\varphi$$

so $\theta=90°-\varphi$ and the angle between the line and the plane is given by (Fig. 6.15)

$$\sin\theta=\cos\varphi=\frac{\boldsymbol{b}\cdot\hat{\boldsymbol{n}}}{|\boldsymbol{b}|}$$

Distance of a point from a plane

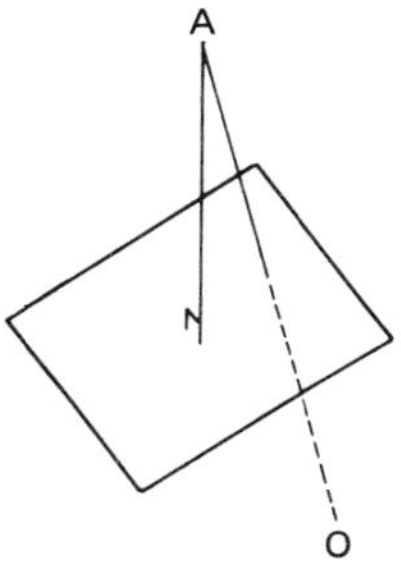

Figure 6.16

Consider a point A with point vector $\boldsymbol{a}$ and a plane π whose equation is $\boldsymbol{r}\cdot\hat{\boldsymbol{n}}=d$. The equation of the plane π' parallel to π and passing through A is $\boldsymbol{r}\cdot\hat{\boldsymbol{n}}=\boldsymbol{a}\cdot\hat{\boldsymbol{n}}$, Therefore the distance of the point A from the plane is

$$\boldsymbol{a}\cdot\hat{\boldsymbol{n}}-d$$

Note If A and O are on opposite sides of the plane (Fig. 6.16) then the result is positive. For example, the distance of the point A (1, 2, 1) from the plane $\boldsymbol{r}\cdot(\boldsymbol{i}+\boldsymbol{j}+\boldsymbol{k})=7$ is given by

$$(\boldsymbol{i}+2\boldsymbol{j}+\boldsymbol{k})\cdot\frac{(\boldsymbol{i}+\boldsymbol{j}+\boldsymbol{k})}{\sqrt{3}}-\frac{7}{\sqrt{3}}=\frac{4}{\sqrt{3}}-\frac{7}{\sqrt{3}}=\frac{-3}{\sqrt{3}}=-\sqrt{3}$$

so the point and the origin are on the same side of the plane.

Problem 6.1

Find the vector equation of the plane through the points A (1, 0, 1), B (2, 1, 0) and C (1, −2, 4) in parametric form and in scalar product form. Hence find the angle CAB and the angle between the plane and the line $\boldsymbol{r}=(\boldsymbol{i}-2\boldsymbol{j})+t(\boldsymbol{i}-\boldsymbol{j}+\boldsymbol{k})$.

(1) $\overrightarrow{AB}$ and $\overrightarrow{AC}$ are vectors contained in the plane. Find $\overrightarrow{AB}=\boldsymbol{i}+\boldsymbol{j}-\boldsymbol{k}$ and $\overrightarrow{AC}=-2\boldsymbol{j}+3\boldsymbol{k}$ so $|\overrightarrow{AB}|=\sqrt{3}$ and $|\overrightarrow{AC}|=\sqrt{13}$.
(2) $\overrightarrow{OA}=\boldsymbol{i}+\boldsymbol{k}$ is the position vector of a point on the plane.
(3) Hence the equation of the plane in parametric form is

$$\boldsymbol{r}=\boldsymbol{a}+s\boldsymbol{b}+t\boldsymbol{c}=\overrightarrow{OA}+s\overrightarrow{AB}+t\overrightarrow{AC}$$

Therefore show that $\boldsymbol{r}=(s+1)\boldsymbol{i}+(s-2t)\boldsymbol{j}+(1-s+3t)\boldsymbol{k}$.
(4) $\overrightarrow{AB}$ and $\overrightarrow{AC}$ are parallel to the plane. Therefore $\overrightarrow{AB}\times\overrightarrow{AC}=\boldsymbol{n}$ is perpendicular to the plane. The scalar product form is $\boldsymbol{r}\cdot(\overrightarrow{AB}\times\overrightarrow{AC})=D$, where $\boldsymbol{r}=\overrightarrow{OA}$ at one point A.

$$\overrightarrow{AB}\times\overrightarrow{AC}=\begin{vmatrix}\boldsymbol{i} & \boldsymbol{j} & \boldsymbol{k}\\ 1 & 1 & -1\\ 0 & -2 & 3\end{vmatrix}=\boldsymbol{i}-3\boldsymbol{j}-2\boldsymbol{k}=\boldsymbol{n}$$

$$\hat{\boldsymbol{n}}=\frac{5}{\sqrt{14}}\boldsymbol{i}-\frac{3}{\sqrt{14}}\boldsymbol{j}-\frac{2}{\sqrt{14}}\boldsymbol{k}$$

Show that $\overrightarrow{OA}\cdot\boldsymbol{n}=-1$. Therefore $\boldsymbol{r}\cdot(\boldsymbol{i}-3\boldsymbol{j}-2\boldsymbol{k})=-1$ is the scalar product form of the equation of the plane.

(5) $(\boldsymbol{b}-\boldsymbol{a})\cdot(\boldsymbol{c}-\boldsymbol{a})=|(\boldsymbol{b}-\boldsymbol{a})||(\boldsymbol{c}-\boldsymbol{a})|\cos\widehat{\mathrm{CAB}}$

$\overrightarrow{\mathrm{AB}}\cdot\overrightarrow{\mathrm{AC}}=(\mathrm{AB})(\mathrm{AC})\cos\theta$

$\cos\widehat{\mathrm{CAB}}=-5/\sqrt{39}$

i.e. $\widehat{\mathrm{CAB}}=143°$

(6) The angle required is given by

$$\sin\theta=\frac{\boldsymbol{b}\cdot\hat{\boldsymbol{n}}}{|\boldsymbol{b}|}=\frac{(\boldsymbol{i}-\boldsymbol{j}+\boldsymbol{k})\cdot(\boldsymbol{i}-3\boldsymbol{j}-2\boldsymbol{k})}{(\sqrt{3})(\sqrt{14})}$$

i.e. $\theta=18°$

Differentiation of a vector with respect to a scalar variable

A vector $\boldsymbol{r}$ can be a function of a scalar quantity.

$$\boldsymbol{r}=f(t)\boldsymbol{i}+g(t)\boldsymbol{j}+h(t)\boldsymbol{k}$$

$$\delta\boldsymbol{r}=\boldsymbol{r}(t+\delta t)-\boldsymbol{r}(t)$$

Then

$$\frac{\mathrm{d}\boldsymbol{r}}{\mathrm{d}t}=\lim_{\delta t\to 0}\frac{\delta\boldsymbol{r}}{\delta t}$$

$$=\lim_{\delta t\to 0}\left(\frac{f(t+\delta t)\boldsymbol{i}+g(t+\delta t)\boldsymbol{j}+h(t+\delta t)\boldsymbol{k}-f(t)\boldsymbol{i}-g(t)\boldsymbol{j}-h(t)\boldsymbol{k}}{\delta t}\right)$$

$$=\left(\lim_{\delta t\to 0}\frac{f(t+\delta t)-f(t)}{\delta t}\right)\boldsymbol{i}+\left(\lim_{\delta t\to 0}\frac{g(t+\delta t)-g(t)}{\delta t}\right)\boldsymbol{j}$$

$$+\left(\lim_{\delta t\to 0}\frac{h(t+\delta t)-h(t)}{\delta t}\right)\boldsymbol{k}$$

i.e. $$\frac{\mathrm{d}\boldsymbol{r}}{\mathrm{d}t}=\frac{\mathrm{d}f}{\mathrm{d}t}\boldsymbol{i}+\frac{\mathrm{d}g}{\mathrm{d}t}\boldsymbol{j}+\frac{\mathrm{d}h}{\mathrm{d}t}\boldsymbol{k}=\dot{\boldsymbol{r}}$$

In general, $\boldsymbol{r}$ and $\mathrm{d}\boldsymbol{r}/\mathrm{d}t$ have different directions.

Problem 6.2

A particle moves along a curve whose parametric equations are $x=2e^{-2t}$, $y=4\sin 2t$, where t is the time. Find: its velocity and acceleration at a time t and the magnitude of its velocity and acceleration at time $t=0$.

(1) Use $\boldsymbol{r}=2e^{-2t}\boldsymbol{i}+4\sin 2t\boldsymbol{j}$ to find the velocity

$$\dot{\boldsymbol{r}}=-4e^{-2t}\boldsymbol{i}+8\cos 2t\boldsymbol{j}$$

and the acceleration

$$\ddot{\boldsymbol{r}}=8e^{-2t}\boldsymbol{i}-16\sin 2t\boldsymbol{j}$$

(2) Substitute $t=0$ to find $\dot{\boldsymbol{r}}=-4\boldsymbol{i}+8\boldsymbol{j}$ at $t=0$, i.e. $|\dot{\boldsymbol{r}}|=\sqrt{80}$ units. The acceleration $\ddot{\boldsymbol{r}}=8\boldsymbol{i}$ at $t=0$, i.e. $|\ddot{\boldsymbol{r}}|=8$ units.

Integration of a vector with respect to a scalar variable

If $\boldsymbol{r}$ is a vector which is a function of a scalar variable, i.e.

$$\boldsymbol{r}=f(t)\boldsymbol{i}+g(t)\boldsymbol{j}+h(t)\boldsymbol{k}$$

then

$$\int \boldsymbol{r}\,\mathrm{d}t=\left(\int f(t)\,\mathrm{d}t\right)\boldsymbol{i}+\left(\int g(t)\,\mathrm{d}t\right)\boldsymbol{j}+\left(\int h(t)\,\mathrm{d}t\right)\boldsymbol{k}$$

In general, $\int \boldsymbol{r}\,\mathrm{d}t$ and $\boldsymbol{r}$ will have different directions. If $\boldsymbol{r}$ is the position vector of the body, $\boldsymbol{v}$ its velocity vector and $\boldsymbol{a}$ its acceleration vector then

$$\boldsymbol{v}=\frac{\mathrm{d}\boldsymbol{r}}{\mathrm{d}t}$$

$$\boldsymbol{a}=\frac{\mathrm{d}\boldsymbol{v}}{\mathrm{d}t}$$

$$\boldsymbol{v}=\int \boldsymbol{a}\,\mathrm{d}t$$

and $\boldsymbol{r}=\int \boldsymbol{v}\,\mathrm{d}t$

Problem 6.3

Evaluate $\int_{t=2}^{t=3} \boldsymbol{A}(t)\,\mathrm{d}t$ if $\boldsymbol{A}(t)=(8t^2-1)\boldsymbol{i}+(3t+6)\boldsymbol{j}$.

Integrate the function and substitute the values at the limits, i.e.

$$\int_{t=2}^{t=3} \boldsymbol{A}(t)\,\mathrm{d}t=\left[\frac{8t^3}{3}-t\right]_2^3\boldsymbol{i}+\left[\frac{3t^2}{2}+6t\right]_2^3\boldsymbol{j}$$

$$=49\tfrac{2}{3}\boldsymbol{i}+13\tfrac{1}{2}\boldsymbol{j}$$

Example 6.8

The equations of two planes are

$$\boldsymbol{r}\cdot(\boldsymbol{i}-2\boldsymbol{j}+\boldsymbol{k})=0$$

$$\boldsymbol{r}\cdot(\boldsymbol{i}-\boldsymbol{j})=1$$

Find the acute angle between the planes.

Show that the point A with position vector $\boldsymbol{i}-\boldsymbol{k}$ lies on L, the line of intersection of the two planes. Hence or otherwise show that a vector equation of L is

$$\boldsymbol{r}=\boldsymbol{i}-\boldsymbol{k}+\lambda(\boldsymbol{i}+\boldsymbol{j}+\boldsymbol{k})$$

where λ is a scalar.

Given that the point B has position vector $3\boldsymbol{i}+\boldsymbol{j}-\boldsymbol{k}$, find the point C on L such that BC is perpendicular to L. Find the area of the triangle ABC. (AEB N82)

The equations of planes 1 and 2 are

$$\boldsymbol{r}\cdot\hat{\boldsymbol{n}}_1=d_1$$

and $\boldsymbol{r}\cdot\hat{\boldsymbol{n}}_2=d_2$

respectively. Therefore

$$\hat{\boldsymbol{n}}_1 = \frac{1}{\sqrt{6}}\boldsymbol{i} - \frac{2}{\sqrt{6}}\boldsymbol{j} + \frac{1}{\sqrt{6}}\boldsymbol{k}$$

and $\hat{\boldsymbol{n}}_2 = \frac{1}{\sqrt{2}}\boldsymbol{i} - \frac{1}{\sqrt{2}}\boldsymbol{j}$

The angle between the planes equals the angle between the normals $\hat{\boldsymbol{n}}_1$ and $\hat{\boldsymbol{n}}_2$ to the plane.

$$\cos\theta = \hat{\boldsymbol{n}}_1 \cdot \hat{\boldsymbol{n}}_2 = \frac{(\boldsymbol{i}-2\boldsymbol{j}+\boldsymbol{k})}{\sqrt{6}} \cdot \frac{(\boldsymbol{i}-\boldsymbol{j})}{\sqrt{2}} = \frac{3}{\sqrt{12}}$$

i.e. $\theta = \underline{30^\circ}$

Let $\boldsymbol{r} = x\boldsymbol{i} + y\boldsymbol{j} + z\boldsymbol{k}$ be a point with a position vector on the line of intersection L of the two planes. Then $\boldsymbol{r}$ must satisfy equations (1) and (2) for the planes as below.

$$(x\boldsymbol{i} + y\boldsymbol{j} + z\boldsymbol{k}) \cdot (\boldsymbol{i} - 2\boldsymbol{j} + \boldsymbol{k}) = 0 \qquad (1)$$

and $(x\boldsymbol{i} + \boldsymbol{j} + z\boldsymbol{k}) \cdot (\boldsymbol{i} - \boldsymbol{j}) = 1$ (2)

Therefore

$$x - 2y + z = 0 \qquad (3)$$

and $x - y = 1$ (4)

so $x = 1 + y$, $x = 2 + z$.

Let $x = \lambda$, a scalar, hence any point on the line has coordinates $(\lambda, \lambda - 1, \lambda - 2)$ so the position vector of any point on the line L is

$$\boldsymbol{r} = \lambda\boldsymbol{i} + (\lambda - 1)\boldsymbol{j} + (\lambda - 2)\boldsymbol{k} = -\boldsymbol{j} - 2\boldsymbol{k} + \lambda(\boldsymbol{i} + \boldsymbol{j} + \boldsymbol{k}) \qquad (5)$$

If the point A lies on L then

$$(\boldsymbol{i} - \boldsymbol{k}) \cdot (\boldsymbol{i} - 2\boldsymbol{j} + \boldsymbol{k}) = 0 \quad \text{i.e. } 1 - 1 = 0$$

$$(\boldsymbol{i} - \boldsymbol{k}) \cdot (\boldsymbol{i} - \boldsymbol{j}) = 1 \quad \text{i.e. } 1 - 0 = 1$$

so A lies on the line L.

The equation of a line is of the form $\boldsymbol{r} = \boldsymbol{a} + t\boldsymbol{b}$. From equation (5) $t\boldsymbol{b} = \lambda(\boldsymbol{i} + \boldsymbol{j} + \boldsymbol{k})$ and $\boldsymbol{b}$ is the direction vector of L so a vector equation of L is

$$\boldsymbol{r} = \boldsymbol{i} - \boldsymbol{k} + \lambda(\boldsymbol{i} + \boldsymbol{j} + \boldsymbol{k})$$

Any point on the line has coordinate $(\lambda, \lambda - 1)$ and $(\lambda - 2)$. Let these be the coordinates of C. Then

$$\overrightarrow{BC} = (\lambda - 3)\boldsymbol{i} + (\lambda - 2)\boldsymbol{j} + (\lambda - 1)\boldsymbol{k}$$

If $\overrightarrow{BC}$ is perpendicular to L then $\overrightarrow{BC} \cdot \boldsymbol{b} = 0$, i.e.

$$[(\lambda - 3)\boldsymbol{i} + (\lambda - 2)\boldsymbol{j} + (\lambda - 1)\boldsymbol{k}] \cdot (\boldsymbol{i} + \boldsymbol{j} + \boldsymbol{k}) = 0$$

$$\lambda - 3 + \lambda - 2 + \lambda - 1 = 0$$

Therefore $\lambda = 2$ for C and the point C has position vector $\underline{2\boldsymbol{i} + \boldsymbol{j}}$.

The area of $\triangle ABC = \frac{1}{2}|\overrightarrow{AC} \times \overrightarrow{AB}| = \frac{1}{2}(AC)(AB)\sin\theta$.

$$\overrightarrow{AB} = 3\boldsymbol{i}+\boldsymbol{j}-\boldsymbol{k}-\boldsymbol{i}+\boldsymbol{k} = 2\boldsymbol{i}+\boldsymbol{j}$$

$$\overrightarrow{AC} = 2\boldsymbol{i}+\boldsymbol{j}-\boldsymbol{i}+\boldsymbol{k} = \boldsymbol{i}+\boldsymbol{j}+\boldsymbol{k}$$

$$\overrightarrow{AC}\times\overrightarrow{AB} = \begin{vmatrix} \boldsymbol{i} & \boldsymbol{j} & \boldsymbol{k} \\ 1 & 1 & 1 \\ 2 & 1 & 0 \end{vmatrix} = -\boldsymbol{i}+2\boldsymbol{j}-\boldsymbol{k}$$

$$|\overrightarrow{AC}\times\overrightarrow{AC}| = \sqrt{6}$$

hence

$$\text{area of } \triangle ABC = \tfrac{1}{2}\sqrt{6} = \underline{\sqrt{(3/2)}(\text{units})^2}$$

Example 6.9

The vector equations of two lines are $\boldsymbol{r}_1 = 6\boldsymbol{j}+\lambda(2\boldsymbol{i}-4\boldsymbol{j}+3\boldsymbol{k})$ and $\boldsymbol{r}_2 = 2\boldsymbol{i}+\mu(\boldsymbol{j}+\boldsymbol{k})$, where λ and μ are scalars. Show that the two lines are skew. Show also that the vector $7\boldsymbol{i}+2\boldsymbol{j}-2\boldsymbol{k}$ is perpendicular to both lines, hence find the shortest distance between the lines.

The lines are not parallel as their direction vectors are not equal. If the lines cross, $\boldsymbol{r}_1 = \boldsymbol{r}_2$ for some value of μ and λ. Hence

$$2\lambda\boldsymbol{i}+(6-4\lambda)\boldsymbol{j}+3\lambda\boldsymbol{k} = 2\boldsymbol{i}+\mu\boldsymbol{j}+\mu\boldsymbol{k}$$

Comparing coefficients of $\boldsymbol{i}$,

$$2\lambda = 2 \quad \text{i.e. } \lambda = 1$$

of $\boldsymbol{j}$,

$$6-4\lambda = \mu \quad \text{i.e. } \mu = 2$$

and of $\boldsymbol{k}$,

$$3\lambda = \mu \quad \text{i.e. } \mu = 3$$

The last two do not agree so the lines do not cross and are skew.

$2\boldsymbol{i}-4\boldsymbol{j}+3\boldsymbol{k}$ is the direction vector of the first line L_1. Now

$$(2\boldsymbol{i}-4\boldsymbol{j}+3\boldsymbol{k})\cdot(7\boldsymbol{i}+2\boldsymbol{j}-2\boldsymbol{k}) = 14-8-6 = 0$$

so $7\boldsymbol{i}+2\boldsymbol{j}-2\boldsymbol{k}$ is perpendicular to L_1. $\boldsymbol{j}+\boldsymbol{k}$ is the direction vector of the second line L_2. Now

$$(\boldsymbol{j}+\boldsymbol{k})\cdot(7\boldsymbol{i}+2\boldsymbol{j}-2\boldsymbol{k}) = 2-2 = 0$$

so $7\boldsymbol{i}+2\boldsymbol{j}-2\boldsymbol{k}$ is perpendicular to L_2. Hence $\boldsymbol{n} = 7\boldsymbol{i}+2\boldsymbol{j}-2\boldsymbol{k}$ is perpendicular to L_1 and L_2. The shortest distance between the two lines is given by $(\boldsymbol{a}_2-\boldsymbol{a}_1)\cdot\hat{\boldsymbol{n}}$, where $\boldsymbol{a}_2$ and $\boldsymbol{a}_1$ are position vectors of points of lines L_1 and L_2 and $\hat{\boldsymbol{n}}$ is a unit vector perpendicular to the two lines. Hence

$$\text{shortest distance} = (2\boldsymbol{i}-6\boldsymbol{j})\cdot(7\boldsymbol{i}+2\boldsymbol{j}-2\boldsymbol{k})(1/\sqrt{57})$$
$$= 2/\sqrt{57}$$

Problem 6.4

The position vector of a particle is given by $\boldsymbol{r} = (3t^2-1)\boldsymbol{i}+t\boldsymbol{j}$. Find the velocity of the particle at a time t and the time when $\boldsymbol{r}$ is perpendicular to $\dot{\boldsymbol{r}}$.

(1) Differentiate $\boldsymbol{r}$ with respect to t to show that $\dot{\boldsymbol{r}}=6t\boldsymbol{i}+\boldsymbol{j}$ when $\boldsymbol{r}$ is perpendicular to $\dot{\boldsymbol{r}}$. Then $\boldsymbol{r}\cdot\dot{\boldsymbol{r}}=0$.
(2) Calculate this to show that $t=0$ or $t=+\sqrt{(5/18)}$.

Summary

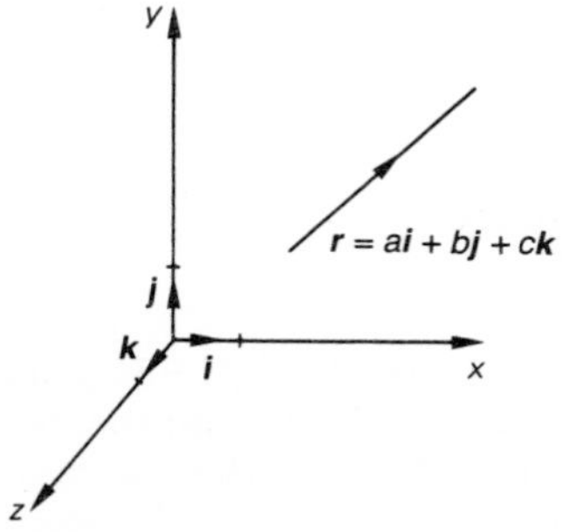

Figure 6.17

(1) If $\boldsymbol{r}=a\boldsymbol{i}+b\boldsymbol{j}+c\boldsymbol{k}$ is a vector (Fig. 6.17) then

$$|\boldsymbol{r}|=\sqrt{(a^2+b^2+c^2)}=r$$

$a:b:c$ are the direction ratios of $\boldsymbol{r}$ and l, m, n are the direction cosines of r, where

$$l=\frac{a}{|\boldsymbol{r}|} \quad m=\frac{b}{|\boldsymbol{r}|} \quad n=\frac{c}{|\boldsymbol{r}|}$$

$$l^2+m^2+n^2=1$$

The unit vector,

$$\hat{\boldsymbol{r}}=l\boldsymbol{i}+m\boldsymbol{j}+n\boldsymbol{k}$$

and $\boldsymbol{r}=r(l\boldsymbol{i}+m\boldsymbol{j}+n\boldsymbol{k})$

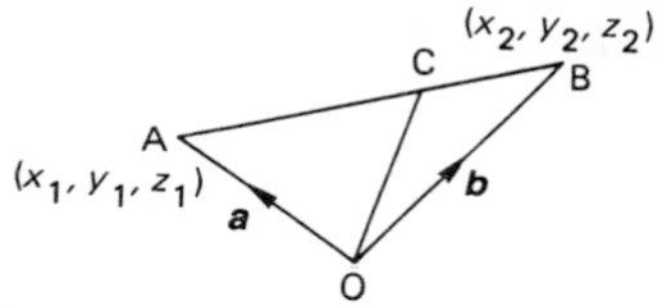

Figure 6.18

(2) If two points A and B have coordinates (x_1, y_1, z_1) and (x_2, y_2, z_2) and position vectors $\boldsymbol{a}$ and $\boldsymbol{b}$ respectively (Fig. 6.18) then

$$\overrightarrow{AB}=\overrightarrow{OB}-\overrightarrow{OA}=\boldsymbol{b}-\boldsymbol{a}$$
$$=(x_2-x_1)\boldsymbol{i}+(y_2-y_1)\boldsymbol{j}+(z_2-z_1)\boldsymbol{k}$$

and $|\overrightarrow{AB}|=\sqrt{[(x_2-x_1)^2+(y_2-y_1)^2+(z_2-z_1)^2]}$

(3) If C divides AB in the ratio $\lambda:\mu$ then

$$\overrightarrow{OC}=\frac{\lambda\boldsymbol{b}+\mu\boldsymbol{a}}{\lambda+\mu}$$

and the coordinates of C are

$$\frac{\lambda x_2+\mu x_1}{\lambda+\mu} \quad \frac{\lambda y_2+\mu y_1}{\lambda+\mu} \quad \frac{\lambda z_2+\mu z_1}{\lambda+\mu}$$

If C is the midpoint of AB then $\overrightarrow{OC}=\frac{1}{2}(\boldsymbol{b}+\boldsymbol{a})$.

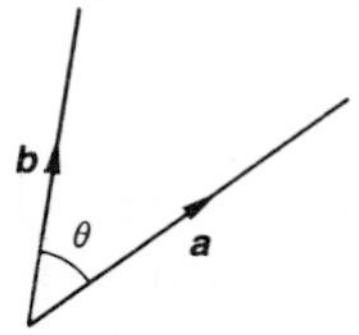

Figure 6.19

(4) The scalar product of two vectors $\boldsymbol{a}$ and $\boldsymbol{b}$ inclined at an angle θ (Fig. 6.19) is written as $\boldsymbol{a}\cdot\boldsymbol{b}$ and defined by $\boldsymbol{a}\cdot\boldsymbol{b}=ab\cos\theta$. Then

$$\boldsymbol{a}\cdot\boldsymbol{b}=x_1x_2+y_1y_2+z_1z_2$$

with $\boldsymbol{a}$ and $\boldsymbol{b}$ defined as in (2).

The cosine of the angle between the vectors $\cos\theta=\boldsymbol{a}\cdot\boldsymbol{b}/ab=0$ for perpendicular vectors and 1 for parallel vectors.

$$\cos\theta=l_1l_2+m_1m_2+n_1n_2$$

where l_1, m_1, n_1 and l_2, m_2, n_2 are the direction cosines of the vectors $\boldsymbol{a}$ and $\boldsymbol{b}$ respectively.

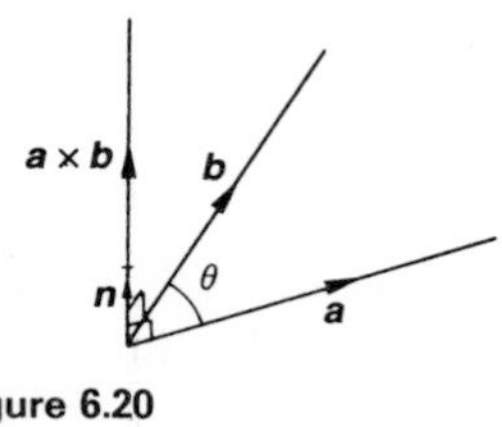

Figure 6.20

(5) The vector product of the two vectors $\boldsymbol{a}$ and $\boldsymbol{b}$ inclined at an angle θ to each other (Fig. 6.20) is written as $\boldsymbol{a}\times\boldsymbol{b}$ and defined

by

$$\boldsymbol{a} \times \boldsymbol{b} = ab \sin \theta \, \hat{\boldsymbol{n}}$$

where $\hat{\boldsymbol{n}}$ is the unit vector in the direction perpendicular to the plane containing $\boldsymbol{a}$ and $\boldsymbol{b}$ in the sense of a right-handed screw from $\boldsymbol{a}$ to $\boldsymbol{b}$. Hence

$$\boldsymbol{a} \times \boldsymbol{b} = -\boldsymbol{b} \times \boldsymbol{a}$$

If two vectors are parallel $\boldsymbol{a} \times \boldsymbol{b} = 0$ and if they are perpendicular $\boldsymbol{a} \times \boldsymbol{b} = ab$. In general,

$$\boldsymbol{a} \times \boldsymbol{b} = \begin{vmatrix} \boldsymbol{i} & \boldsymbol{j} & \boldsymbol{k} \\ x_1 & y_1 & z_1 \\ x_2 & y_2 & z_2 \end{vmatrix}$$

(6) The vector equation of a straight line is given by $\boldsymbol{r} = \boldsymbol{a} + \lambda \boldsymbol{b}$, where $\boldsymbol{r}$ is the position vector of a point P on the line, $\boldsymbol{a}$ is the position vector of a point $A\,(x_1, y_1, z_1)$ on the line and $\boldsymbol{b}$ the direction vector of the line (Fig. 6.21). If $\boldsymbol{b} = (x_2\boldsymbol{i} + y_2\boldsymbol{j} + z_2\boldsymbol{k})$ then

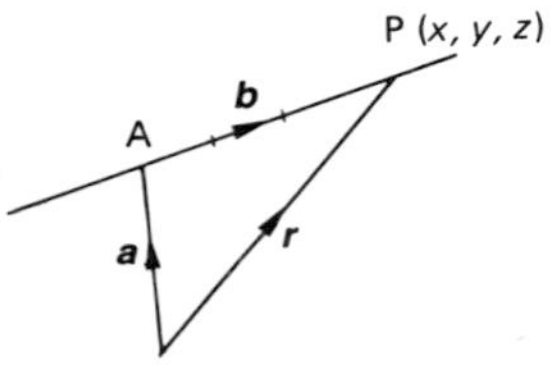

Figure 6.21

$$\boldsymbol{r} = x_1\boldsymbol{i} + y_1\boldsymbol{j} + z_1\boldsymbol{k} + \lambda(x_2\boldsymbol{i} + y_2\boldsymbol{j} + z_2\boldsymbol{k})$$

and $\dfrac{x - x_1}{x_2} = \dfrac{y - y_1}{y_2} = \dfrac{z - z_1}{z_2} = \lambda$

or $\quad x = x_1 + \lambda x_2 \quad y = y_1 + \lambda y_2 \quad z = z_1 + \lambda z_2$

$x_2 : y_2 : z_2 = l : m : n$, where l, m, n are the direction cosines of the line.

(7) Two lines $\boldsymbol{r}_1 = \boldsymbol{a}_1 + \lambda \boldsymbol{b}_1$ and $\boldsymbol{r}_2 = \boldsymbol{a}_2 + \boldsymbol{b}_2$ are

(a) parallel if $\boldsymbol{b}_1$ and $\boldsymbol{b}_2$ have equal direction ratios (Fig. 6.22(a)),
(b) intersect if there exists values of λ and μ such that $\boldsymbol{a}_1 + \lambda \boldsymbol{b}_1 = \boldsymbol{a}_2 + \mu \boldsymbol{b}_2$ for the position vector of the point of intersection (Fig. 6.22(b)),
(c) skew if neither of the above (Fig. 6.22(c)).

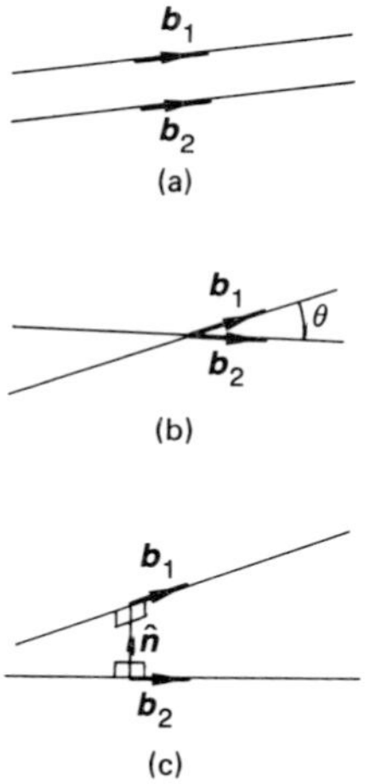

Figure 6.22

The shortest distance between two skew lines is given by $(\boldsymbol{a}_1 - \boldsymbol{a}_2) \cdot \hat{\boldsymbol{n}}$, where $\hat{\boldsymbol{n}}$ is the unit vector in the direction perpendicular to both lines and equals $(\boldsymbol{b}_1 \times \boldsymbol{b}_2)/|\boldsymbol{b}_1 \times \boldsymbol{b}_2|$ so a second condition of intersection is

$$(\boldsymbol{a}_1 - \boldsymbol{a}_2) \cdot (\boldsymbol{b}_1 \times \boldsymbol{b}_2) = 0$$

(8) The distance d of a point P with position vector $\boldsymbol{p}$ from a line $\boldsymbol{r} = \boldsymbol{a} + \lambda \boldsymbol{b}$ is given by $d = |\boldsymbol{b} \times (\boldsymbol{p} - \boldsymbol{a})|/b$.

(9) The angle between two lines is given by $\cos\theta = \hat{\boldsymbol{b}}_1 \cdot \hat{\boldsymbol{b}}_2$, where $\boldsymbol{b}_1$ and $\boldsymbol{b}_2$ are the direction vectors of the lines.

(10) The vector equation of a plane can be written

$$\boldsymbol{r} \cdot \hat{\boldsymbol{n}} = d \quad \text{or} \quad \boldsymbol{r} \cdot \boldsymbol{n} = D$$

where d is the distance of the plane from the origin and $\boldsymbol{n}$ is a vector perpendicular to the plane, or by

$$\boldsymbol{r} = \boldsymbol{a} + s\boldsymbol{b} + t\boldsymbol{c}$$

where $\boldsymbol{a}$ is a position vector of a point on the plane and $\boldsymbol{b}$ and $\boldsymbol{c}$ are two non-parallel vectors parallel to the plane, or by

$$lx + my + nz = d$$

where $P\,(x, y, z)$ is any point on the plane and (l, m, n) are the direction cosines of the normal to the plane.

(11) The angle θ between two planes $\boldsymbol{r}\cdot\boldsymbol{n}_1 = d_1$ and $\boldsymbol{r}\cdot\boldsymbol{n}_2 = d_2$ is given by $\cos\theta = \hat{\boldsymbol{n}}_1\cdot\hat{\boldsymbol{n}}_2$.

(12) The angle θ between a line $\boldsymbol{r} = \boldsymbol{a} + t\boldsymbol{b}$ and the plane $\boldsymbol{r}\cdot\hat{\boldsymbol{n}} = d$ is given by $\sin\theta = (\boldsymbol{b}\cdot\hat{\boldsymbol{n}})/b$.

(13) The distance of the point P with position vector $\boldsymbol{a}$ from the plane $\boldsymbol{r}\cdot\hat{\boldsymbol{n}} = d$ is given by $\boldsymbol{a}\cdot\hat{\boldsymbol{n}} - d$.

(14) If $\boldsymbol{r}$ is a function of a scalar, i.e. $\boldsymbol{r} = f(t)\boldsymbol{i} + g(t)\boldsymbol{j} + h(t)\boldsymbol{k}$, then

$$\frac{\mathrm{d}\boldsymbol{r}}{\mathrm{d}t} = \frac{\mathrm{d}f}{\mathrm{d}t}\boldsymbol{i} + \frac{\mathrm{d}g}{\mathrm{d}t}\boldsymbol{j} + \frac{\mathrm{d}h}{\mathrm{d}t}\boldsymbol{k}$$

and $\displaystyle\int \boldsymbol{r}\,\mathrm{d}t = \int f(t)\,\mathrm{d}t\,\boldsymbol{i} + \int g(t)\,\mathrm{d}t\,\boldsymbol{j} + \int h(t)\,\mathrm{d}t\,\boldsymbol{k}$

7
Projectiles

Objectives

The student should be able to:

(1) recognise a projectile as moving under the action of its own weight and so have an acceleration of g vertically downwards and zero horizontally,
(2) express the velocity, position and acceleration of a particle in terms of $\boldsymbol{i}, \boldsymbol{j}$ notation,
(3) express the velocity and position in parametric notation and so derive the equation for the path of a projectile,
(4) derive particular properties of a parabolic flight such as the range and time of flight:

(a) on a horizontal plane,
(b) on an inclined plane.

Introduction

A projectile is a particle which moves entirely under the action of its own weight after having been given an initial velocity. Air resistance is neglected. The vertical acceleration is $-g$ (the acceleration due to gravity) and the horizontal acceleration is zero, taking the vertically upwards direction as being positive.

Projectile on a horizontal plane

Vector notation

Taking positive vertically upwards, let the particle have an initial velocity $\dot{\boldsymbol{r}}_0 = u\boldsymbol{i} + v\boldsymbol{j}$ at time $t=0$ (Fig. 7.1) and the acceleration $= 0\boldsymbol{i} - g\boldsymbol{j}$. Then the velocity at a time t is given by

$$\dot{\boldsymbol{r}}_t = u\boldsymbol{i} + (v - gt)\boldsymbol{j}$$

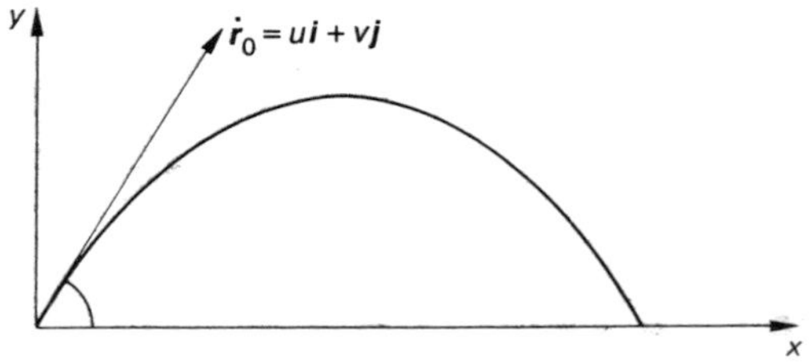

Figure 7.1

and the position vector at time t,

$$\boldsymbol{r}_t = \int \dot{\boldsymbol{r}}_t \, \mathrm{d}t = ut\boldsymbol{i} + (vt - \tfrac{1}{2}gt^2)\boldsymbol{j} + \boldsymbol{c}$$

but $\boldsymbol{r} = 0$ when $t = 0$ so $\boldsymbol{c} = 0$. Now let

$$\boldsymbol{r}_t = x\boldsymbol{i} + y\boldsymbol{j} = ut\boldsymbol{i} + (vt - \tfrac{1}{2}gt^2)\boldsymbol{j}$$

Comparing coefficients,

$$x = ut$$

$$y = vt - \tfrac{1}{2}gt^2$$

where x and y are the coordinates of the particle at a time t.

Example 7.1

A particle is projected from a point (0, 0) with an initial velocity vector of $3\boldsymbol{i} + 2\boldsymbol{j}$. Find the velocity vector of the particle after t seconds and the position vector after 3 seconds.

The velocity vector at a time t,

$$\dot{\boldsymbol{r}}_t = u\boldsymbol{i} + (v - gt)\boldsymbol{j} = 3\boldsymbol{i} + (2 - gt)\boldsymbol{j}$$

Taking $g = 10 \text{ m s}^{-2}$,

$$\dot{\boldsymbol{r}}_t = \underline{3\boldsymbol{i} + (2 - 10t)\boldsymbol{j}}$$

The position vector at a time $t = 3$ s,

$$\boldsymbol{r}_t = ut\boldsymbol{i} + (vt - \tfrac{1}{2}gt^2)\boldsymbol{j} = 9\boldsymbol{i} + (6 - 45)\boldsymbol{j} = \underline{9\boldsymbol{i} - 39\boldsymbol{j}}$$

Note If a problem on projectiles is phrased in vector terms it is generally best to use the above method, otherwise the parametric method is often easier.

Parametric notation

Consider a particle projected upwards with an initial velocity u at an angle α to the horizontal. The acceleration $= -g$ acting downwards.

Taking axes as shown in Fig. 7.2,

$\rightarrow \quad \ddot{x} = 0$

$\uparrow \quad \ddot{y} = -g$

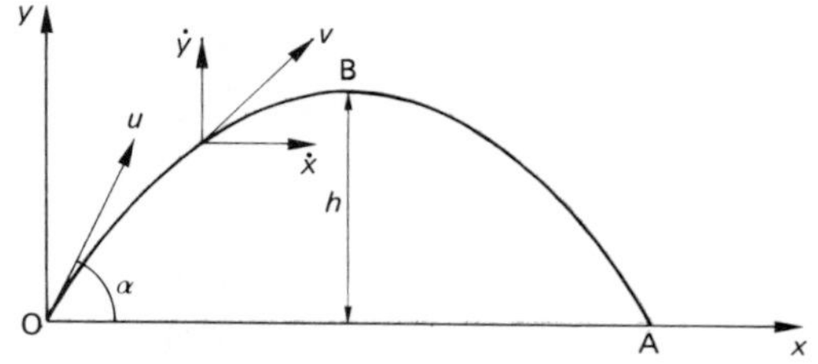

Figure 7.2

and integrating with respect to t gives

$$\dot{x} = u \cos \alpha \qquad \dot{y} = u \sin \alpha - gt \qquad (v = u + at)$$

$$x = ut \cos \alpha \qquad y = ut \sin \alpha - \tfrac{1}{2}gt^2 \qquad (s = ut + \tfrac{1}{2}at^2)$$

Substituting in the equation for y with $t = (u \cos \alpha)/x$ gives the parametric equation of the path of the projectile and is the equation of a parabola:

$$y = x \tan \alpha - \frac{x^2 g}{2u^2} \sec^2 \alpha \qquad (1)$$

At any instant t the velocity of the particle v is given by $v = \sqrt{(\dot{x}^2 + \dot{y}^2)}$ in a direction of $\tan^{-1}(\dot{y}/\dot{x})$ to the horizontal, i.e. $\tan^{-1}[(u \sin \alpha - gt)/u \cos \alpha)]$, using

$$\frac{\dot{y}}{\dot{x}} = \frac{\mathrm{d}y}{\mathrm{d}t} \bigg/ \frac{\mathrm{d}x}{\mathrm{d}t} = \frac{\mathrm{d}y}{\mathrm{d}x}$$

so the direction of the velocity is along the tangent.

Particular properties of parabolic flight

The properties listed below are frequently required but care must be taken if the problem involves, for example, projection from a position where $y \neq 0$ initially. The equations of motion for constant acceleration must be applied to each problem as it is set.

Time of flight

T = time to travel from O to A in Fig. 7.2. When the particle is at B

$$\dot{y} = 0 = u \sin \alpha - gt$$

$$t = \frac{u \sin \alpha}{g}$$

Therefore

$$\text{time of flight } T = 2t = \frac{2u \sin \alpha}{g}$$

Maximum height

The height h is a maximum when $y = h$. Then $\dot{y} = 0$ and the particle is moving horizontally. The height h is a maximum when using $v^2 = u^2 + 2as$,

$$0 = u^2 \sin^2 \alpha - 2gh$$

$$h = \frac{u^2 \sin^2 \alpha}{2g}$$

Horizontal range

$$R = \text{horizontal velocity} \times \text{time of flight}$$

$$= (u \cos \alpha)\left(\frac{2u \sin \alpha}{g}\right)$$

i.e. $$R = \frac{u^2 \sin 2\alpha}{g}$$

Maximum range

The maximum range occurs when $\sin 2\alpha = 1$, i.e. when $\alpha = 45°$.

$$R_{max} = \frac{u^2}{g}$$

so the maximum horizontal range can be achieved by projecting the particle at 45° for a given value of *u*.

To achieve a given range,

$$R_G = \frac{u^2 \sin 2\alpha}{g}$$

if $R_G < R_{max}$. Therefore

$$\sin 2\alpha = \frac{gR_G}{u^2}$$

$$2\alpha = \sin^{-1}\left(\frac{gR_G}{u^2}\right) \quad \text{or} \quad 180° - \sin^{-1}\left(\frac{gR_G}{u^2}\right)$$

i.e. two angles of projection produce the same given range R_G (Fig. 7.3). The smaller angle will give the faster time of flight because it gives a larger horizontal component of the velocity.

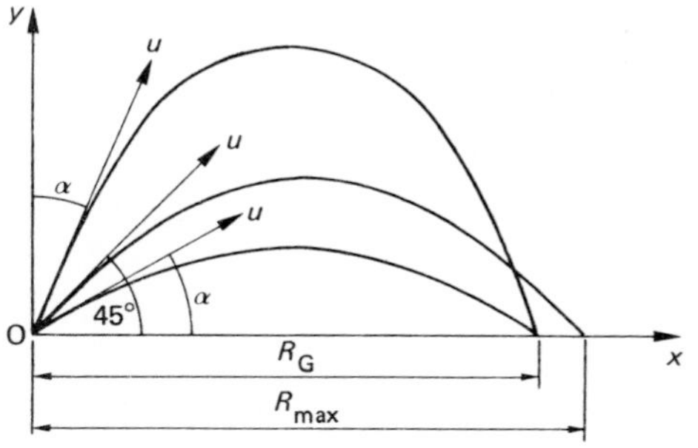

Figure 7.3

Angle of projection to pass through a particular point

See Fig. 7.4. Using the equation of the path,

$$y = x \tan \theta - \frac{gx^2}{2u^2}(1 + \tan^2 \theta)$$

For point A (a, b)

$$b = a \tan \theta - \frac{ga^2}{2u^2}(1 + \tan^2 \theta)$$

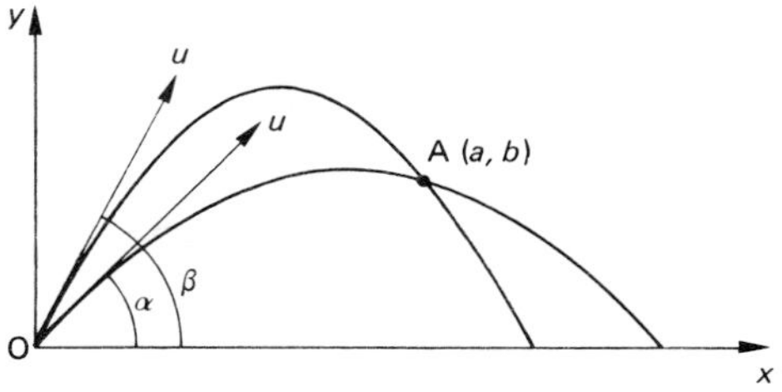

Figure 7.4

Rearranging gives

$$\frac{a^2 g}{2u^2}\tan^2\theta - a\tan\theta + \left(b + \frac{a^2 g}{2u^2}\right) = 0$$

This is a quadratic equation in $\tan\theta$ with two solutions. If these are both real and positive there will be two angles of projection, α and β, for the particle to pass through $A\,(a, b)$ with initial speed u.

Example 7.2

A particle is projected with an initial speed of $50\ \text{m s}^{-1}$ at 60° to the horizontal. Find:

(a) the horizontal range of the particle,
(b) an alternative angle of projection to give the same range,
(c) the maximum range.

(Take $g = 10\ \text{m s}^{-2}$.)

(a) $u = 50\ \text{m s}^{-1}$ and $\alpha = 60°$ (Fig. 7.5). Using $R = (u^2 \sin 2\alpha)/g$,

$R = (50^2 \times \sin 120°)/10 = \underline{216.5\ \text{m}}$

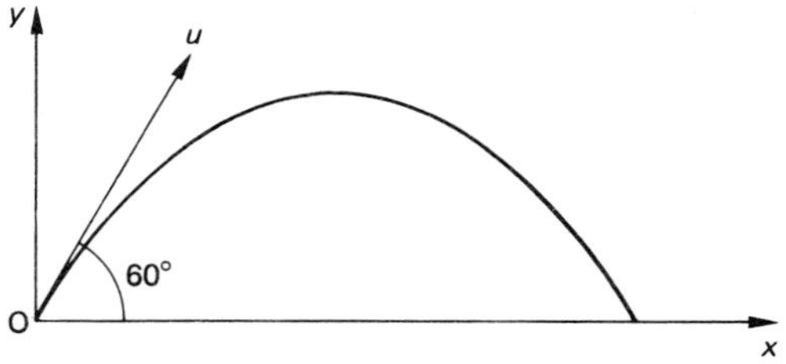

Figure 7.5

(b) $\sin 2\alpha = gR/u^2 = 0.8660$

$$2\alpha = 60° \quad \text{or} \quad 180° - 60°$$

$$\alpha = 30° \quad \text{or} \quad 60°$$

Therefore

alternative angle of projection $= \underline{30°}$

(c) The maximum range $R_{max} = u^2/g$ when $\alpha = 45°$. Therefore

$R_{max} = 50^2/10 = \underline{250\ \text{m}}$

Example 7.3

A particle is projected from a point O on a horizontal plane with speed u at an angle α to the horizontal and it next strikes the plane at a distance R from O.

(a) In the special case when $u = 40 \text{ m s}^{-1}$ and $R = 100$ m find, correct to the nearest degree, the possible values of α.
(b) The angle between the direction of motion of P and the horizontal at time t after projection is denoted by β. In the general case when u and R are not given, express $\tan\beta$ in terms of u, α, t and g.

Given that $\tan\beta$ is of magnitude $\frac{1}{2}\tan^2\alpha$, at two points whose horizontal distance apart is $R/5$, find $\tan\alpha$. (AEB J85)

(a) The range $R = (u^2 \sin 2\alpha)/g$. Therefore

$$\sin 2\alpha = gR/u^2 = (10 \times 100)/40^2 = 0.625$$

$$2\alpha = 38.7° \quad \text{or} \quad 180° - 38.7°$$

$$\alpha = \underline{19° \quad \text{or} \quad 71°}$$

(b) The horizontal velocity $= u\cos\alpha$ and the vertical velocity $= u\sin\alpha - gt$ after a time t. Therefore

$$\underline{\tan\beta = \frac{u\sin\alpha - gt}{u\cos\alpha}} \tag{1}$$

Let the particle move a further $R/5$ at a time t' so it makes an angle $-\tan\beta$ as shown in Fig. 7.6. Then

$$-\tan\beta = \frac{u\sin\alpha - gt'}{u\cos\alpha} \tag{2}$$

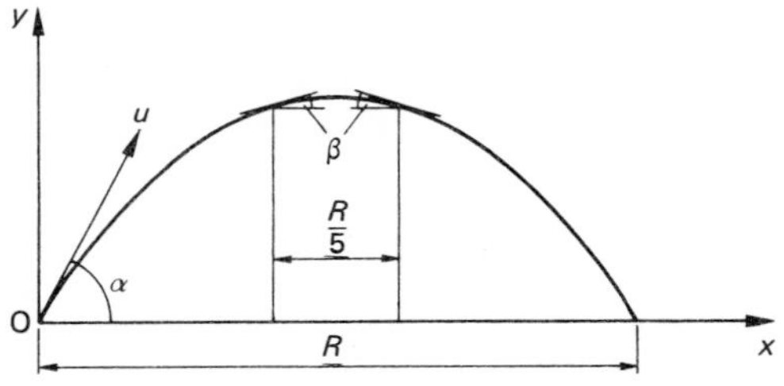

Figure 7.6

Subtracting equation (2) from equation (1),

$$2\tan\beta = \frac{g(t'-t)}{u\cos\alpha} \tag{3}$$

but horizontally, distance = time × velocity, therefore

$$R/5 = u\cos\alpha\,(t'-t) \tag{4}$$

Substituting into equation (3) from equation (4) for $(t'-t)$ gives

$$2\tan\beta = \frac{gR}{5u^2\cos^2\alpha}$$

but $2\tan\beta = \tan^2\alpha$, therefore

$$\tan^2\alpha = \frac{gR}{5u^2\cos^2\alpha}$$

Using $R = (u^2 \sin 2\alpha)/g$,

$$\tan^2 \alpha = \frac{gu^2 \sin 2\alpha}{5u^2 g \cos^2 \alpha} = \tfrac{2}{5} \tan \alpha$$

or $\quad \underline{\tan \alpha = \tfrac{2}{5}}$

Problem 7.1

A particle is projected from a point O with a velocity vector $4\boldsymbol{i} + 2\boldsymbol{j}$. Find the direction in which it is moving a second later. Two seconds after the launch of the first particle a second particle is projected from the same point with a velocity vector $8\boldsymbol{i} - 26\boldsymbol{j}$. Show that the two particles collide and find the time at which this occurs.

(1) Use $\dot{\boldsymbol{r}} = u\boldsymbol{i} + (v - gt)\boldsymbol{j}$ to show that $\dot{\boldsymbol{r}} = 4i - 8\boldsymbol{j}$ after one second. Hence the particle is moving in a direction $\tan^{-1} 2$ below the horizon.
(2) Now use $\boldsymbol{r} = ut\boldsymbol{i} + (vt - \frac{1}{2}gt^2)\boldsymbol{j}$ to find after t seconds

$$\boldsymbol{r}_1 = 4t\boldsymbol{i} + (2t - 5t^2)\boldsymbol{j}$$

for the first particle and

$$\boldsymbol{r}_2 = 8(t-2)\boldsymbol{i} + [-26(t-2) - 5(t-2)^2]\boldsymbol{j}$$

for the second particle.
(3) Equate the coefficients of $\boldsymbol{i}$ to solve for a value of t when they are equal. Hence find $t = 4$ s at $x = 16$ units.
(4) Substitute this value into the coefficient of $\boldsymbol{j}$ for both particles to show that $y = -72$ units at $t = 4$ *s* for both particles. Hence they collide as they both have coordinates (16, −72) after 4 s.

Problem 7.2

A particle is projected from a point O on a cliff-top at a speed of 15 m s^{-1} and at an angle of elevation of 45° and strikes the sea at the point A whose horizontal distance from O is 60 m. Given that $g = 10$ m s^{-2}, calculate the vertical height of O above A and the time of flight of the particle.

(1) Draw and label a diagram (Fig. 7.7).
(2) Using the equation of the path

$$y = x \tan \alpha - \frac{x^2 g}{2u^2} \sec^2 \alpha$$

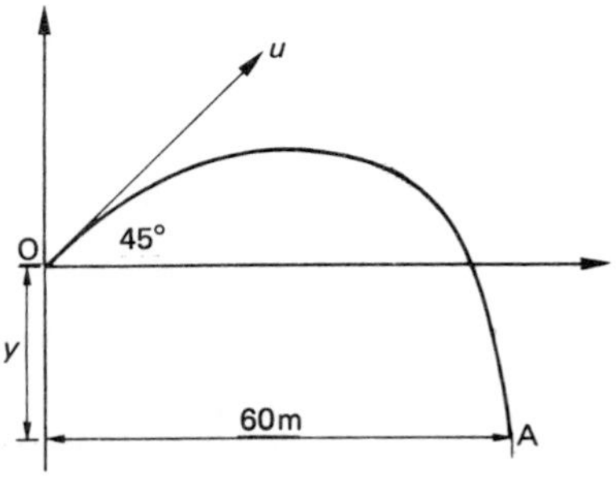

Figure 7.7

and the coordinates of A as $(60, y)$, substitute the given values of u and α to find $y=-100$ *m*, i.e. A is 100 m vertically below O. (3) The horizontal velocity $= u \cos\alpha$ and the horizontal range $= 60$ m. Using time = distance/velocity, find that the time of flight is 5.7 s.

Example 7.4

A particle is projected with a speed u and at an angle of elevation α from a point O. Show that, at time t after projection, the position vector of the particle relative to O is $\boldsymbol{r}$, where

$$\boldsymbol{r}=(u\cos\alpha)t\boldsymbol{i}+[(u\sin\alpha)t-\tfrac{1}{2}gt^2]\boldsymbol{j}$$

and $\boldsymbol{i}$ and $\boldsymbol{j}$ are unit vectors directed horizontally and vertically upwards respectively. Given that $u=40 \text{ m s}^{-1}$ and that the particle strikes a target A on the same horizontal level as O, where OA = 60 m, find the least possible time, to the nearest tenth of a second, that elapses before the particle hits the target A. (Take $g=10 \text{ m s}^{-2}$.) (UL J83)

Initial velocity $=(u\cos\alpha)\boldsymbol{i}+(u\sin\alpha)\boldsymbol{j}$ resolving parallel to Ox and Oy. Now acceleration $=0\boldsymbol{i}-g\boldsymbol{j}$. Therefore the velocity at a time t,

$$\dot{\boldsymbol{r}}=(u\cos\alpha)\boldsymbol{i}+(u\sin\alpha-gt)\boldsymbol{j}$$

and the position vector

$$\boldsymbol{r}=\int\dot{\boldsymbol{r}}\,\mathrm{d}t=(u\cos\alpha)t\boldsymbol{i}+[(u\sin\alpha)t-\tfrac{1}{2}gt^2]\boldsymbol{j}+\boldsymbol{D}$$

but $\boldsymbol{r}=0$ when $t=0$ so $\boldsymbol{D}=0$. Therefore

$$\boldsymbol{r}=(u\cos\alpha)t\boldsymbol{i}+[(u\sin\alpha)t-\tfrac{1}{2}gt^2]\boldsymbol{j}$$

When the coefficient of $\boldsymbol{j}$ is zero then t = the time of flight T.

$$Tu\sin\alpha=\tfrac{1}{2}gT^2$$
$$T=(2u\sin\alpha)/g$$

Hence

$$\text{range}=u\cos\alpha T=(2u^2\sin\alpha\cos\alpha)/g$$
$$60=(u^2\sin 2\alpha)/g$$

i.e.

$$\sin 2\alpha=0.375$$
$$2\alpha=22^\circ \quad\text{or}\quad 180^\circ-22^\circ$$
$$\alpha=11^\circ \quad\text{or}\quad 79^\circ$$

Therefore

$$\text{minimum time of flight}=(2u\sin 11^\circ)/g=\underline{1.5\text{ s}}$$

as using 79° gives a smaller horizontal component of velocity and a longer flight time.

Projectile on an inclined plane

Consider a particle projected with a speed u from a plane inclined at an angle α to the horizontal (Fig. 7.8). Let the initial velocity of the particle make an angle β with the line of greatest slope of the plane.

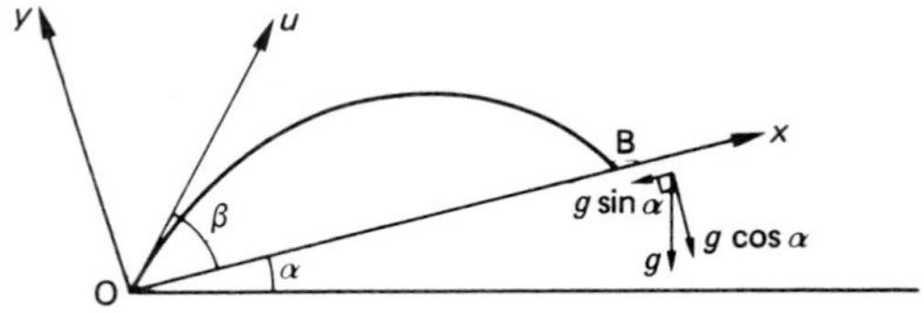

Figure 7.8

Taking the y-axis perpendicular to the plane and the x-axis parallel to it,

$$\ddot{y} = -g \cos \alpha$$

$$\dot{y} = u \sin \beta - gt \cos \alpha \qquad (v = u + at)$$

$$y = ut \sin \beta - \tfrac{1}{2}gt^2 \cos \alpha \qquad (s = ut + \tfrac{1}{2}at^2)$$

$$\ddot{x} = -g \sin \alpha$$

$$\dot{x} = u \cos \beta - gt \sin \alpha$$

$$x = ut \cos \beta - \tfrac{1}{2}gt^2 \sin \alpha$$

Time of flight

Let $t = T$ when $y = 0$. Therefore

$$0 = uT \sin \beta - \tfrac{1}{2}gT^2 \cos \alpha$$

$$T = 0 \quad \text{or} \quad T = \frac{2u \sin \beta}{g \cos \alpha}$$

Range up the plane

Let $R = \text{OB}$ when $t = T$. Therefore

$$R = u\left(\frac{2u \sin \beta \cos \beta}{g \cos \alpha}\right) - \tfrac{1}{2}g\left(\frac{4u^2 \sin^2 \beta \sin \alpha}{g^2 \cos^2 \alpha}\right)$$

i.e. $$R = \frac{2u^2 \sin \beta \cos(\beta + \alpha)}{g \cos^2 \alpha}$$

Maximum range up the plane

The maximum range up the plane (Fig. 7.9) for a given α and u occurs when

$$\frac{d}{d\beta}[\sin \beta \cos(\beta + \alpha)] = 0$$

i.e. $\cos\beta\cos(\beta+\alpha)-\sin\beta\sin(\beta+\alpha)=0$

$$\cos(2\beta+\alpha)=0$$

$$2\beta+\alpha=90°$$

$$\beta=45°-\alpha/2$$

Substituting for β gives

$$\text{maximum range up the plane}=\frac{u^2}{g\cos^2\alpha}(1-\sin\alpha)$$

i.e. the range up the plane is a maximum when the angle of projection bisects the angle between the upward slope and the vertical. This expression simplifies to $(u^2/g)(1+\sin\alpha)$.

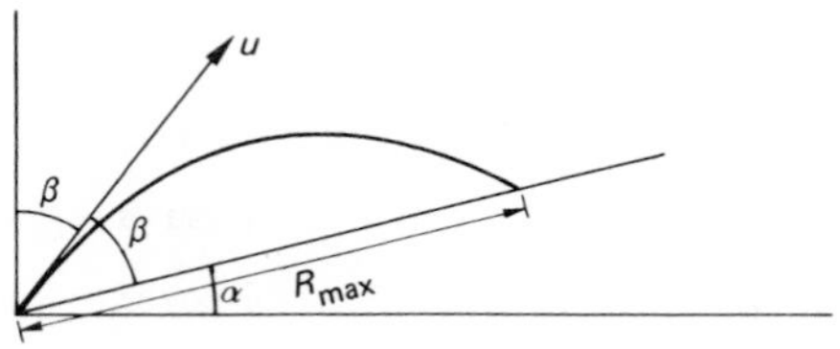

Figure 7.9

Range down the plane

If the particle is projected down the plane (Fig. 7.10)

$$\ddot{y}=-g\cos\alpha$$

$$\dot{y}=u\sin\beta-gt\cos\alpha \qquad (v=u+at)$$

$$y=ut\sin\beta-\tfrac{1}{2}gt^2\cos\alpha \qquad (s=ut+\tfrac{1}{2}at^2)$$

$$\ddot{x}=g\sin\alpha$$

$$\dot{x}=u\cos\beta+gt\sin\alpha$$

$$x=ut\cos\beta+\tfrac{1}{2}gt^2\sin\alpha$$

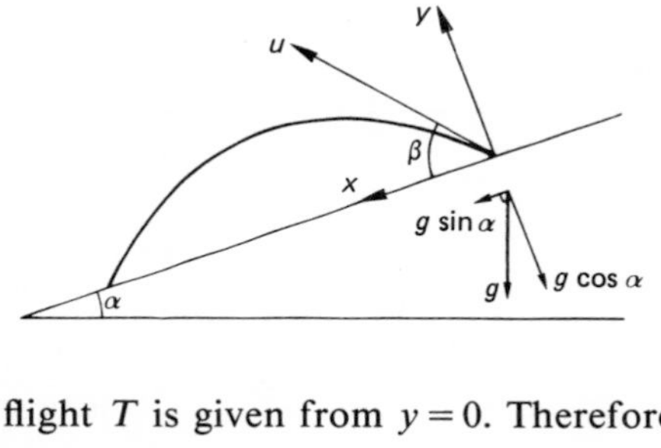

Figure 7.10

The time of flight T is given from $y=0$. Therefore

$$T=\frac{2u\sin\beta}{g\cos\alpha}$$

as before. Substituting for x gives the range down the plane.

$$R=\frac{u(2u\sin\beta)}{g\cos\alpha}(\cos\beta)+\tfrac{1}{2}g\sin\alpha\left(\frac{4u^2\sin^2\beta}{g\cos^2\alpha}\right)$$

i.e. $R = \dfrac{2u^2 \sin\beta \cos(\beta - \alpha)}{g \cos^2 \alpha}$

Maximum range down the plane

The maximum range down the plane (Fig. 7.11) for a given α and u occurs when

$$\frac{d}{d\beta}[\sin\beta \cos(\beta - \alpha)] = 0$$

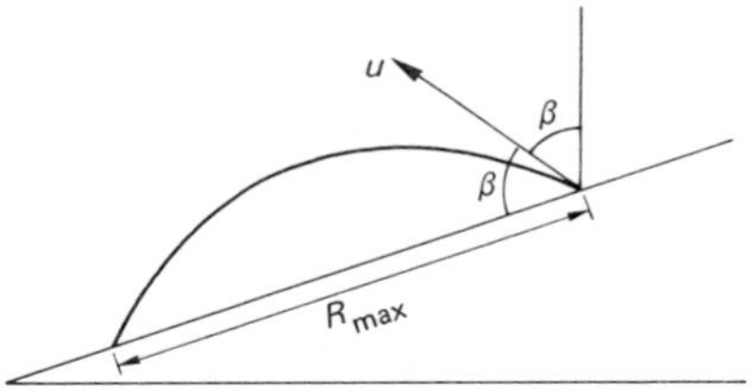

Figure 7.11

i.e. $\cos\beta \cos(\beta - \alpha) - \sin\beta \sin(\beta - \alpha) = 0$

$$\cos(2\beta - \alpha) = 0$$

$$2\beta - \alpha = 90°$$

$$\beta = 45° + \alpha/2$$

i.e. the range down the plane is a maximum when the angle of projection bisects the angle between the downward slope of the plane and the vertical.

Maximum height above the plane

The height h above the plane for a particle travelling up (Fig. 7.12) is given by

$$\cos\alpha = y/h$$

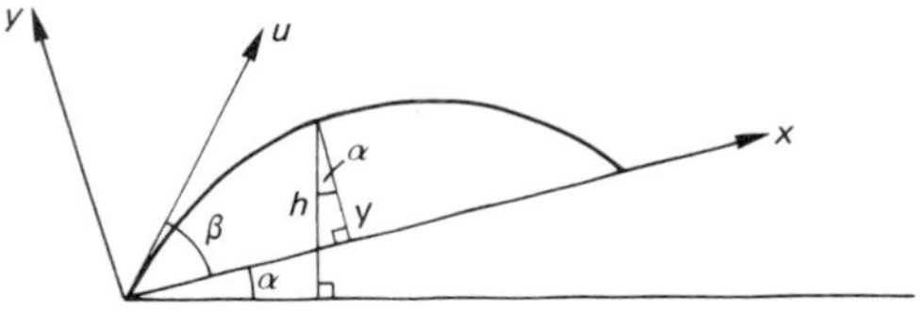

Figure 7.12

i.e. $h = y \sec\alpha$

α is constant. Therefore

maximum y produces maximum h

This occurs when $\dot{y} = 0$, i.e. at a time equal to half the time of flight.

Example 7.5

A particle is projected under gravity up a plane which makes an angle α with the horizontal. The velocity of projection V makes an angle β with the slope and the motion takes place in a vertical plane through a line of greatest slope. Given that the y-axis and x-axis are perpendicular and parallel to the plane respectively, show that the range up the inclined plane can be expressed as

$$\frac{V^2[\sin(2\beta+\alpha)-\sin\alpha]}{g\cos^2\alpha}$$

Hence find the maximum value of the range as α values. When the range of the particle is $(\sqrt{2}-1)$ times its maximum range and $\alpha=\pi/6$ find the two values of β with which this can be achieved.

From p. 83

$$x = Vt\cos\beta - \tfrac{1}{2}gt^2\sin\alpha \qquad (1)$$

and $y = Vt\sin\beta - \tfrac{1}{2}gt^2\cos\alpha$

Hence the time of flight when $y=0$ is given by

$$T=\frac{2V\sin\beta}{g\cos\alpha}$$

Substituting in equation (1) for t, when

$$R = x = \frac{2V^2\cos\beta\sin\beta}{g\cos\alpha} - \tfrac{1}{2}g\frac{(4V^2\sin^2\beta\sin\alpha)}{g^2\cos^2\alpha}$$

$$= \frac{V^2}{g\cos^2\alpha}[2\cos\beta\sin\beta\cos\alpha - 2\sin^2\beta\sin\alpha]$$

$$= \frac{V^2}{g\cos^2\alpha}[\sin 2\beta\cos\alpha + (1-2\sin^2\beta)\sin\alpha - \sin\alpha]$$

i.e. $$R = \frac{V^2}{g\cos^2\alpha}[\sin(2\beta+\alpha)-\sin\alpha] \qquad (2)$$

As β varies, the maximum value of R is given by

$$\frac{d}{d\beta}[\sin(2\beta+\alpha)-\sin\alpha]=0$$

i.e. $\cos(2\beta+\alpha)=0$

$$2\beta+\alpha = 90°$$

$$\beta = 45° - \alpha/2$$

Substituting in equation (2) gives

$$\underline{R_{max} = \frac{V^2}{g\cos^2\alpha}[1-\sin\alpha]}$$

When the range of the particle is $(\sqrt{2}-1)$ times R_{max} and $\alpha=\pi/6$

$$(\sqrt{2}-1)\frac{V^2}{g\cos^2\alpha}[1-\sin\alpha] = \frac{V^2}{g\cos^2\alpha}[\sin(2\beta+\alpha)-\sin\alpha]$$

$$(\sqrt{2}-1)\times 0.5 = \sin(2\beta+\alpha) - 0.5$$

$$\sin(2\beta+\alpha) = \frac{\sqrt{2}}{2} = \frac{1}{\sqrt{2}}$$

$$2\beta + \frac{\pi}{6} = \frac{\pi}{4} \quad \text{or} \quad \frac{3\pi}{4}$$

$$\beta = \frac{\pi}{24} \quad \text{or} \quad \frac{7\pi}{24}$$

Example 7.6

A particle is projected up a plane with an initial speed of 50 m s^{-1} from a point O on a plane inclined at 45° to the horizontal. The plane containing the path passes through a line of greatest slope of the inclined plane. Find:

(a) the maximum range of the particle,
(b) the time of flight for this maximum range.

(a) From p. 83

$$R = \frac{2u^2 \sin\beta \cos(\beta + \alpha)}{g \cos^2 \alpha}$$

This is a maximum when $\beta = 45° - \alpha/2 = 22.5°$ and

$$R_{max} = \frac{u^2}{g \cos^2 \alpha}(1 - \sin\alpha)$$

Now $\alpha = 45°$. Therefore

$$R_{max} = \frac{50^2}{10 \cos^2 45°}(1 - \sin 45°) = \underline{146.4 \text{ m}}$$

(b) The time of flight T is given by

$$T = \frac{2u \sin\beta}{g \cos\alpha} = \frac{2 \times 50 \times \sin 22.5°}{10 \cos 45°} = \underline{5.4 \text{ s}}$$

Summary

(1) A projectile is a particle moving under the action of its own weight therefore its acceleration is given by $0\boldsymbol{i} - g\boldsymbol{j}$, where $\boldsymbol{i}$ and $\boldsymbol{j}$ are unit vectors in the horizontal and vertical directions.

(2) If its velocity is given in $\boldsymbol{i}, \boldsymbol{j}$ notation it is usually simpler to express its position vector, velocity at a later time and acceleration in this notation to solve the problem.

(3) If its velocity is given as u m s^{-1} at an angle α to the horizontal then either it can be expressed at a time t as $\boldsymbol{u} = (u \cos\alpha)\boldsymbol{i} + (u \sin\alpha - gt)\boldsymbol{j}$ or it can be expressed in parametric notation and an expression derived for the path of the projectile.

The methods are equivalent but correct choice in a problem can simplify the solution.

(4) The particle may be projected on a horizontal plane in which case the axes are conveniently taken as the vertical and horizontal directions. If the particle is projected on an inclined plane then axes parallel and perpendicular to the line of greatest slope of the plane are most convenient to use.

8
Work, energy and power

Objectives

The student should be able to:

(1) define work done by a variable force and calculate it,
(2) define work done by a constant force and calculate it,
(3) define power as the rate of doing work and calculate it,
(4) define energy and use potential and kinetic energy in calculations,
(5) state Hooke's law and use it to calculate the elastic potential energy stored in a stretched spring or string or a compressed spring,
(6) define a conservative force,
(7) use the principles of conservation of energy, of conservation of mechanical energy and of work.

Work

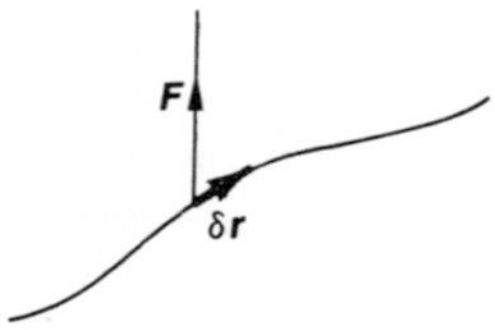

Figure 8.1

When a force $\boldsymbol{F}$ acts on a body and gives it a displacement $\delta\boldsymbol{r}$ (Fig. 8.1) then, assuming $\boldsymbol{F}$ to be constant while moving the point of application $\delta\boldsymbol{r}$, the work done δW by the force on the body is defined as

$$\delta W = \boldsymbol{F} \cdot \delta\boldsymbol{r}$$

since only the component of $\boldsymbol{F}$ in the direction of $\delta\boldsymbol{r}$ is effective in producing the motion.

Work done by a variable force

For a variable force let it have values $\boldsymbol{F}_1, \boldsymbol{F}_2, \ldots, \boldsymbol{F}_n$ while moving through displacements $\delta\boldsymbol{r}_1, \delta\boldsymbol{r}_2, \ldots, \delta\boldsymbol{r}_n$ along AB (Fig. 8.2). Then

$$W = \lim_{\delta r \to 0} \sum \boldsymbol{F} \cdot \delta\boldsymbol{r} = \int_{\mathrm{A}}^{\mathrm{B}} \boldsymbol{F} \cdot \mathrm{d}\boldsymbol{r}$$

where $\boldsymbol{r}_1$ is the position vector of A and $\boldsymbol{r}_2$ is the position vector of B. Therefore

$$W = \int_{\mathrm{A}}^{\mathrm{B}} F \cos\theta \, \mathrm{d}r$$

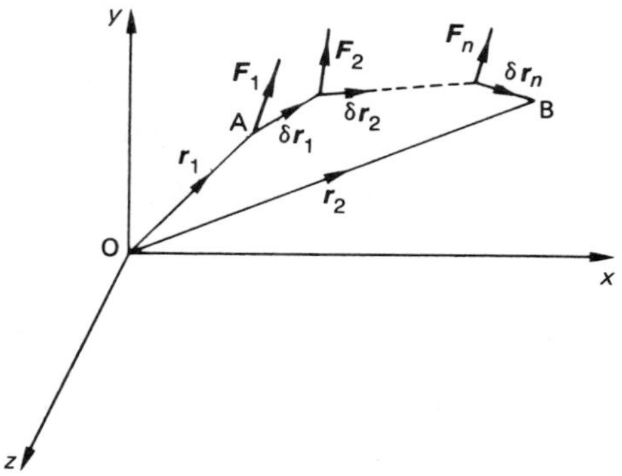

Figure 8.2

Work done by a constant force

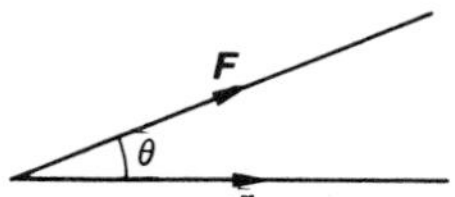

Figure 8.3

For a constant force $\boldsymbol{F}$ moved through a displacement $\boldsymbol{r}$ (Fig. 8.3) the work done is given by

$$W = \boldsymbol{F} \cdot \boldsymbol{r} = Fr \cos \theta$$

and is the product of the magnitude of the component of the force in the direction of motion with the distance moved by the point of application of the force.

Units

Work is a **scalar** and has units of N m or joules since 1 joule is the amount of work done in moving the point of application of 1 newton by 1 metre in the direction of the force.

Example 8.1

Three forces: $\boldsymbol{F}_1 = 2\boldsymbol{i}+\boldsymbol{j}+\boldsymbol{k}$, $\boldsymbol{F}_2 = 3\boldsymbol{i}-3\boldsymbol{j}+\boldsymbol{k}$ and $\boldsymbol{F}_3 = 2\boldsymbol{i}+\boldsymbol{j}$ are acting on a particle and give it a displacement of $6\boldsymbol{i}-\boldsymbol{j}+2\boldsymbol{k}$. Find:

(a) the work done by each of the forces,
(b) the work done by the resultant force.

(a) The work done by $\boldsymbol{F}_1$,

$$W_1 = (2\boldsymbol{i}+\boldsymbol{j}+\boldsymbol{k}) \cdot (6\boldsymbol{i}-\boldsymbol{j}+2\boldsymbol{k})$$
$$= 12-1+2 = \underline{13 \text{ units}}$$

The work done by $\boldsymbol{F}_2$,

$$W_2 = (3\boldsymbol{i}-3\boldsymbol{j}+\boldsymbol{k}) \cdot (6\boldsymbol{i}-\boldsymbol{j}+2\boldsymbol{k})$$
$$= 18+3+2 = \underline{23 \text{ units}}$$

The work done by $\boldsymbol{F}_3$,

$$W_3 = (2\boldsymbol{i}+\boldsymbol{j}) \cdot (6\boldsymbol{i}-\boldsymbol{j}+2\boldsymbol{k})$$
$$= 12-1 = \underline{11 \text{ units}}$$

(b) The total work done,

$$W = \boldsymbol{F}_1 \cdot \boldsymbol{r} + \boldsymbol{F}_2 \cdot \boldsymbol{r} + \boldsymbol{F}_3 \cdot \boldsymbol{r}$$

where $\boldsymbol{r} = (6\boldsymbol{i} - \boldsymbol{j} + 2\boldsymbol{k})$.

$$W = (\boldsymbol{F}_1 + \boldsymbol{F}_2 + \boldsymbol{F}_3) \cdot \boldsymbol{r}$$

Let the resultant force $= \boldsymbol{F}$, i.e.

$$\boldsymbol{F} = \boldsymbol{F}_1 + \boldsymbol{F}_2 + \boldsymbol{F}_3$$

Therefore

$$W = \boldsymbol{F} \cdot \boldsymbol{r} = (7\boldsymbol{i} - \boldsymbol{j} + 2\boldsymbol{k}) \cdot (6\boldsymbol{i} - \boldsymbol{j} + 2\boldsymbol{k})$$
$$= \underline{47 \text{ units}}$$

Note When a set of forces acts on a particle and displaces it then the sum of the work done by the individual forces equals the work done by the resultant force.

Power

Power P is the rate of doing work by a force:

$$P = \frac{\mathrm{d}}{\mathrm{d}t}(\boldsymbol{F} \cdot \boldsymbol{r})$$

where a body is working with power P exerting a force $\boldsymbol{F}$ and causing a displacement $\boldsymbol{r}$.

If $\boldsymbol{F}$ is constant then

$$P = \boldsymbol{F} \cdot \frac{\mathrm{d}\boldsymbol{r}}{\mathrm{d}t}$$

i.e. $P = \boldsymbol{F} \cdot \boldsymbol{V}$

Units

Power is a **scalar** and its units are joules per second, i.e. watts, where 1 joule per second = 1 watt.

Example 8.2

Find the instantaneous power applied to a body moving with velocity $(6\boldsymbol{i} + 2\boldsymbol{j} + \boldsymbol{k})$ units by a force of $(3\boldsymbol{i} + 6\boldsymbol{j} + \boldsymbol{k})$ units.

$$P = \boldsymbol{F} \cdot \boldsymbol{v}$$
$$= (3\boldsymbol{i} + 6\boldsymbol{j} + \boldsymbol{k}) \cdot (6\boldsymbol{i} + 2\boldsymbol{j} + \boldsymbol{k})$$

i.e. $P = \underline{31 \text{ units}}$

Example 8.3

A car of mass 500 g is acted on by a constant frictional resistance of 1000 N as it travels along a level road at a constant speed of 20 m s^{-1}. Find in kW the rate of working of the engine.

force acting on the car = resistive force + ma

i.e. $F = R + ma$

but $a = 0$ so

$$F = R$$

Now

$$\text{power} = \boldsymbol{F} \cdot \boldsymbol{v}$$

Therefore

$$\text{power} = Rv$$

as R and v are parallel. Therefore

$$\text{power} = 1000 \times 20 = 20 \text{ kW}$$

i.e. the rate of working of the engine is 20 kW.

Energy

Energy is the capacity of a body to do work and so is measured in joules. It can have many different forms, e.g. heat energy, chemical energy, light energy, potential energy and kinetic energy.

Kinetic energy (KE)

Kinetic energy is the capacity of a body to do work due to its motion.

Consider a particle of mass m moving under the action of a force $\boldsymbol{F}$ so that its velocity is $\boldsymbol{v}_1$ at time t_1 and $\boldsymbol{v}_2$ at time t_2. Work has been done to change the velocity of the body.

$$\text{work done} = \int_{t_1}^{t_2} \boldsymbol{F} \cdot \frac{\mathrm{d}\boldsymbol{r}}{\mathrm{d}t}\,\mathrm{d}t = \int_{t_1}^{t_2} \boldsymbol{F} \cdot \boldsymbol{v}\,\mathrm{d}t$$

$$= \int_{t_1}^{t_2} m\frac{\mathrm{d}\boldsymbol{v}}{\mathrm{d}t} \cdot \boldsymbol{v}\,\mathrm{d}t = m\int_{\boldsymbol{v}_1}^{\boldsymbol{v}_2} \boldsymbol{v} \cdot \mathrm{d}\boldsymbol{v}$$

$$= \tfrac{1}{2}m\int_{\boldsymbol{v}_1}^{\boldsymbol{v}_2} d(\boldsymbol{v} \cdot \boldsymbol{v}) = \tfrac{1}{2}m[v^2]_{\boldsymbol{v}_1}^{\boldsymbol{v}_2}$$

i.e. $\text{work done} = \tfrac{1}{2}mv_2^2 - \tfrac{1}{2}mv_1^2 = \tfrac{1}{2}m\boldsymbol{v}_2 \cdot \boldsymbol{v}_2 - \tfrac{1}{2}m\boldsymbol{v}_1 \cdot \boldsymbol{v}_1$

Hence the kinetic energy of a body of mass m travelling at a speed $v = \tfrac{1}{2}mv^2$ or $\tfrac{1}{2}m\boldsymbol{v} \cdot \boldsymbol{v}$ and is always positive and the increase in kinetic energy of a particle during a displacement is equal to the net work done. The result is often called the **principle of work.**

For a body of mass m accelerated from a speed u to a speed v by a constant force $F = ma$ over a distance s

$$mas = \tfrac{1}{2}mv^2 - \tfrac{1}{2}mu^2$$

Potential energy (PE)

Potential energy is the capacity of a body to do work by virtue of its position or state.

Gravitational potential energy

Gravitational potential energy is the work a body can do in moving from its position to some standard position under the action of its own weight. A mass m at height h above a standard level would require work of mgh in moving to the standard level and this is the gravitational potential energy of the body. If h were below the standard level then the gravitational potential energy would be $-mgh$. The level chosen is arbitrary but must be made clear in a given problem.

Elastic potential energy and Hooke's law

A string or spring may possess elastic potential energy if the string is stretched or the spring stretched or compressed. The length of a spring or string when no forces act on it, is its natural length a and the difference in length between the stretched length or compressed length and the natural length is the extension or compression x.

Hooke's law is an experimental law which states that the extension is directly proportional to the tension provided that elastic limit is not exceeded for a spring or string and the thrust in a compressed spring is directly proportional to the compression, i.e.

$$T = \frac{\lambda x}{a}$$

where T is the tension or thrust, a is the natural length and λ is the modulus of elasticity of the spring. λ has the dimensions of force and is a measure of the 'stiffness' of a spring or the 'elasticity' of a string and is a constant for a given spring or string.

Once the elastic limit is exceeded the spring or string will no longer return to its original length a when the tension is removed and so will not obey Hooke's law.

The work done in stretching a spring or string or compressing a spring by an amount x is given by

$$\delta W = T\,\delta x = \frac{\lambda x}{a}\,\delta x$$

where T is the tension and a is the natural length. Hence the work done in stretching it from an extension x_A to an extension x_B is given by

$$W = \int_A^B \frac{\lambda x \, dx}{a} = \left[\frac{\lambda x^2}{2a}\right]_{x_A}^{x_B}$$

and

$$\text{elastic potential energy} = W = \frac{1}{a}\lambda x_B^2 - \frac{1}{2a}\lambda x_A^2$$

If the original extension is zero and the final extension is x then

$$\text{elastic potential energy} = W = \frac{\lambda}{2a}x^2$$

and is never negative. This is also the work done and the potential energy stored in compressing a spring by an amount x.

Conservation forces

The work done when a force has its point of application displaced from point A to point B

$$W = \int_A^B \boldsymbol{F} \cdot \mathrm{d}\boldsymbol{r}$$

For a block of wood moved on a table top in a circle against friction the work done depends on the circumference of the circle. If the same block of wood is moved in a vertical circle against gravity then as the path is closed no work is done, hence gravity is a conservative force. The work done by any conservative force when its point of application follows a closed path is zero. Other examples of conservative forces are tension in an elastic spring, tension or thrust in a spring and any constant force because

$$\sum \boldsymbol{F} \cdot \delta\boldsymbol{r} = 0$$

if $\Sigma\ \delta\boldsymbol{r} = 0$ and $\boldsymbol{F}$ is constant.

Principle of conservation of energy

Energy can never be created or destroyed.

Kinetic and potential energy are forms of mechanical energy.

Principle of mechanical energy

In a conservative system of forces the total mechanical energy remains constant and it follows that if work is done by a non-conservative force then that work is equal to the change in mechanical energy it produces.

The principle of mechanical energy can be a very useful tool in problem solving.

If a body of mass m falls from a height A with velocity v_A to a height B with velocity v_B then

$$\text{PE at A} + \tfrac{1}{2}mv_A^2 = \text{PE at B} + \tfrac{1}{2}mv_B^2$$

from the principle of mechanical energy.

Example 8.4

A pump working at an effective rate of 50 kW raises 100 kg of water per second from a depth of 20 m. Calculate the speed at which it is delivered. (Take $g = 10\ \text{m s}^{-2}$.)

The energy supplied per second $= 50 \times 10^3$ J. Therefore

$$(\text{gain in KE} + \text{gain in PE}) \text{ per second} = 50 \times 10^3$$

$$\tfrac{1}{2}mv^2 + mgh = 50 \times 10^3$$

$$50v^2 + 100 \times 10 \times 20 = 50 \times 10^3$$

Therefore

$$v = 24.5\ \text{m s}^{-1}$$

i.e. the water is delivered at $\underline{24.5\ \text{m s}^{-1}}$.

Problem 8.1

A car of mass 500 kg is travelling up a hill of inclination α to the horizontal where $\sin \alpha = \frac{1}{2}$. If the total resistive force is 200 N and the car is working at 30 kW, calculate the acceleration a of the car when the speed is 10 m s^{-1} and the maximum speed that can be attained by the car up this hill.

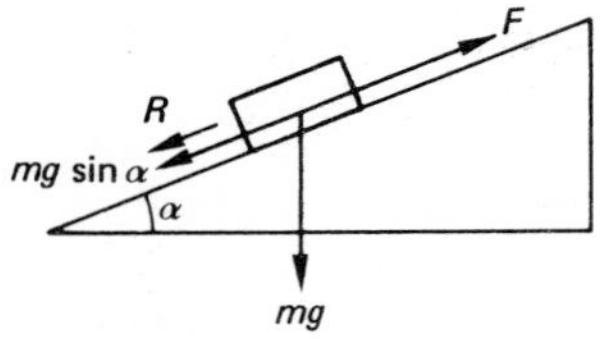

Figure 8.4

(1) Draw a diagram (Fig. 8.4).
(2) Resolve parallel to the slope to show that the pull of the car is given by

$$F = mg \sin \alpha + R + ma$$

where R is the resistive force.
(3) Now $P = \mathbf{F} \cdot \mathbf{v} = Fv$ because they are parallel. Therefore calculate F and hence a using $v = 10$ m s^{-1} to show that $a = 0.6$ m s^{-1}.
(4) When the car attains its maximum speed v_m then the acceleration is zero. Therefore use $F_m = mg \sin \alpha + R$ and $F_m = P/v_m$ to find $v_m = 11.1$ m s^{-1}.

Note Had the car been travelling down the hill then the resistive force would have been acting up the hill and the force equation parallel to the slope would be

$$F = mg \sin \alpha - R + ma$$

Example 8.5

A light spring obeys Hooke's law. A force of 20 N extends the spring by 0.01 m. Show that the work done in extending the spring by b m from the unstretched state is $10^3 b^2$ J.

This spring is placed in a long smooth straight cylindrical tube with one end fixed to the tube. The tube is fixed in the vertical plane with the free end of the spring uppermost. The dimensions of the tube and the spring are such that the spring can only move vertically and the spring always remains inside the tube. A particle of mass 4 kg is held firmly attached to the free end of the spring. The particle is held so that the spring is compressed a distance of 0.1 m from its uncompressed state. The particle is then released. Show that subsequently

$$v^2 = 3 + 20y - 500y^2$$

where v m s^{-1} is the speed of the particle and y m is the compression of the spring.

Find:

(a) v^2 when the *extension* of the spring is 0.1 m,
(b) the value of y when the speed is a maximum,
(c) the maximum extension of the spring.
(Take $g = 10$ m s^{-2}.) (AEB J83)

From Hooke's law

$$T = \lambda x/a$$

$$20 = \lambda(0.01)/a$$

$$\lambda/a = 2000 \text{ N m}^{-1}$$

The work done in extending the spring by b m from zero extension is given by

$$W = \frac{1}{2a}\lambda x^2 = \frac{\lambda}{a}\frac{b^2}{2} = 10^3 b^2$$

i.e. the work done is $10^3 b^2$ J.

When the spring is released the compression reduces to y (Fig. 8.5). Therefore

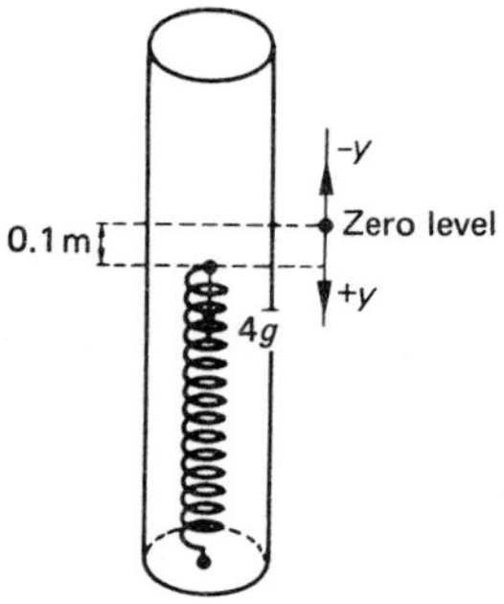

Figure 8.5

$$\text{loss in elastic PE of the spring} = 10^3\,(0.1^2 - y^2)$$

The particle of mass 4 kg gains KE and PE

$$\text{gain in KE of 4 kg} = 2v^2$$

$$\text{gain in PE of 4 kg} = 4 \times g \times (0.1 - y)$$

From the principle of conservation of mechanical energy gain in (KE + PE) of the 4 kg mass = loss in elastic PE of the spring.

Therefore

$$2v^2 + 40(0.1 - y) = 10^3(0.1^2 - y^2)$$

$$2v^2 + 4 - 40y = 10 - 1000y^2$$

Therefore

$$v^2 = 3 + 20y - 500y^2$$

(a) When the extension = 0.01 m then $y = -0.01$ m. Therefore

$$v^2 = 3 - 20 \times 0.01 - 500 \times 0.01^2$$

$$= \underline{2.75\ (\text{m s}^{-1})^2}$$

(b) v^2 is a maximum when $3 + 20y - 500y^2$ is a maximum, i.e. when

$$\frac{\text{d}}{\text{d}y}(3 + 20y - 500y^2) = 0$$

$$20 - 1000y = 0$$

$$y = \underline{0.02\ \text{m}}$$

Note v^2 is a minimum when $v = 0$.

(c) The maximum extension of the spring occurs when the KE is zero and the work done to increase the PE of the mass = the loss in elastic PE of the spring. Therefore

$$4g \times (0.1 - y) = 10^3(0.1^2 - y^2)$$

$$40/10^3 = 0.1 + y$$

$$y = 0.04 - 0.1 = -0.06\ \text{m}$$

but y is a compression so the maximum extension is $\underline{+0.06\ \text{m}}$.

Problem 8.2

The external resistance to the motion of a bicycle and rider consists of a constant force together with a force proportional to the square of the speed. The mass of the bicycle and rider is

90 kg. The speed is constant at 3 m s^{-1} when freewheeling (i.e. not pedalling) down a slope inclined at an angle $\sin^{-1}(1/50)$ to the horizontal and constant at 7 m s^{-1} when freewheeling down a slope inclined at an angle $\sin^{-1}(1/25)$ to the horizontal. Show that when the cyclist is moving at a speed of v m s^{-1} the external resistance is $(13.95+0.45v^2)$ N.

Assuming that 10% of the work is lost in friction in the pedalling gear, find the amount of power that has to be expended in climbing a slope inclined at an angle $\sin^{-1}(1/40)$ to the horizontal, at a steady speed of 4 m s^{-1}. (AEB N84)

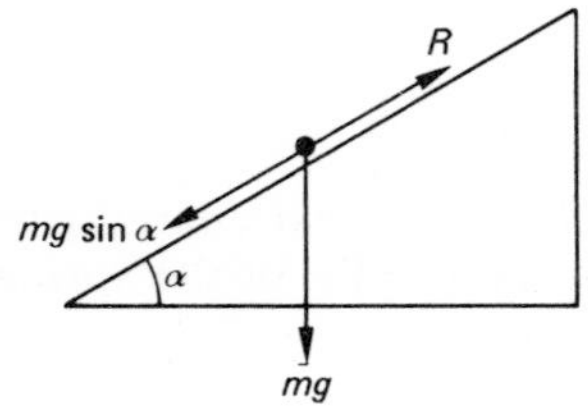

Figure 8.6

Let the external resistance $R = C + Dv^2$ and draw a diagram (Fig. 8.6).

As the cyclist is freewheeling down, R acts up the slope and the pull $F = 0$. At constant speed the acceleration $a = 0$. Therefore

$$0 = mg \sin \alpha - R$$

parallel to the slope. Substitute in this for both slopes and constant speeds given to obtain

$$900/50 = C + 9D \qquad (1)$$

and $$900/25 = C + 49D \qquad (2)$$

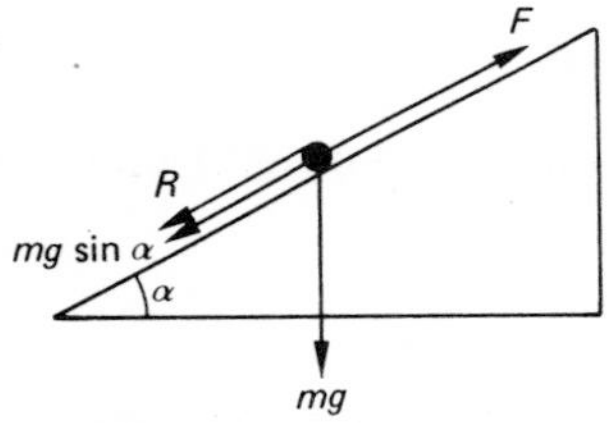

Figure 8.7

Subtracting equation (1) from equation (2) gives D and then C can be found to show

$$R = (13.95 + 0.45v^2) \text{ N}$$

When the cyclist pedals up the slope $F \neq 0$ and R acts down so parallel to the slope in this case,

$$F = mg \sin \alpha + R + 0$$

because $a = 0$ for steady speeds. Substitution of the given values gives $F = 43.7$ N and

$$P = Fv = 174.8 \text{ N}$$

but this is 90% of the required power as 10% is lost. Therefore

amount of power that has to be expended = <u>194 W</u>

Example 8.6

Prove that the elastic energy of a light spring of natural length a and modulus of elasticity λ, stretched by an amount x, is $\lambda x^2/2a$.

A trolley of mass m runs down a smooth track of constant inclination $\pi/6$ to the horizontal, carrying at its front end a light spring of natural length a and modulus mga/c, where c is constant. When the spring is fully compressed it is of length $a/4$ and it obeys Hooke's law up to this point. After the trolley has travelled a distance b from rest the spring meets a fixed stop. Show that, when the spring has been compressed a distance x, where $x < 3a/4$, the speed v of the trolley is given by

$$cv^2/g = c(b+x) - x^2$$

Given that $c = a/10$ and $b = 2a$, find the total distance covered by the trolley before it momentarily comes to rest for the first time.
(UL J82)

The first part $W = \lambda x^2/2a$ is proved previously in this chapter (p. 92).

Parallel to the slope

$$\text{acceleration} = g \sin \alpha$$

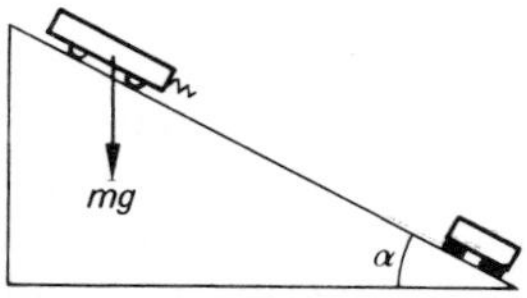

Figure 8.8

(Fig. 8.8). Therefore using $v^2 = u^2 + 2as$, after a distance b,

$$V^2 = 2g \sin \alpha b = gb$$

(as $\sin \pi/6 = \frac{1}{2}$) when the spring reaches the stop.

From the principle of conservation of energy

gain in elastic PE of the spring upon compression a distance x

= loss in KE of the trolley + loss in PE of the trolley (1)

Loss in KE of the trolley $= \frac{1}{2}m(gb - v^2)$ when it reduces to a speed v and loss in PE of the trolley $= mgx \sin \alpha$ when the spring is compressed a distance x. Then in equation (1),

$$\frac{\lambda x^2}{2a} = \frac{1}{2}m(gb - v^2) + mgx \sin \alpha$$

Substituting for λ,

$$\left(\frac{mga}{c}\right)\left(\frac{x^2}{2a}\right) = \frac{1}{2}m(gb - v^2) + \frac{1}{2}mgx$$

dividing by $mg/2$,

$$\frac{x^2}{c} = b - \frac{v^2}{g} + x$$

multiplying by c,

$$x^2 = bc - \frac{v^2 c}{g} + xc$$

and collecting terms,

$$c(b + x) - x^2 = \frac{cv^2}{g}$$

When the trolley comes to rest $v = 0$. Therefore

$$c(b + x) = x^2$$

Substituting for $c = a/10$ and $b = 2a$,

$$\frac{a}{10}(2a + x) = x^2$$

multiplying by 10,

$$2a^2 + ax = 10x^2$$

or $\quad 10x^2 - ax - 2a^2 = 0$

Therefore

$$x = \frac{a \pm \sqrt{(a^2 + 80a^2)}}{20} = \frac{a \pm 9a}{20}$$

Now a is positive so

$$x = a/2$$

Hence the total distance covered by the trolley before it momentarily comes to rest $= \underline{b + x = 5a/2}$.

Example 8.7

A fast cruiser is propelled at a constant speed of 60 km h^{-1} when its engines deliver power of 30 000 kW. Calculate the resistance to motion of the cruiser. Given that the resistance to motion is proportional to the square of the speed of the cruiser, calculate the resistance when the cruiser is moving at a speed of 72 km h^{-1}. (AEB J86)

$$60 \text{ km h}^{-1} = 100/6 \text{ m s}^{-1} \quad \text{and} \quad 72 \text{ km h}^{-1} = 20 \text{ m s}^{-1}.$$

As the speed is constant, $ma = 0$. There is no slope so the pulling force $F = R$.

$$\text{power } P = \boldsymbol{F} \cdot \boldsymbol{v} = Fv$$

Therefore

$$R = \frac{P}{v} = \frac{30 \times 10^6}{100/6} = 1.8 \times 10^6 \text{ N}$$

i.e. the resistance to motion of the cruiser when it moves at 60 km h^{-1} is $\underline{1800 \text{ KN}}$.

As $R \propto v^2$,

$$\frac{R_2}{R_1} = \frac{V_2^2}{V_1^2}$$

$$R_2 = \frac{1.8 \times 10^6 \times 20^2}{(100/6)^2} = 2590 \times 10^3 \text{ N}$$

i.e. the resistance to motion of the cruiser when it moves at 72 km h^{-1} is $\underline{2590 \text{ KN}}$.

Summary

(1) Work is a scalar and its units are joules.

(2) The work done by a variable force $\boldsymbol{F}$ acting in the same direction as the motion in moving its point of application a displacement $\boldsymbol{r}$ in a straight line from A to B is given by

$$W = \int_A^B \boldsymbol{F} \cdot d\boldsymbol{r} = \int_A^B F \cos\theta \, dr$$

If the force $\boldsymbol{F}$ is constant then

$$W = \boldsymbol{F} \cdot \boldsymbol{r} = Fr \cos\theta$$

(3) Power P is the rate of doing work, it is a scalar and its units are watts.

$$P = \frac{d}{dt}(\boldsymbol{F} \cdot \boldsymbol{r})$$

If $\boldsymbol{F}$ is constant $P = \boldsymbol{F} \cdot \boldsymbol{V} = Fv \cos \theta$.
If $\boldsymbol{F}$ and $\boldsymbol{v}$ are parallel $P = Fv$.
The pull of an engine $F = P/v$ for a given v.

(4) Energy is the capacity to do work, it is a scalar and its units are joules.

Energy can be converted into many forms. The kinetic energy of a mass m moving with speed v is $\frac{1}{2}mv^2$. The gravitational potential energy of a mass m a height h above an arbitrary zero potential energy level is mgh and a height h below the level is $-mgh$.

(5) Hooke's law states that the extension of a spring or string is proportional to the tension provided that the elastic limit is not exceeded. The elastic potential energy of a spring or string is the work done in stretching or compressing the spring or stretching the string x m from its natural length of a, i.e.

$$\text{elastic potential energy} = \frac{\lambda x^2}{2a} \text{ J}$$

(6) A conservative force is such that the work done when its point of application follows a closed path is zero, e.g. gravity. An example of a non-conservative force is friction.

(7) The principle of conservation of energy states that energy can be neither created nor destroyed.

(8) Mechanical energy is either kinetic or potential energy and the principle of conservation of mechanical energy states that in a conservative system of forces the total mechanical energy remains constant, i.e. KE + PE is constant.

9
Motion of particles in two dimensions

Objectives

The student should be able to:

(1) calculate the velocity and acceration of a particle given its position vector in cartesian coordinates,
(2) calculate the velocity and acceleration of a particle given its position vector in polar coordinates,
(3) calculate the velocity and acceleration of a vector given its position vector in intrinsic coordinates.

Note Differentiation of vectors can be applied to the motion of a particle in two dimensions, i.e. a plane, using cartesian, polar or intrinsic coordinates.

Motion in two dimensions using cartesian coordinates

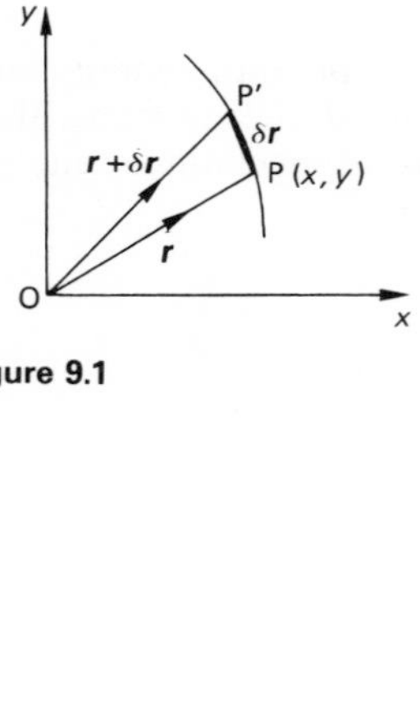

Figure 9.1

Let $\boldsymbol{r}$ be the position vector of a particle P at a time t, where $\boldsymbol{r}$ is a function of time and P moves on a curve (Fig. 9.1). Therefore

$$\boldsymbol{r}(t)=f(t)\boldsymbol{i}+g(t)\boldsymbol{j}$$

and the velocity

$$\dot{\boldsymbol{r}}=\frac{\mathrm{d}\boldsymbol{r}}{\mathrm{d}t}=\lim_{\delta t\to 0}\frac{\delta\boldsymbol{r}}{\delta t}$$

where $\delta\boldsymbol{r}$ is the small change in $\boldsymbol{r}$ over time δt so $\dot{\boldsymbol{r}}$ will be in the direction of the tangent to the curve at P.

$$\dot{\boldsymbol{r}}=\frac{\mathrm{d}(f(t))}{\mathrm{d}t}\boldsymbol{i}+\frac{\mathrm{d}(g(t))}{\mathrm{d}t}\boldsymbol{j}$$

The acceleration vector

$$\boldsymbol{a}=\ddot{\boldsymbol{r}}=\frac{\mathrm{d}^2\boldsymbol{r}}{\mathrm{d}t^2}$$

$$\ddot{\boldsymbol{r}}=\frac{\mathrm{d}^2}{\mathrm{d}t^2}(f(t))\boldsymbol{i}+\frac{\mathrm{d}^2}{\mathrm{d}t^2}(g(t))\boldsymbol{j}$$

Example 9.1

A particle moves so that its position vector is given by $a\cos\omega t\,\boldsymbol{i}+a\sin\omega t\,\boldsymbol{j}$, where ω is constant. Show that:

(a) the velocity $\boldsymbol{v}$ of the particle is perpendicular to $\boldsymbol{r}$,

(b) the acceleration $\boldsymbol{a}$ is directed towards the origin of the coordinate system.

(a) $\boldsymbol{r} = a \cos \omega t\, \boldsymbol{i} + a \sin \omega t\, \boldsymbol{j}$ (1)

and $\dot{\boldsymbol{r}} = -a\omega \sin \omega t\, \boldsymbol{i} + a\omega \cos \omega t\, \boldsymbol{j}$

$$\boldsymbol{r} \cdot \boldsymbol{v} = (a \cos \omega t\, \boldsymbol{i} + a \sin \omega t\, \boldsymbol{j}) \cdot (-a\omega \sin \omega t\, \boldsymbol{i} + a\omega \cos \omega t\, \boldsymbol{j})$$

$$= -a^2\omega \sin \omega t \cos \omega t + a^2\omega \sin \omega t \cos \omega t$$

so $\boldsymbol{r} \cdot \boldsymbol{v} = 0$ and $\boldsymbol{r}$ and $\boldsymbol{v}$ are perpendicular.

(b) acceleration $\ddot{\boldsymbol{r}} = -a\omega^2 \sin \omega t\, \boldsymbol{i} - a\omega^2 \cos \omega t\, \boldsymbol{j}$

$$= -\omega^2 \boldsymbol{r}$$

so the acceleration is opposed to the direction of $\boldsymbol{r}$, i.e. is always directed towards the origin.

Note Equation (1) is the vector equation of a circle.

Motion in two dimensions using polar coordinates

First we must consider the differentiation of a unit vector with respect to a scalar. Consider a unit vector $\hat{\boldsymbol{r}}$ which has variable direction,

$$\hat{\boldsymbol{r}} = l\boldsymbol{i} + m\boldsymbol{j} + n\boldsymbol{k}$$

where l, m and n are the variable direction cosines of $\hat{\boldsymbol{r}}$ and

$$l^2 + m^2 + n^2 = 1$$

$$\frac{d\hat{\boldsymbol{r}}}{dt} = \frac{dl}{dt}\boldsymbol{i} + \frac{dm}{dt}\boldsymbol{j} + \frac{dn}{dt}\boldsymbol{k}$$

hence

$$\hat{\boldsymbol{r}} \cdot \frac{d\hat{\boldsymbol{r}}}{dt} = (l\boldsymbol{i} + m\boldsymbol{j} + n\boldsymbol{k}) \cdot \left(\frac{dl}{dt}\boldsymbol{i} + \frac{dm}{dt}\boldsymbol{j} + \frac{dn}{dt}\boldsymbol{k}\right)$$

$$= l\frac{dl}{dt} + m\frac{dm}{dt} + n\frac{dn}{dt}$$

$$= \frac{1}{2}\frac{d}{dt}(l^2 + m^2 + n^2)$$

Therefore

$$\hat{\boldsymbol{r}} \cdot \frac{d\hat{\boldsymbol{r}}}{dt} = 0$$

so a unit vector and its derivative with respect to a scalar variable are perpendicular. (*Note* $d\hat{\boldsymbol{r}}/dt$ is not necessarily a unit vector.)

Now consider a particle P moving along a curve in the (x, y) plane so that at a time t its polar coordinates are (r, θ) (Fig. 9.2). The position vector of P at time t,

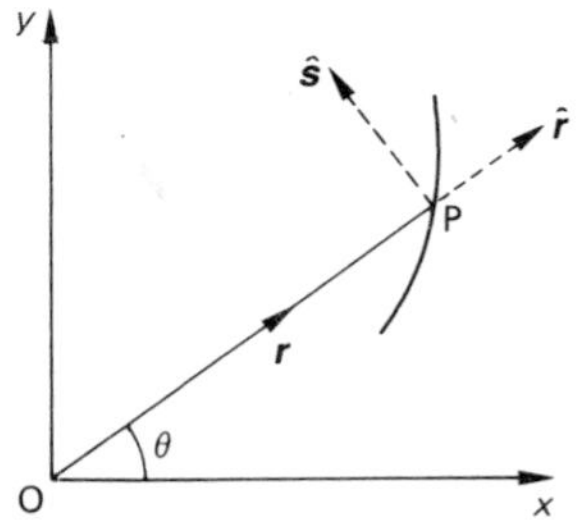

Figure 9.2

$$\boldsymbol{r} = r \cos \theta\, \boldsymbol{i} + r \sin \theta\, \boldsymbol{j}$$

Then the velocity vector $\boldsymbol{v}$ is given by

$$\boldsymbol{v} = \frac{\mathrm{d}\boldsymbol{r}}{\mathrm{d}t} = \dot{r}(\cos\theta\,\boldsymbol{i} + \sin\theta\,\boldsymbol{j}) + r\dot{\theta}(-\sin\theta\,\boldsymbol{i} + \cos\theta\,\boldsymbol{j})$$

but $\hat{\boldsymbol{r}} = \cos\theta\,\boldsymbol{i} + \sin\theta\,\boldsymbol{j}$ and is a unit vector along $\boldsymbol{r}$. Let $\hat{\boldsymbol{s}} = -\sin\theta\,\boldsymbol{i} + \cos\theta\,\boldsymbol{j}$, where $\hat{\boldsymbol{s}}$ is a unit vector inclined at $\theta + \pi/2$ to Ox. Then

$$\boldsymbol{v} = \dot{r}\hat{\boldsymbol{r}} + r\dot{\theta}\hat{\boldsymbol{s}}$$

The acceleration of P at time t is given by

$$\boldsymbol{a} = \frac{\mathrm{d}\boldsymbol{v}}{\mathrm{d}t} = \ddot{r}\hat{\boldsymbol{r}} + \dot{r}\frac{\mathrm{d}\hat{\boldsymbol{r}}}{\mathrm{d}t} + \dot{r}\dot{\theta}\hat{\boldsymbol{s}} + r\ddot{\theta}\hat{\boldsymbol{s}} + r\dot{\theta}\frac{\mathrm{d}\hat{\boldsymbol{s}}}{\mathrm{d}t}$$

Now

$$\frac{\mathrm{d}\hat{\boldsymbol{r}}}{\mathrm{d}t} = \frac{\mathrm{d}\hat{\boldsymbol{r}}}{\mathrm{d}\theta}\frac{\mathrm{d}\theta}{\mathrm{d}t} = (-\sin\theta\,\boldsymbol{i} + \cos\theta\,\boldsymbol{j})\dot{\theta} = \hat{\boldsymbol{s}}\dot{\theta}$$

and similarly

$$\frac{\mathrm{d}\hat{\boldsymbol{s}}}{\mathrm{d}t} = \dot{\theta}(-\hat{\boldsymbol{r}})$$

Therefore

$$\boldsymbol{a} = \ddot{r}\hat{\boldsymbol{r}} + \dot{r}\dot{\theta}\hat{\boldsymbol{s}} + \dot{r}\dot{\theta}\hat{\boldsymbol{s}} + r\ddot{\theta}\hat{\boldsymbol{s}} - r\dot{\theta}^2\hat{\boldsymbol{r}}$$

i.e. $\boldsymbol{a} = (\ddot{r} - r\dot{\theta}^2)\hat{\boldsymbol{r}} + (r\ddot{\theta} + 2\dot{r}\dot{\theta})\hat{\boldsymbol{s}}$

θ is the angle that the radius vector $\overrightarrow{\mathrm{OP}}$ makes with Ox at a time t. Hence $\dot{\theta}$ is the angular velocity of $\overrightarrow{\mathrm{OP}}$ and $\ddot{\theta}$ is the angular acceleration of $\overrightarrow{\mathrm{OP}}$.

The velocity and acceleration vectors of P can be considered as the sum of two component vectors: the radial component in the direction of $\overrightarrow{\mathrm{OP}}$ and the transverse component in the direction given by rotating $\overrightarrow{\mathrm{OP}}$ through a positive right angle.

Example 9.2

A particle moves around the curve $r = 2(1 + \sin\theta)$ with constant angular velocity ω. Find the radial and transverse components of the velocity and acceleration of the particle at a time t in terms of ω and θ.

$$\omega = \dot{\theta}$$

As ω is constant,

$$\ddot{\theta} = 0$$

$$r = 2(1 + \sin\theta)$$

$$\dot{r} = +(2\cos\theta)\dot{\theta} = 2\omega\cos\theta$$

$$\ddot{r} = -(2\omega\sin\theta)\dot{\theta} = -2\omega^2\sin\theta$$

so the radial component of the velocity

$$\dot{r} = \underline{2\omega\cos\theta}$$

the transverse component of the velocity

$$r\dot{\theta} = \underline{2\omega(1 + \sin\theta)}$$

the radial component of the acceleration

$$\ddot{r} - r\dot{\theta}^2 = -2\omega^2 \sin\theta - 2\omega^2(1 + \sin\theta)$$
$$= \underline{-2\omega^2(1 + 2\sin\theta)}$$

and the transverse component of the acceleration

$$r\ddot{\theta} + 2\dot{r}\dot{\theta} = \underline{4\omega^2 \cos\theta}$$

Motion in two dimensions using intrinsic coordinates

Let A be a fixed point on the path of a moving particle at position P at some time t (Fig. 9.3). Let the arc AP $= s$ and let the tangent

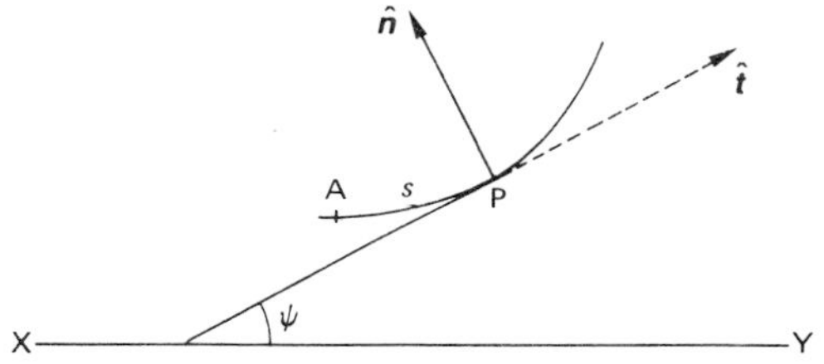

Figure 9.3

at P be inclined at an angle ψ to a fixed straight line XY. The intrinsic coordinates of P are then (s, ψ). Let P′ $(s + \delta s, \psi + \delta\psi)$ be the position of P at time $t + \delta t$. Then as for cartesian coordinates, the velocity v of P is given by

$$v = \lim_{\delta t \to 0} \frac{\text{PP}'}{\delta t} = \lim_{\delta t \to 0} \frac{\delta \boldsymbol{r}}{\delta t} = \lim_{\delta t \to 0} \frac{\delta \boldsymbol{r}}{\delta s}\frac{\delta s}{\delta t}$$

Now as $\delta t \to 0$ then the modulus of $\delta \boldsymbol{r} \to \delta s$, i.e. $\delta \boldsymbol{r}/\delta s \to 1$, and the direction of $\delta \boldsymbol{r}$ tends to that of the tangent at P.

Let $\hat{\boldsymbol{t}}$ be the unit vector in the direction of the tangent at P and let $\hat{\boldsymbol{n}}$ be the unit vector in the direction of the positive normal at P. Therefore

$$\boldsymbol{v} = \frac{\mathrm{d}s}{\mathrm{d}t}\hat{\boldsymbol{t}} = \dot{s}\hat{\boldsymbol{t}}$$

and $$\frac{\mathrm{d}\hat{\boldsymbol{t}}}{\mathrm{d}t} = \frac{\mathrm{d}\hat{\boldsymbol{t}}}{\mathrm{d}\psi}\frac{\mathrm{d}\psi}{\mathrm{d}t} = \hat{\boldsymbol{n}}\frac{\mathrm{d}\psi}{\mathrm{d}t}$$

as for polar coordinates so

$$\dot{\boldsymbol{v}} = \ddot{s}\hat{\boldsymbol{t}} + \dot{s}\frac{\mathrm{d}\hat{\boldsymbol{t}}}{\mathrm{d}t}$$

i.e. $$\dot{\boldsymbol{v}} = \ddot{s}\hat{\boldsymbol{t}} + \dot{s}\dot{\psi}\hat{\boldsymbol{n}}$$

so the velocity has a tangential component $= \dot{s}$ and the acceleration has a tangential component $= \ddot{s}$ plus a normal component $= \dot{s}\dot{\psi}$.

Example 9.3

A particle is moving with constant speed u along the circumference of a circle of radius a. Find the magnitude of the acceleration and its direction.

$$u = \frac{\mathrm{d}s}{\mathrm{d}t} = \dot{s}$$

The radius of curvature of the path

$$\rho = \frac{\mathrm{d}s}{\mathrm{d}\psi}$$

by definition. Now

$$\text{normal component of the acceleration} = \dot{s}\dot{\psi} = \dot{s}\frac{\mathrm{d}\psi}{\mathrm{d}s}\frac{\mathrm{d}s}{\mathrm{d}t} = \dot{s}^2/\rho$$

In this example u is constant. Therefore

$$\dot{u} = 0$$

and the radius of curvature

$$\frac{\mathrm{d}s}{\mathrm{d}\psi} = a$$

$$\ddot{s} = \dot{u}$$

but u is constant so

$$\ddot{s} = 0$$

i.e. the tangential component of the acceleration $\ddot{s}$ is zero and the acceleration is of magnitude $\dot{s}^2/\rho$ or u^2/a and is directed towards the centre of the circle.

Example 9.4

A particle moves along a curve with position vector $\boldsymbol{r}$ at time t given by

$$\boldsymbol{r} = 2\cos t\,\boldsymbol{i} + 2\sin t\,\boldsymbol{j}$$

Find the velocity and acceleration of the particle in terms of the normal and tangential unit vectors $\hat{\boldsymbol{n}}$ and $\hat{\boldsymbol{t}}$.

$$\frac{\mathrm{d}\boldsymbol{r}}{\mathrm{d}t} = \boldsymbol{v} = \dot{s}\hat{\boldsymbol{t}}$$

In this example

$$\frac{\mathrm{d}\boldsymbol{r}}{\mathrm{d}t} = -2\sin t\,\boldsymbol{i} + 2\cos t\,\boldsymbol{j}$$

$$\left|\frac{\mathrm{d}\boldsymbol{r}}{\mathrm{d}t}\right| = 2\sqrt{(\sin^2 t + \cos^2 t)} = 2$$

Now

$$\hat{\boldsymbol{t}} = \frac{\mathrm{d}\boldsymbol{r}}{\mathrm{d}t}\Bigg/\left|\frac{\mathrm{d}\boldsymbol{r}}{\mathrm{d}t}\right| = -\sin t\,\boldsymbol{i} + \cos t\,\boldsymbol{j}$$

Therefore

$$\boldsymbol{v} = 2(-\sin t\,\boldsymbol{i} + \cos t\,\boldsymbol{j})$$

i.e. $\boldsymbol{v} = 2\hat{\boldsymbol{t}}$

and the normal component is zero.

Since $\hat{\boldsymbol{n}}$ and $\hat{\boldsymbol{t}}$ are perpendicular unit vectors

$$\hat{\boldsymbol{n}} = \cos t\,\boldsymbol{i} + \sin t\,\boldsymbol{j}$$

then

$$\hat{\boldsymbol{t}} \cdot \hat{\boldsymbol{n}} = 0$$

$$\frac{\mathrm{d}\boldsymbol{v}}{\mathrm{d}t} = 2(-\cos t\,\boldsymbol{i} - \sin t\,\boldsymbol{j}) + 0$$

i.e. $\dfrac{\mathrm{d}\boldsymbol{v}}{\mathrm{d}t} = \underline{-2\hat{\boldsymbol{n}}}$

and the tangential component is zero.

Example 9.5.

A particle describes the curve $r = 2\mathrm{e}^{\theta}$. Find the radial and transverse components of the acceleration if the particle moves with uniform angular velocity ω about the origin.

Let the postion vector of a point P relative to the origin be $\boldsymbol{r}$ and the unit vectors in the directions $\overrightarrow{\mathrm{OP}}$ and perpendicular to $\overrightarrow{\mathrm{OP}}$ be $\hat{\boldsymbol{r}}$ and $\hat{\boldsymbol{s}}$ respectively.

$$\dot{r} = 2\mathrm{e}^{\theta}\dot{\theta} = r\omega$$

$$\ddot{\theta} = \dot{\omega} = 0$$

$$\ddot{r} = \dot{r}\omega + 0 = r\omega^2$$

Now

$$\ddot{\boldsymbol{r}} = (\ddot{r} - r\dot{\theta}^2)\hat{\boldsymbol{r}} + (2\dot{r}\dot{\theta} + r\ddot{\theta})\hat{\boldsymbol{s}}$$

$$= (r\omega^2 - r\omega^2)\hat{\boldsymbol{r}} + (2r\omega^2 + 0)\hat{\boldsymbol{s}}$$

$$= 0\hat{\boldsymbol{r}} + 2r\omega^2\hat{\boldsymbol{s}}$$

Hence the radial component of the acceleration is $\underline{\text{zero}}$ and the transverse component is $\underline{2r\omega^2}$.

Problem 9.1

The position vector of a particle at a time t is $2t\boldsymbol{i} + \mathrm{e}^t\boldsymbol{j}$. Show that the acceleration has no component in the direction of $\boldsymbol{i}$ and find the speed when $t = 2$ s.

(1) Differentiate with respect to time to show that $\boldsymbol{v} = 2\boldsymbol{i} + \mathrm{e}^t\boldsymbol{j}$ and again with respect to time to show that $\boldsymbol{a} = \mathrm{e}^t\boldsymbol{j}$. Hence the acceleration has no component in the direction of $\boldsymbol{i}$.

(2) Find the speed $= |\boldsymbol{v}| = \sqrt{(4 + \mathrm{e}^4)} = 77\ \mathrm{m\,s^{-1}}$.

Summary

(1) In general,

$$\hat{\boldsymbol{r}} \cdot \frac{\mathrm{d}\hat{\boldsymbol{r}}}{\mathrm{d}t} = 0$$

as a unit vector and its derivative with respect to a scalar variable are perpendicular.

(2) Using cartesian components, where $\boldsymbol{r}$ is the position vector of a particle P at a time t, then if

$$\boldsymbol{r} = f(t)\boldsymbol{i} + g(t)\boldsymbol{j}$$

$$\dot{\boldsymbol{r}} = \dot{f}(t)\boldsymbol{i} + \dot{g}(t)\boldsymbol{j}$$

and $\ddot{\boldsymbol{r}} = \ddot{f}(t)\boldsymbol{i} + \ddot{g}(t)\boldsymbol{j}$

as shown in Fig. 9.4(a).

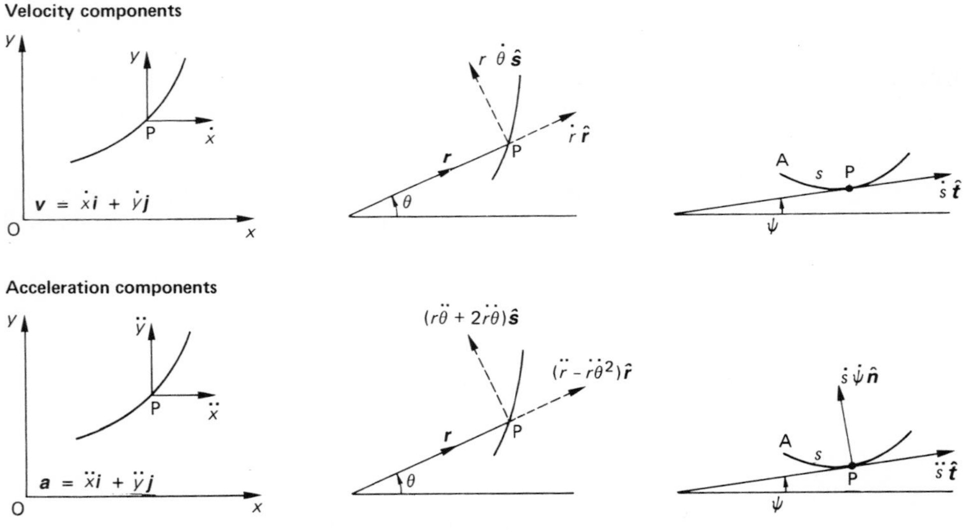

(a) Cartesian (b) Polar (c) Intrinsic

Figure 9.4

(3) Using polar coordinates (r, θ) at a time t for a particle P moving along a curve then

$$\boldsymbol{r} = r\cos\theta\,\boldsymbol{i} + r\sin\theta\,\boldsymbol{j}$$

$$\dot{\boldsymbol{r}} = \boldsymbol{v} = \dot{r}\hat{\boldsymbol{r}} + r\dot{\theta}\hat{\boldsymbol{s}}$$

and $\ddot{\boldsymbol{r}} = \boldsymbol{a} = (\ddot{r} - r\dot{\theta}^2)\hat{\boldsymbol{r}} + (r\ddot{\theta} + 2\dot{r}\dot{\theta})\hat{\boldsymbol{s}}$

where $\hat{\boldsymbol{r}}$ is a radial unit vector along $\overline{\mathrm{OP}}$ (from the origin O) and $\hat{\boldsymbol{s}}$ is a transverse unit vector inclined at $\theta + \pi/2$ to Ox, as shown in Fig. 9.4(b).

(4) Using intrinsic coordinates (s, ψ) for a particle P at a time t then

$$\boldsymbol{v} = \dot{s}\hat{\boldsymbol{t}}$$

and $\boldsymbol{a} = \ddot{s}\hat{\boldsymbol{t}} + \dot{s}\dot{\psi}\hat{\boldsymbol{n}}$

where $\hat{\boldsymbol{t}}$ is a unit vector in the direction of the tangent at P and $\hat{\boldsymbol{n}}$ is a unit vector in the direction of the normal at P, as shown in Fig. 9.4(c).

10
Circular motion

Objectives

The student should be able to:

(1) define angular velocity,
(2) state the conditions necessary for circular motion and define the acceleration experienced in circular motion,
(3) use Newton's laws and the principle of conservation of mechanical energy to analyse problems involving horizontal and vertical circular motion of particles.

Angular velocity

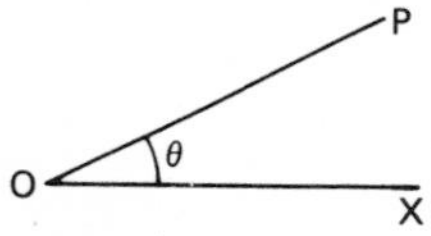

Figure 10.1

Let P be a particle moving in a plane, where O is a fixed point and OX a fixed line (Fig. 10.1). The angular velocity ω of the particle about O is the rate at which $\widehat{POX}$ increases, i.e.

$$\omega = \frac{d\theta}{dt}$$

in units of radians per second.

Circular motion at constant speed

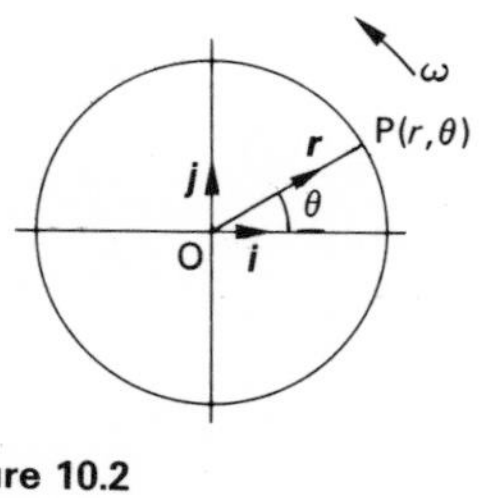

Figure 10.2

If the particle P describes a circle with centre O and radius r at constant speed v then its speed at any instant v is $r\omega$ (Fig. 10.2). The speed is not changing in magnitude but the particle is changing direction so a force must be acting on it as its velocity is changing.

The position vector of the particle P is given by

$$\boldsymbol{r} = r\cos\theta\, \boldsymbol{i} + r\sin\theta\, \boldsymbol{j}$$

so $\quad \boldsymbol{v} = \dot{\boldsymbol{r}} = -r\sin\theta\, \dot{\theta}\, \boldsymbol{i} + r\cos\theta\, \dot{\theta}\, \boldsymbol{j}$

since $\dot{r} = 0$ and

$$\boldsymbol{a} = \ddot{\boldsymbol{r}} = -r\cos\theta\, \dot{\theta}^2\, \boldsymbol{i} - r\sin\theta\, \dot{\theta}^2\, \boldsymbol{j}$$

since $\ddot{\theta} = 0$ so

$$\boldsymbol{a} = -\dot{\theta}^2 \boldsymbol{r}$$

i.e. $\quad \boldsymbol{a} = -\omega^2 \boldsymbol{r} = -\dfrac{v^2}{r^2}\boldsymbol{r}$

Hence the acceleration of P is directed towards O and has magnitude $r\omega^2$ or v^2/r. A force of constant magnitude $mr\omega^2$ or mv^2/r must be acting on the particle, where m is the mass of the particle. The force is not constant because its direction varies.

Example 10.1

A particle of mass 0.5 kg is attached to one end of a light inextensible string of length 1 m. The other end is fixed to a point on a smooth horizontal table and the particle is set moving in a circular path with a speed of 10 m s^{-1}. What is the tension in the string and the reaction with the table?

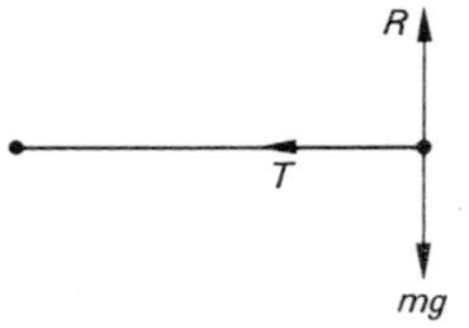

Figure 10.3

See Fig. 10.3. Resolving vertically,

$$\text{reaction } R = mg$$

as there is no vertical acceleration. Horizontally,

$$a = v^2/r = 10^2/1 = 100 \text{ m s}^{-2}$$

Resolving horizontally,

$$\text{tension } T = ma = \underline{50 \text{ N}}$$

Conical pendulum

A particle P of mass m is attached to one end of a light inextensible string of length l; the other end of the string is attached to a fixed point (Fig. 10.4). The particle is made to rotate in a horizontal circle with constant angular velocity ω.

As P rotates, AP traces out the surface of a cone, hence the name. Let $\widehat{OAP} = \theta$. Horizontally,

$$T \sin\theta = mr\omega^2$$

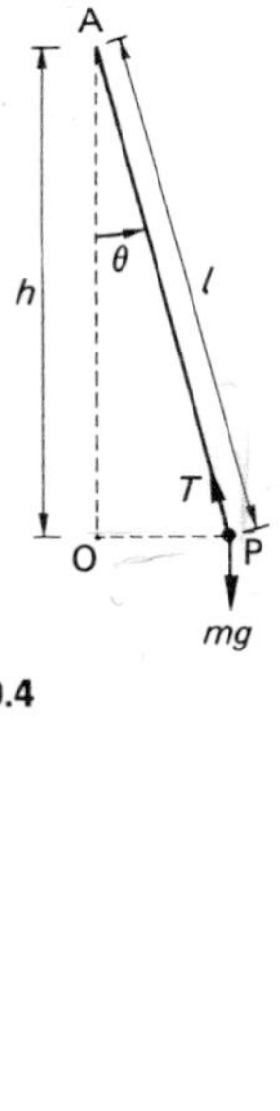

Figure 10.4

and the horizontal component of the tension in the string provides the force to maintain the circular motion. Vertically, the forces balance and there is no acceleration. Resolving vertically,

$$T \cos\theta = mg$$

$$\tan\theta = \frac{r\omega^2}{g} = \frac{v^2}{rg} \quad (1)$$

Since $r = l \sin\theta$,

$$T = ml\omega^2 \quad (2)$$

$$\text{and } h = l\cos\theta = \frac{lmg}{T} = \frac{g}{\omega^2} \quad (3)$$

Equations (1), (2) and (3) are relationships that are often useful in problem solving.

Example 10.2

Two particles of mass 5 kg and 8 kg are connected by a light inextensible string of length 1.5 m which passes through a smooth swivel at a fixed height. The 5 kg particle hangs at rest at a depth 0.5 m below the swivel. The second particle describes a horizontal circle below the first with its centre vertically below the swivel.

Find the angular velocity of the second particle. (Take $g = 10\text{ m s}^{-2}$.)

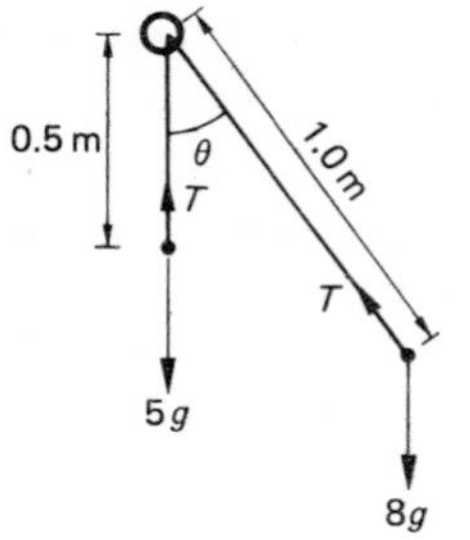

Figure 10.5

See Fig. 10.5. Resolving vertically for the 5 kg mass,

$$T = 5g$$

The swivel is smooth so the tension is the same throughout the string. Horizontally for the 8 kg mass,

$$T \sin\theta = 8r\omega^2 = 8l \sin\theta\, \omega^2$$

and $l = 1.5 - 0.5 = 1.0$ m. Therefore

$$T = 8l\omega^2$$

$$5g = 8 \times 1 \times \omega^2$$

so $\quad \omega = 2.5 \text{ rad s}^{-1}$

i.e. the angular velocity of the 8 kg particle is $\underline{2.5 \text{ rad s}^{-1}}$.

Cyclist

A vehicle which travels round a bend on horizontal ground relies upon the frictional force on the rough ground to provide the inwards horizontal force for the circular motion. The frictional force produces a turning effect and the cyclist must lean inwards to counteract it.

Let PQ represent the bicycle and rider, where G is their centre of mass, mg is their weight and R is the normal reaction (Fig. 10.6). The frictional force F must act inwards. Let μ be the coefficient of friction between the cyclist and the ground. As there is no vertical motion,

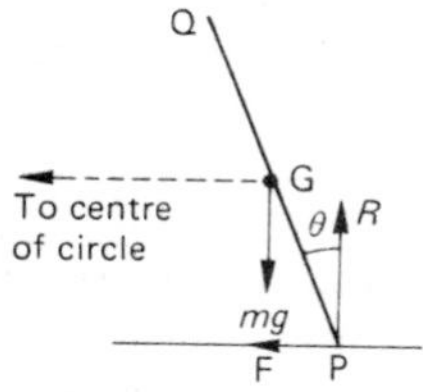

Figure 10.6

$$R = mg$$

From Newton's law, horizontally,

$$F = \frac{mv^2}{r}$$

where $F_{max} = \mu R$. As there is no rotation about G,

$$F \times \text{PG} \cos\theta = R \times \text{PG} \sin\theta$$

Therefore

$$\frac{F}{R} = \tan\theta = \frac{v^2}{rg}$$

$$v = \sqrt{(rg \tan\theta)}$$

and this velocity is a maximum when $\tan\theta = \mu$.

Banked tracks

The maximum speed at which a vehicle can travel without side slip around a circle of radius r on horizontal ground is given by $v = \sqrt{(\mu rg)}$, where μ is the coefficient of friction. This situation is helped by a banked track. Consider a vehicle of mass m

travelling at a speed v around a bend of radius r on a road which is banked at an angle of θ.

When there is no tendency to side slip

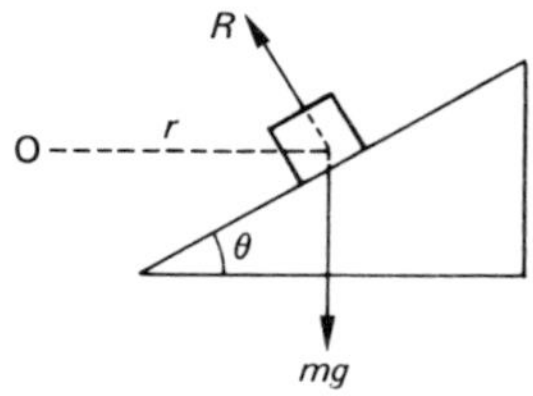

Figure 10.7

Frictional forces are not brought into action (Fig. 10.7). Vertically, with no acceleration,

$$R \cos \theta = mg$$

and horizontally,

$$R \sin \theta = \frac{mv^2}{r}$$

so, eliminating R,

$$\tan \theta = \frac{v^2}{rg}$$

and so the cyclist leans inwards at the same angle that the track is banked to prevent any side slip for the speed $v = \sqrt{(rg \tan \theta)}$.

When there is a tendency to side slip

If the speed is greater than v the vehicle will tend to side slip up and if it is less than v the vehicle will tend to side slip down.

The maximum speed v_1 will occur when $F = \mu R_1$ acts down the track, where μ is the coefficient of friction between the bank and the vehicle (Fig. 10.8). With v_1 greater than v, horizontally,

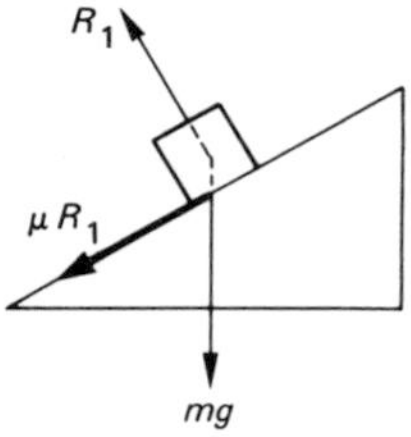

Figure 10.8

$$\frac{mv_1^2}{r} = R_1 \sin \theta + \mu R_1 \cos \theta \qquad (1)$$

and vertically,

$$mg = R_1 \cos \theta - \mu R_1 \sin \theta \qquad (2)$$

Dividing equation (1) by equation (2) gives

$$\frac{v_1^2}{rg} = \frac{\sin \theta + \mu \cos \theta}{\cos \theta - \mu \sin \theta}$$

so $$v_1 = \sqrt{\left[rg\left(\frac{\sin \theta + \mu \cos \theta}{\cos \theta + \mu \sin \theta}\right)\right]}$$

is the maximum speed at which the vehicle can travel around a bend of radius r on a track banked at an angle of θ, without slipping.

If the speed is less than v and the vehicle is tending to slip down then the minimum speed v_2 will occur when $F = \mu R_2$ acts up the track (Fig. 10.9) so, in a similar analysis to that above,

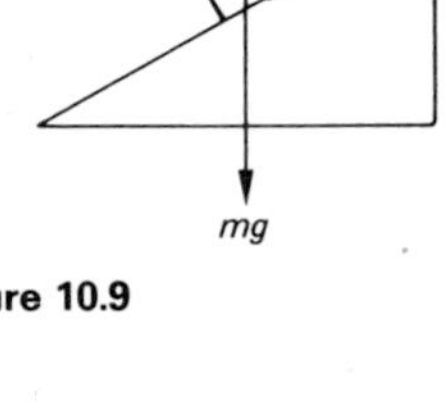

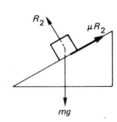

Figure 10.9

$$\frac{v_2^2}{rg} = \frac{\sin \theta - \mu \cos \theta}{\cos \theta + \mu \sin \theta}$$

$$v_2 = \sqrt{\left[rg\left(\frac{\sin \theta - \mu \cos \theta}{\cos \theta + \mu \sin \theta}\right)\right]}$$

Example 10.3

A car is moving in a horizontal circle of radius 50 m on a track which is banked at an angle of θ to the horizontal, where $\sin\theta = \frac{3}{5}$. Calculate:

(a) the speed of the car when there is no tendency for it to side slip,
(b) the greatest speed at which the car could move in this circle without slipping sideways given that the coefficient of friction between the car and the ground is 0.2.

(Take $g = 10\text{ m s}^{-2}$.)

(a) $v = \sqrt{(gr\tan\theta)}$

from the above theory. Therefore

$$v = \sqrt{(10 \times 50 \times \tfrac{3}{4})} = 19.4\text{ m s}^{-1}$$

The speed of the car when there is *no* tendency to side slip is $\underline{19.4\text{ m s}^{-1}}$.
(b) The maximum speed

$$v_1 = \sqrt{\left[rg\left(\frac{\sin\theta + \mu\cos\theta}{\cos\theta - \mu\sin\theta}\right)\right]}$$

from the above theory. Therefore

$$v_1 = \sqrt{\left[\frac{500(\frac{3}{5} + 0.2 \times \frac{4}{5})}{(\frac{4}{5} - 0.2 \times \frac{3}{5})}\right]} = \sqrt{\left[\frac{500 \times 3.8}{3.4}\right]}$$
$$= 23.6\text{ m s}^{-1}$$

The greatest speed at which the car can move without slipping sideways is $\underline{23.6\text{ m s}^{-1}}$.

Motion in a vertical circle

Examples of motion in a vertical circle are a particle rotating at the end of a light string whose other end is fixed, a ring sliding on a smooth vertical wire, a particle sliding down the outside of a smooth circular surface or a particle rotating on the inside of a smooth circular surface. In general, the weight of the particle will have a component along the tangent so we can apply $F = m\,\mathrm{d}v/\mathrm{d}t$ along the tangent as well as towards the centre. It is usually more convenient to obtain a second equation from the principle of work (see Chapter 8) if this is applicable.

There are broadly two groups of problems concerning motion in a vertical circle: those where the particle is restricted to the circular path as in (1) and (5) below and those where it is not as in (2), (3) and (4) below.

(1) Motion of a bead threaded on a smooth vertical wire

Consider a small bead of mass m threaded on a smooth circular vertical wire of radius r (Fig. 10.10). Let A be the lowest point in the plane and let the bead pass this point with speed u and let it subsequently pass a point B with speed v.

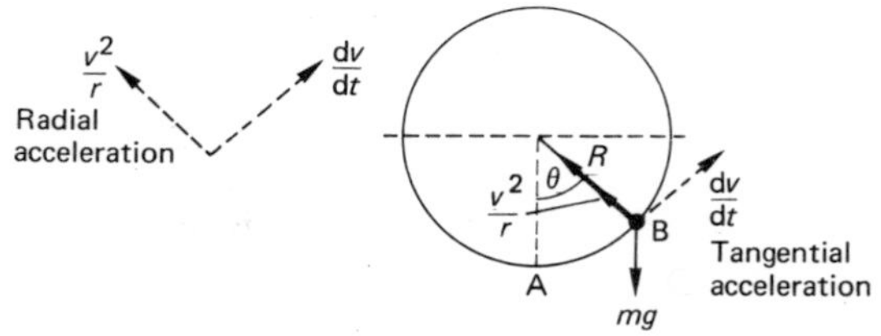

Figure 10.10

Applying Newton's law radially at B,

$$R - mg\cos\theta = \frac{mv^2}{r} = \text{mass} \times \text{radial acceleration} \qquad (1)$$

Applying Newton's law tangentially at B,

$$-mg\sin\theta = m\frac{dv}{dt} = \text{mass} \times \text{tangential acceleration} \qquad (2)$$

Energy is conserved because the normal reaction is perpendicular to the wire and so does no work. Therefore by the conservation of energy, loss in KE = gain in PE,

$$\tfrac{1}{2}m(u^2 - v^2) = mg(r - r\cos\theta)$$

$$u^2 - v^2 = 2rg(1 - \cos\theta) \qquad (3)$$

The ring is restricted to move on the wire so there are two possibilities for the motion.

(a) It may pass through the highest point of the wire and go on to describe complete circles. In this case, $v > 0$ at the top when $\cos\theta = -1$. Therefore in equation (3),

$$u^2 = v^2 + 4rg \quad \text{or} \quad v^2 = u^2 - 4rg$$

Since $v > 0$,

$$u^2 > 4gr$$

If $u^2 = 4gr$ the ring will come to rest at the highest point.
(b) It may come momentarily to rest before reaching the highest point and then oscillate. If the bead comes to rest at some angle $\theta = \alpha$ then from equation (3), with $v = 0$ at $\theta = \alpha$,

$$u^2 = 2rg(1 - \cos\alpha)$$

(2) Motion of a particle rotating on the end of a light inextensible string where the other end is fixed

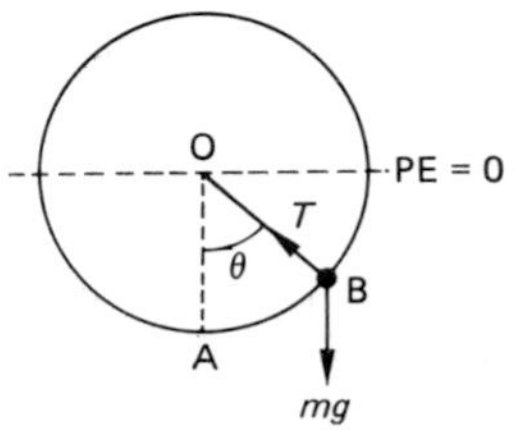

Figure 10.11

The equations are similar to those of the bead, where T is the tension in the string (Fig. 10.11).

$$T - mg\cos\theta = \frac{mv^2}{r} \qquad (1)$$

$$mg\sin\theta = -m\frac{dv}{dt} \qquad (2)$$

$$u^2 - v^2 = 2rg(1 - \cos\theta) \qquad (3)$$

In this case there are three possibilities for the motion.

(a) It may describe complete circles. The tension must never be zero other than instantaneously at the top of the circle. Even if $v>0$ the particle could be moving as a projectile rather than a circle at the highest point. From equations (1) and (3),

$$\frac{mv^2}{r}=T-mg\cos\theta=\frac{mu^2}{r}-2mg(1-\cos\theta)$$

so $$T=m\left(\frac{u^2}{r}-2g+3g\cos\theta\right)$$

so if $T\geqslant 0$ then

$$\frac{u^2}{r}\geqslant 2g-3g\cos\theta$$

but the maximum value of $2g-3g\cos\theta$ occurs when $\cos\theta=-1$ and $\theta=180°$ so $u^2\geqslant 5rg$ ensures that T is never zero other than instantaneously at the highest point.

(b) It may come to instantaneous rest below the level of O and then oscillate. As

$$T=\frac{mv^2}{r}+mg\cos\theta$$

then $T>0$ for $\theta\leqslant 90°$. So to test for oscillations $v=0$ for $\theta\leqslant 90°$. When $v=0$

$$u^2=2rg(1-\cos\theta)$$

$$\cos\theta=1-\frac{u^2}{2rg}$$

As $\cos\theta\geqslant 0$ below O, then

$$u^2\leqslant 2gr$$

In cases (a) and (b) the string is always taut and the particle always moves on a vertical circular path so for this to be the case

$$u\leqslant\sqrt{(2gr)}\quad\text{or}\quad u\geqslant\sqrt{(5gr)}$$

(c) Circular motion may cease when the string becomes slack, i.e. when $T=0$. Therefore

$$\cos\theta=\frac{2gr-u^2}{3gr}$$

This is the case for $\sqrt{(2gr)}<u<\sqrt{(5gr)}$ from (a) and (b) but also $-1<\cos\theta<0$ and $T=0$ for circular motion to cease.

(3) Motion of a particle rotating on the inside of a smooth circular surface of radius *r*

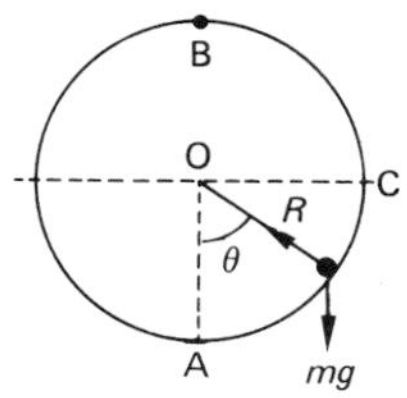

Figure 10.12

For the particle to complete vertical circles $R \geqslant 0$ at B (Fig. 10.12). For oscillations the velocity $v = 0$ below OC and

$$R - mg \cos \theta = \frac{mv^2}{r}$$

(4) Motion of a particle rotating on the outside of a smooth circular surface

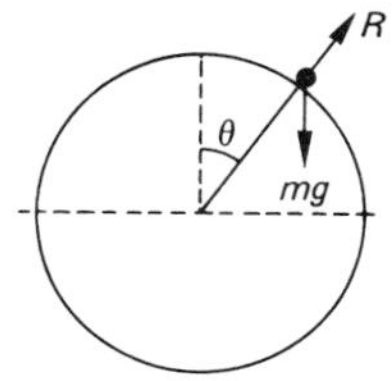

Figure 10.13

The reaction R acts outwards (Fig. 10.13). Therefore

$$mg \cos \theta - R = \frac{mv^2}{r}$$

and the particle leaves the surface when $R = 0$ and $\theta = \alpha$, where $mg \cos \alpha = mv^2/r$.

(5) Motion of a particle attached to one end of a light rod

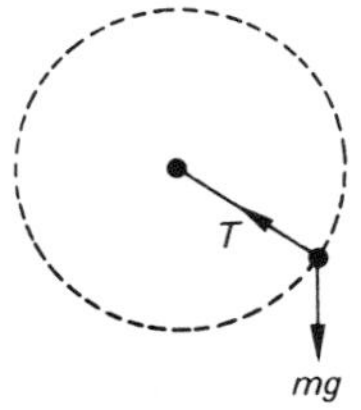

Figure 10.14

The light rod is free to rotate about a smooth fixed axis through the other end of the rod (Fig. 10.14). The force T in the rod acts in the same direction as the reaction R between the wire and the bead. In this case the particle cannot move off the circular path.

Example 10.4

Prove that when a particle moves with constant angular speed ω in a circle of radius r the acceleration towards the centre of the circle is $\omega^2 r$.

A particle P of mass m is attached to one end of a light elastic string of natural length a and whose other end is fixed. In the equilibrium position with the string vertical the extension is $a/4$. The string is then moved out of the vertical position and P is projected so that it describes a horizontal circle with constant angular speed and period t. The length of the string during this motion is $a + x$. Write down the equations of motion of P and show that the motion is only possible for $x > a/4$.

Obtain expressions in terms of x, a and g for the angular speed and hence find t. (AEB J83)

The proof is given at the start of this chapter.

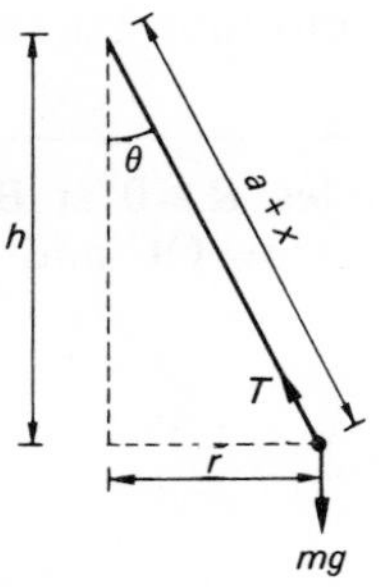

Figure 10.15

See Fig. 10.15. As $T = \lambda x/l$,

$$mg = \frac{\lambda(a/4)}{a}$$

$$\lambda = 4mg \text{ for the string}$$

Newton's law horizontally gives

$$T \sin\theta = mr\omega^2 \qquad (1)$$

and vertically there is no motion so

$$T \cos\theta = mg \qquad (2)$$

$$T = \frac{\lambda x}{a} = \frac{4mgx}{a} \qquad (3)$$

Using $r = (a+x)\sin\theta$ and substituting for T from equation (3) into equation (1),

$$4mg\frac{x}{a}\sin\theta = m(a+x)\sin\theta\,\omega^2$$

$$x = \frac{a}{4}(a+x)\frac{\omega^2}{g} \qquad (4)$$

Now equation (1) divided by equation (2) gives

$$\tan\theta = \frac{r\omega^2}{g}$$

$$\frac{\tan\theta}{r} = \frac{\omega^2}{g} = \frac{1}{h}$$

Substituting in equation (4) for ω^2/g gives

$$x = \frac{a}{4}\frac{(a+x)}{h}$$

The motion is only possible if $a + x > h$, i.e.

$$\frac{a+x}{h} > 1$$

Therefore

$$x > \frac{a}{4}$$

Rearranging equation (4) gives

$$\omega^2 = \frac{4gx}{a(a+x)}$$

Hence the angular speed

$$\omega = 2\sqrt{\left(\frac{xg}{a(a+x)}\right)}$$

The period $t = 2\Pi/\omega$. Therefore

$$t = \Pi\sqrt{\left(\frac{a(a+x)}{xg}\right)}$$

Problem 10.1

A ring of mass 0.5 kg is attached to a point P on a string of length 1.7 m, where AP = 1.2 m. The ends A and B are attached to two points in a vertical line, A being above B. The ring is made to travel in horizontal circles at v m s^{-1}. What is the smallest possible value of v if neither portion of the string is slack?

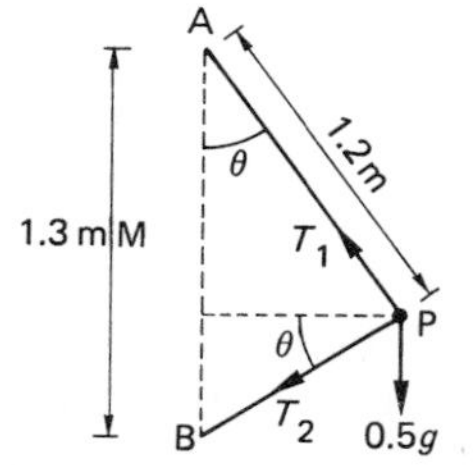

Figure 10.16

(1) Draw a diagram (Fig. 10.16).
(2) Recognise a 5:12:13 right-angled triangle. Therefore $\widehat{BAP} = \theta = \widehat{MPB}$, where MP $= r$ for the motion.
(3) In general, $T_1 \neq T_2$. When $T_2 = 0$ neither string is slack. Use Newton's law horizontally to show that

$$\frac{mv^2}{r} = T_1 \sin\theta + T_2 \cos\theta \qquad (1)$$

and vertically to show that

$$T_1 \cos\theta - T_2 \sin\theta = 0.5g \qquad (2)$$

From equation (1), v^2 is a minimum when $T_2 = 0$. Then show that

$$v^2 = rg \tan\theta = 1.2g \sin\theta \tan\theta$$

Hence show that the smallest possible value, $v = 1.4$ m s^{-1}.

Problem 10.2

A particle P of mass 0.1 kg moving on a smooth horizontal table with constant speed v m s^{-1} describes a circle of centre O such that OP $= r$ metres. The particle is attracted towards O by a force of magnitude $4v$ newtons and repelled from O by a force of magnitude k/r newtons, where k is a constant.

(a) Given that $v = 40$ and the time of one revolution is $\pi/10$ s, find r and k.
(b) Given that $k = 30$ and $r = 1$, find the possible values of v.
(c) Find the range of values of k if $r = 1$.

(AEB J84)

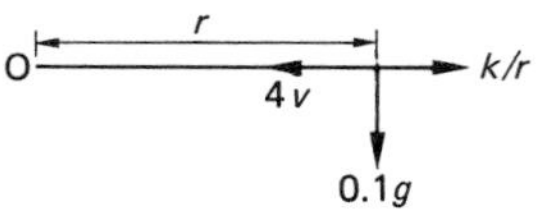

Figure 10.17

(a) Draw a diagram (Fig. 10.17). Since the motion is circular, the acceleration is given by

$$\frac{mv^2}{r} = 4v - \frac{k}{r} \qquad (1)$$

Use the definition of the period $T = 2\pi r/v$ and the values given to show that $r = 2m$. Now substitute $v = 40$ and $r = 2$ in equation (1) to show that $k = 160$.
(b) For $k = 30$ and $r = 1$, equation (1) becomes $4v - 30 = 0.1v^2$ or

$$0.1v^2 - 4v + 30 = 0$$

Use

$$x = \frac{-b \pm \sqrt{(b^2 - 4ac)}}{2a}$$

to solve this quadratic, to give $v = 30 \text{ m s}^{-1}$ or 10 m s^{-1}.
(c) For $r = 1$, $4v - k = 0.1v^2$ or

$$v^2 - 40v + 10k = 0$$

The roots are

$$v = \frac{4 \pm \sqrt{(16 - 0.4k)}}{0.2}$$

For real values of v, $16 - 0.4k > 0$, i.e. $k < 40$. The minimum value of $v = 0$ occurs when $4 - \sqrt{(16 - 0.4k)} = 0$, i.e. $k = 0$. Therefore the range of values of k is $0 < k < 40$.

Example 10.5

One end of a light inextensible string of length a is fastened to a fixed point and a particle is attached to the other end. The particle is held so that the string is taut and horizontal and is then projected vertically upwards with speed u. Given that the string slackens when it is inclined at an angle of 30° to the horizontal, find u in terms of a and g. (JMB 1984)

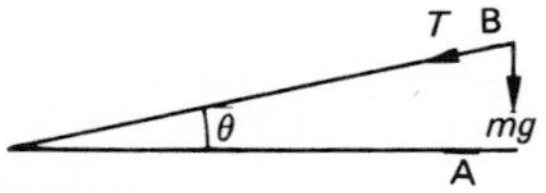

Figure 10.18

Let the particle move from A to some general point B in a time t through an angle θ, where v is the velocity of the particle at the point B (Fig. 10.18). Let T be the tension in the string.

From Newton's law, radially,

$$T + mg \sin \theta = \frac{mv^2}{a} \quad (1)$$

and tangentially,

$$mg \cos \theta = -m\frac{dv}{dt} \quad (2)$$

Applying the conservation of mechanical energy to the system,

$$\tfrac{1}{2}m(u^2 - v^2) = mga \sin \theta$$

This rearranges to

$$\frac{mv^2}{a} = \frac{mu^2}{a} - 2mg \sin \theta \quad (3)$$

Equating equations (1) and (3),

$$T = -mg \sin \theta + \frac{mu^2}{a} - 2mg \sin \theta$$

$$= \frac{mu^2}{a} - 3mg \sin \theta$$

The angle $\theta = 30°$ and the string slackens when $T = 0$ so

$$u^2 = 3ga/2$$

Hence the speed of projection

$$u = \sqrt{(3ga/2)}$$

Example 10.6

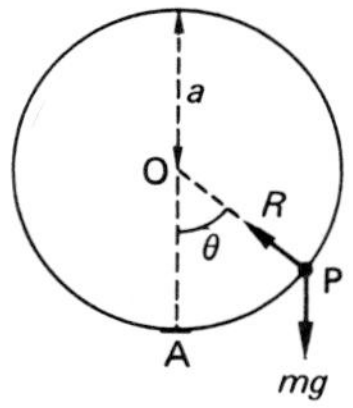

Figure 10.19

A small bead P of mass m is threaded on a smooth thin wire in the form of a circle of radius a and centre O which is fixed in a vertical plane. The bead is initially at the lowest point A of the circle and is projected along the wire with a velocity which is just sufficient to carry it to the highest point. Denoting the angle $\widehat{POA}$ by θ, find, in terms of m, g and θ, the magnitude of the reaction of the wire on the bead. Express $d\theta/dt$, where t denotes time, in the form $C \cos(\theta/2)$, where C is a constant. Show that the time taken for the bead to reach the horizontal diameter is

$$\sqrt{(a/g)} \ln(\sqrt{2}+1) \qquad \text{(JMB 1985)}$$

The bead has just sufficient energy to carry it to the top of the wire so from the principle of conservation of energy,

$$2mga = \tfrac{1}{2}mu^2 \qquad (1)$$

$$u^2 = 4ga$$

Let v be the velocity of the particle at the point P. From Newton's law, radially, from Fig. 10.19

$$R - mg \cos\theta = \frac{mv^2}{a} \qquad (2)$$

and tangentially,

$$mg \sin\theta = -m\frac{dv}{dt}$$

where R is the normal reaction.

At P from the conservation of mechanical energy,

$$\tfrac{1}{2}m(u^2 - v^2) = mg(a - a\cos\theta)$$

rearranging,

$$\frac{mv^2}{a} = \frac{mu^2}{a} - 2mg(1 - \cos\theta) \qquad (3)$$

Equating equations (2) and (3) gives

$$R - mg\cos\theta = \frac{mu^2}{a} - 2mg(1 - \cos\theta)$$

$$R = \frac{mu^2}{a} + mg\cos\theta - 2mg + 2mg\cos\theta$$

Substituting for $u^2 = 4ga$,

$$R = mg(2 + 3\cos\theta)$$

Now from equation (2),

$$R = mg\cos\theta + \frac{mv^2}{a} = mg(2+3\cos\theta)$$

$$\frac{mv^2}{a} = mg(2+2\cos\theta)$$

In general, $v = a\,\mathrm{d}\theta/\mathrm{d}t$ so

$$a\left(\frac{\mathrm{d}\theta}{\mathrm{d}t}\right)^2 = 2g(1+\cos\theta) = 2g[1+2\cos^2(\theta/2)-1]$$

so $$\frac{\mathrm{d}\theta}{\mathrm{d}t} = 2\surd(g/a)\cos(\theta/2)$$

Therefore

$$\int_0^{\pi/2} \frac{\mathrm{d}\theta}{\cos(\theta/2)} = 2\surd(g/a)\int_0^t \mathrm{d}t$$

$$\int_0^{\pi/2} \sec(\theta/2)\,\mathrm{d}\theta = 2\surd(g/a)\int_0^t \mathrm{d}t$$

$$2[\ln\{\sec(\theta/2)+\tan(\theta/2)\}]_0^{\pi/2} = 2\surd(g/a)[t]_0^t$$

$$\ln(\surd 2+1) - \ln(1) = \surd(g/a)t$$

Hence the time taken to reach the horizontal diameter

$$t = \surd(a/g)\ln(\surd 2+1)$$

Summary

(1) Angular velocity ω is the rate of change of angular displacement, i.e.

$$\omega = \frac{\mathrm{d}\theta}{\mathrm{d}t} = \dot{\theta}$$

(2) For circular motion to occur the resultant force acting on a particle must have a radial component of magnitude mv^2/r, where v is the speed of the particle, m is its mass and r is the radius of the circle. The radial component is directed towards the centre of the circle. The tangential component of the force has magnitude $m\,\mathrm{d}v/\mathrm{d}t$. The radial component of the acceleration is thus of magnitude v^2/r and is directed towards the centre of the circle.

(3) Motion in a vertical circle divides broadly into two cases.

(a) Where motion is restricted to a circular path (e.g. a bead on a wire)—the condition that complete vertical circles should be described by the particle is that its velocity is greater than zero at the highest point. If its velocity is zero before it reaches the highest point the particle will oscillate.
(b) Where motion is not restricted to a circular path (e.g. a particle attached to one end of a string fixed at the other end)—for complete circles to be described then when it is in a vertical line

with the highest point the force which has been restricting it to a circle (e.g. tension) must be greater than or equal to zero. If oscillation occurs then the velocity of the particle must be instantaneously zero before it goes above the level of the centre of the circle.

11
Momentum and impact

Objectives

The student should be able to:

(1.) define linear momentum,
(2) define the impulse of a constant and variable force,
(3) state the principle of conservation of linear momentum,
(4) apply the principle to impulsive tensions in strings,
(5) distinguish between elastic and inelastic impacts,
(6) state Newton's experimental law and distinguish between direct and oblique impact applying the conservation of momentum and Newton's experimental law to each case along the line of impact.

Definitions

The **linear momentum** of a body is the product of its mass and its velocity so is a vector in the direction of the velocity. It is usually referred to as the momentum of the body and has units of $\mathrm{kg\,m\,s^{-1}}$.

The **impulse** $\boldsymbol{I}$ exerted by a constant force $\boldsymbol{F}$ acting for a time t is the product of the force and the time for which it acts. The force acting on a mass m will produce a change in velocity from $\boldsymbol{u}$ to $\boldsymbol{v}$.

$$\boldsymbol{F}t = \boldsymbol{I} = m(\boldsymbol{v} - \boldsymbol{u})$$

If the force is variable

$$\boldsymbol{I} = \int_0^t \boldsymbol{F}\,\mathrm{d}t = \int_{\boldsymbol{u}}^{\boldsymbol{v}} m\frac{\mathrm{d}\boldsymbol{v}}{\mathrm{d}t}\,\mathrm{d}t = m(\boldsymbol{v} - \boldsymbol{u})$$

so generally the impulse of a force is equal to the change in momentum produced. It is measured in units of N s and is a vector.

Impact of two bodies

If two bodies A and B collide then from Newton's third law they exert equal and opposite forces of action and reaction on each other. They are in contact for the same length of time so the impulse that A exerts on B is equal and opposite to the impulse that B exerts on A and the change of momenta of A and B are equal and opposite and cancel so the sum of the momenta of the two bodies, measured in the same direction, is unaltered by the collision.

Example 11.1

Two bodies A and B of masses 2 and 3 kg respectively are travelling along the same line in the same sense with constant speeds of 4 and 3 m s^{-1} respectively. If they collide and coalesce find their common speed just after impact.

$$\text{total momentum before impact} = 2\times4+3\times3 = 17 \text{ N s}$$

Let v be the common velocity after impact. Then

$$\text{total momentum after impact} = 5v$$

Equating,

$$17 = 5v$$

or the common speed

$$v = \underline{3.4 \text{ m s}^{-1}}$$

Principle of conservation of linear momentum

If in a specified direction no external force affects the motion of a system, then the total linear momentum remains constant in that direction.

Impulsive tensions in strings

If a string is jerked, equal and opposite impulsive tensions act in the string. For a light string the impulses act in the direction of the string and so have an equal but opposite effect on the objects to which the two ends of the string are attached. The momentum is unchanged by an impulse perpendicular to the direction in which the impulse acts.

Example 11.2

The particles A and B of masses $2m$ and $3m$ lie at rest on a smooth horizontal table connected by a taut light inextensible string. The mass A is given an impulse of 10 N s in a direction inclined at 60° to the string BA, away from A. Find the velocities of A and B immediately after the impulse, in terms of m.

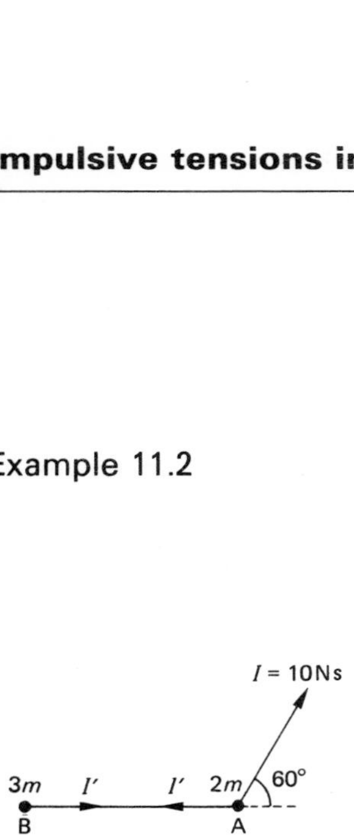

Figure 11.1

See Fig. 11.1. Parallel to AB, the impulse I is given by

$$I = 10 \cos 60° = 5 \text{ N s}$$

Let I' = internal impulsive tensions in the string. From the conservation of momentum parallel to AB, where u = velocities of A and B parallel to AB after the impulse,

$$5 = 2mu - I' + I' + 3mu$$

$$u = 1/m \text{ m s}^{-1}$$

and perpendicular to AB, where v = velocity of B after the impulse,

$$10 \cos 30° = 2mv$$
$$5\sqrt{3}/2m = v$$

Hence

$$\text{velocity of A} = \sqrt{[(1/m)^2 + (5\sqrt{3}/2m)^2]} = \underline{4.44/m \text{ m s}^{-1}}$$

at an angle $\tan^{-1}(5\sqrt{3}/2)$ to BA produced because A was subject to 10 N s at 60° to BA and I' along AB.

$$\text{velocity of B} = \underline{1/m \text{ m s}^{-1}}$$

and acts along BA as the only impulsive tension I' acting on it acted along BA.

Elastic and inelastic impacts

When two objects collide and coalesce the impact is said to be **inelastic**; if they collide and bounce the impact is said to be **elastic**. A perfectly elastic impact is one in which there is no loss of mechanical energy.

Direct impact of elastic bodies

During the impact of two bodies that are smooth, the mutual reaction acts only along the common normal at the point of impact. Direct impact occurs if the direction of motion of each is along the common normal just before impact. The bodies are usually taken as spheres. Consider two bodies of masses m_1 and m_2 and velocities u_1 and u_2 before impact and velocities v_1 and v_2 after impact, all velocities measured in the *same direction* along the direction of impact.

It it always useful to draw and label a diagram with the given information before and after impact (Fig. 11.2).

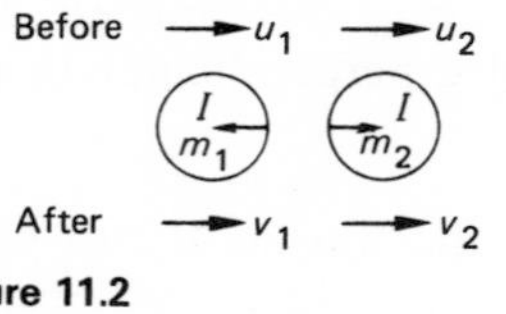

Figure 11.2

From the principle of conservation of momentum

$$m_1u_1 + m_2u_2 = m_1v_1 + m_2v_2 \qquad (1)$$

Another equation is needed to calculate the two unknowns v_1 and v_2 and this is given by **Newton's experimental law** which states that when two bodies made of given substances collide directly then the relative velocity after impact is in a constant ratio to the relative velocity before impact, and in the opposite direction. For oblique impact where the two bodies were not moving along the line of impact just before impact then the same result holds for the component velocities along the common normal. Hence for the direct impact in Fig. 11.2

$$\frac{v_1 - v_2}{u_1 - u_2} = -e \qquad (2)$$

where e is a positive constant called the coefficient of restitution for the two bodies in collision. Bodies for which e is zero are inelastic while $e = 1$ for perfectly elastic collisions and the bodies bounce back with the same speed with which they collided. The limits for e are

$$0 \leqslant e \leqslant 1$$

Equations (1) and (2) can be used to find the values of v_1 and v_2.

Example 11.3

Two smooth spheres A and B of equal radii and masses m and $2m$ lie at rest on a smooth horizontal table. Their centres are in a straight line and A is projected towards B and strikes it with a speed u. After impact B continues along the line of centres with a speed $u/2$. Find:

(a) the coefficient of restitution between A and B,
(b) the velocity of A after the collision,
(c) the loss of KE in the collision.

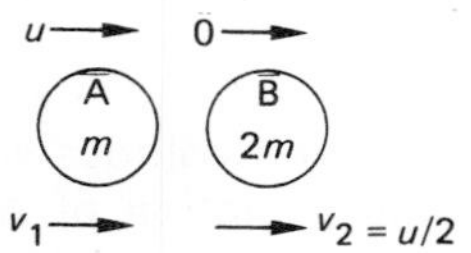

Figure 11.3

(a) By the conservation of momentum for the A–B collision (Fig. 11.3),

$$mu = mv_1 + 2mv_2$$

Since $v_2 = u/2$,

$$u = v_1 + u \qquad (1)$$

$$v_1 = 0$$

From Newton's experimental law

$$v_2 - v_1 = -e(0-u) = eu$$

Substituting,

$$\frac{u}{2} - 0 = eu \qquad (2)$$

so $\quad e = 1/2$

i.e. the coefficient of restitution $e = \underline{1/2}$.
(b) From equation (1), $v_1 = 0$, i.e. the velocity of A after the collision is zero.

(c) initial $\text{KE} = \frac{1}{2}mu^2$

final $\text{KE} = \frac{1}{2}(2m)(u^2/4) = mu^2/4$

so loss in KE close to the collision $= \underline{mu^2/4 \text{ units}}$

Oblique impact of elastic bodies

Let two spheres which impinge obliquely have masses m_1 and m_2. Let their velocities before impact be u_1 and u_2 in directions making angles of α and β with the common normal as shown in (Fig. 11.4).

Perpendicular to the line of impact, for smooth contact, there will be no impulsive forces acting so $u_1 \sin\alpha$ and $u_2 \sin\beta$, the velocities perpendicular to the common normal, are unaltered. Along the line of impact Newton's law holds for the component

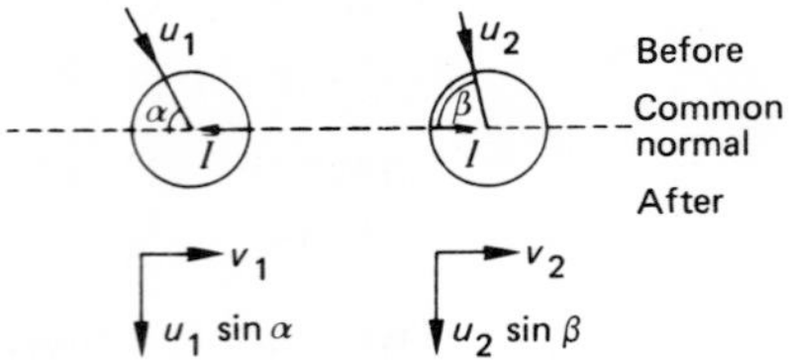

Figure 11.4

velocities. Therefore

$$v_2 - v_1 = -e(u_2 \cos\beta - u_1 \cos\alpha) \tag{1}$$

Momentum is conserved along the line of impact since no external forces act.

$$m_1 u_1 \cos\alpha + m_2 u_2 \cos\beta = mv_1 + mv_2 \tag{2}$$

Equations (1) and (2) allow the calculation of v_1 and v_2 in the same manner as for direct impact.

Example 11.4

A smooth A moves along a horizontal plane and collides with an equal stationary sphere B. The direction of motion of A is such that it makes an angle $\pi/6$ with the line of centres drawn from A to B immediately before the collision. Given that the coefficient of restitution between the spheres is $1/3$, prove that as a result of the collision sphere A is deflected through $\pi/6$ radians.

Express the kinetic energy lost as a percentage of the original kinetic energy. (AEB N82)

Draw a diagram and label the velocities (Fig. 11.5).

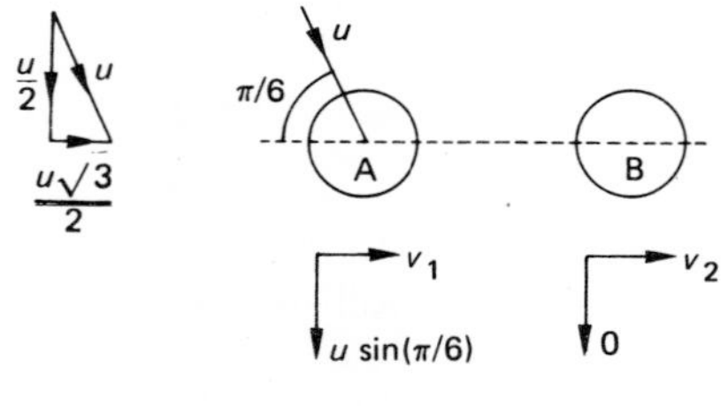

Figure 11.5

From Newton's experimental law, along the line of impacts,

$$v_2 - v_1 = -\frac{1}{3}\left(0 - \frac{u\sqrt{3}}{2}\right)$$

i.e. $$v_2 - v_1 = \frac{u\sqrt{3}}{6} \tag{1}$$

By the conservation of momentum along the line of impacts,

$$mu \cos 30° + 0 = m(v_1 + v_2)$$

Therefore

$$v_1 + v_2 = \frac{u\sqrt{3}}{2} \tag{2}$$

Subtracting equation (1) from equation (2) gives

$$v_1 = \frac{u}{2}\left(\frac{\surd 3}{2} - \frac{\surd 3}{6}\right) = \frac{u\surd 3}{6} = \frac{u}{2\surd 3}$$

so from equation (1)

$$v_2 = \frac{2u\surd 3}{6} = \frac{u}{\surd 3}$$

After collision the direction of A is given by

$$\phi = \tan^{-1}\frac{[u\sin(\pi/6)]}{v_1}$$

(see Fig. 11.6).

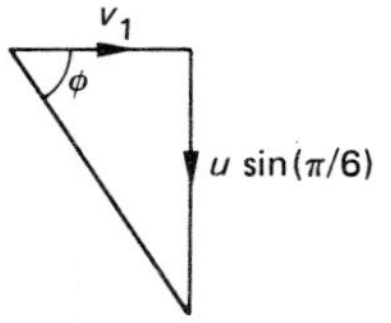

Figure 11.6

$$\phi = \tan^{-1}\left(\frac{u/2}{u/2\surd 3}\right) = \tan^{-1}(\surd 3) = \pi/3 \text{ radians}$$

Therefore A has been deflected through $\pi/3 - \pi/6$, i.e. $\pi/6$ radians.

No KE is lost perpendicular to the line of centres as there are no impulsive forces acting along this line.

Along the line of centres:

$$\text{initial KE} = \frac{1}{2}m\left(\frac{\surd 3}{2}\right)^2 u^2 = \frac{3mu^2}{8}$$

$$\text{final KE} = \frac{1}{2}mv_1^2 + \frac{1}{2}mv_2^2 = \frac{1}{2}\frac{mu^2}{12} + \frac{1}{2}\frac{mu^2}{3} = \frac{5mu^2}{24}$$

Therefore

$$\text{loss in KE} = \frac{9mu^2}{24} - \frac{5mu^2}{24} = \frac{mu^2}{6}$$

and % of the original KE lost $= \left(\frac{mu^2/6}{mu^2/2}\right) \times 100 = \underline{33\%}$

Example 11.5

A particle of mass 8 kg is connected by means of a light inextensible string over a smooth pulley to a particle of mass 6 kg. The system is released from rest with the 8 kg mass 1.4 m above the ground. It hits the ground with a speed v and does not rebound from the floor. Find the impulsive tension in the string when it is jerked off the ground by the 6 kg mass, given that the 6 kg mass does not rise to the height of the pulley during the motion.

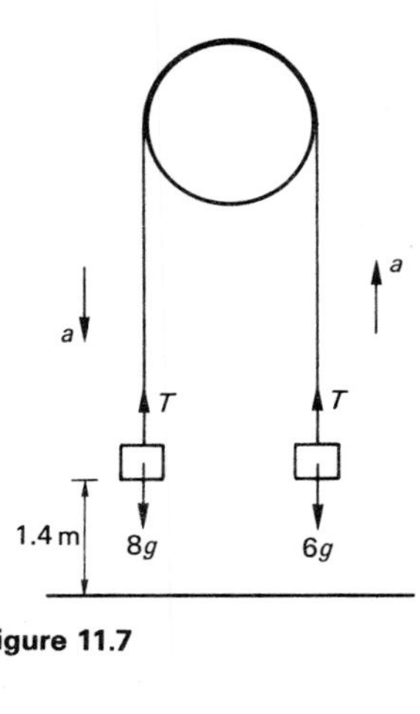

Figure 11.7

The tension is the same throughout the string so let the 8 kg mass move down with an acceleration a (Fig. 11.7). Applying $F = ma$,

$$8g - T = 8a$$

and $T - 6g = 6a$

Therefore

$$a = g/7 \text{ m s}^{-1}$$

Using $v^2 = u^2 + 2as$ to find the speed v with which the 8 kg mass hits the floor,

$$v = 2 \text{ m s}^{-2}$$

The 6 kg mass rises against an acceleration of $-g$, reaches zero velocity and falls. It jerks the string impulsively when its speed is 2 m s^{-1} downwards. Let the velocities of the two masses directly after the impulse be v_1 and let the impulsive tension in the string be I. By the conservation of momentum, for the 6 kg mass

$$6 \times 2 = I + 6v_1 \qquad (1)$$

and for the 8 kg mass

$$I = 8v_1 \qquad (2)$$

Therefore

$$v_1 = 12/14 \text{ m s}^{-1}$$

and $T = 6.9$ N s

i.e. the impulsive tension in the string is 6.9 N s.

Problem 11.1

A jet is discharging water at the rate of 100 litres per second. The water hits a wall and does not bounce off it, exerting a force of 500 N. Calculate the speed of the water when it impinges on the wall. (The mass of one litre of water is 1 kg.)

(1) Calculate the mass of water discharged per second, M. If v is the speed of the water then the momentum destroyed per second $= Mv$.
(2) The impulse exerted by the wall in 1 second $= 500 \times 1$. Therefore $500 \times 1 = Mv$ so calculate v which is 5 m s^{-1}.

Example 11.6

A smooth hemispherical bowl is fixed with its circular rim uppermost. Two particles A and B of masses $2m$ and m respectively are released from rest at opposite ends of a diameter of the rim. The particles collide at N, the lowest point of the bowl when each is moving with speed u. The particle A is brought to rest by the impct. Show that the coefficient of restitution between the particles is 1/2 and find the speed of B immediately after the collision. Also find, in terms of m and u,

(a) the magnitude of the impulse of the blow received by A,
(b) the kinetic energy lost in this collision.

Show that, immediately after the second collision of the particles, the speed of A is $u/2$. By considering conservation of energy, find, in terms of u and g, the height above N to which A rises after this second collision. (UL J83)

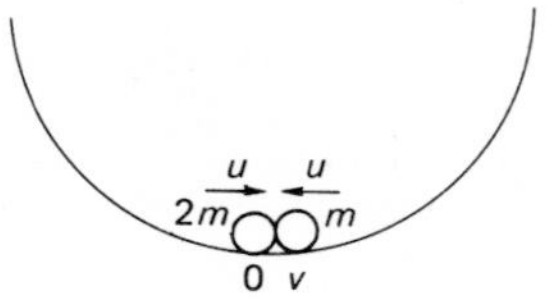

Figure 11.8

Take W–E as the positive direction.

By the conservation of momentum along the line of centres (Fig. 11.8),

$$2mu - mu = 0 + mv$$

Therefore

$$v = \underline{u}$$

where v is the speed of B immediately after the collision.

Applying Newton's experimental law along the line of centres,

$$v - 0 = -e(-u - u) = 2eu$$

Since $v = u$,

$$e = 1/2$$

(a) The impulse received by A,

$$I_A = 2m(u - 0) = \underline{2mu}$$

(b) KE before collision $= \frac{1}{2}2mu^2 + \frac{1}{2}mu^2 = \frac{3}{2}mu^2$

Therefore

$$\text{KE lost in this first collision} = \underline{mu^2}$$

B will rise until its velocity is zero then fall gaining velocity until it strikes A again. In this collision by the conservation of momentum along the line of centres (Fig. 11.9),

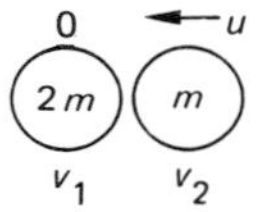

Figure 11.9

$$0 - mu = 2mv_1 + mv_2$$

$$-u = 2v_1 + v_2 \qquad (1)$$

Applying Newton's experimental law along the line of centres,

$$v_2 - v_1 = -e(-u - 0) = u/2 \qquad (2)$$

Subtracting equation (2) from equation (1) gives

$$3v_1 = -3u/2$$

$$v_1 = -u/2$$

so the speed of A after the second collision is $u/2$ and it acts in the direction E–W.

By the conservation of mechanical energy, A rises until its KE is reduced to zero at a height h above N. Therefore

$$\text{loss in KE} = \text{gain in PE}$$

$$\tfrac{1}{2}(2m)(u^2/4) = 2mgh$$

The height to which A rises,

$$h = \underline{u^2/8g}$$

Example 11.7

Relative to a fixed origin at a time $t = 0$, a squash ball has position vector $a(-\boldsymbol{i} + \boldsymbol{j} + \boldsymbol{k})$ and velocity $\sqrt{(ag)}(\boldsymbol{i} - \boldsymbol{j} + \boldsymbol{k})$, where a is a constant, g is the magnitude of the acceleration due to gravity and $\boldsymbol{i}$, $\boldsymbol{j}$ and $\boldsymbol{k}$ are unit vectors along Ox, Oy and Oz respectively. The ball moves freely under gravity with an acceleration $-g\boldsymbol{k}$, and meets a vertical wall, $y = 0$, at time $t = \sqrt{(a/g)}$. Show that the position vector and the velocity of the ball immediately before impact are $\frac{3}{2}a\boldsymbol{k}$ and $\sqrt{(ag)}(\boldsymbol{i} - \boldsymbol{j})$ respectively.

The ball bounces off the wall with velocity $\sqrt{(ag)}(\boldsymbol{i} + \frac{1}{2}\boldsymbol{j})$. What is the coefficient of restitution between the ball and the wall?

Show that the ball meets the floor, $z=0$, at a point P, where OP is $\frac{1}{2}a\sqrt{15}$. (AEB J84)

Initially for the ball, the position vector $\boldsymbol{r}$, the velocity $\boldsymbol{v}$ and the acceleration $\boldsymbol{a}$ are

$$\boldsymbol{r}=a(-\boldsymbol{i}+\boldsymbol{j}+\boldsymbol{k})$$

$$\boldsymbol{v}=\sqrt{(ag)}(\boldsymbol{i}-\boldsymbol{j}+\boldsymbol{k})$$

and $\boldsymbol{a}=-g\boldsymbol{k}$

respectively.

The position vector at a time t is given by

$$\boldsymbol{r}_t=\boldsymbol{r}+\boldsymbol{v}t+\tfrac{1}{2}\boldsymbol{a}t^2$$

Therefore

$$\boldsymbol{r}_t=a(-\boldsymbol{i}+\boldsymbol{j}+\boldsymbol{k})+t\sqrt{(ag)}(\boldsymbol{i}-\boldsymbol{j}+\boldsymbol{k})-\tfrac{1}{2}t^2g\boldsymbol{k}$$

When $t=\sqrt{(a/g)}$,

$$\boldsymbol{r}_t=a(-\boldsymbol{i}+\boldsymbol{j}+\boldsymbol{k})+\sqrt{(a/g)}\sqrt{(ag)}(\boldsymbol{i}-\boldsymbol{j}+\boldsymbol{k})-\tfrac{1}{2}(a/g)g\boldsymbol{k}$$

$$=-a\boldsymbol{i}+a\boldsymbol{j}+a\boldsymbol{k}+a\boldsymbol{i}-a\boldsymbol{j}+a\boldsymbol{k}-\tfrac{1}{2}a\boldsymbol{k}$$

i.e. $\boldsymbol{r}_t=\frac{3}{2}a\boldsymbol{k}$

The velocity vector at a time t is given by

$$\boldsymbol{v}_t=\boldsymbol{v}+\boldsymbol{a}t=\boldsymbol{v}-gt\boldsymbol{k}$$

When $t=\sqrt{(a/g)}$,

$$\boldsymbol{v}_t=\sqrt{(ag)}(\boldsymbol{i}-\boldsymbol{j}+\boldsymbol{k})-g\sqrt{(a/g)}\boldsymbol{k}$$

$$=\sqrt{(ag)}\boldsymbol{i}-\sqrt{(ag)}\boldsymbol{j}+\sqrt{(ag)}\boldsymbol{k}-\sqrt{(ag)}\boldsymbol{k}$$

i.e. the velocity vector before impact (Fig. 11.10),

$$\boldsymbol{v}_t=\sqrt{(ag)}(\boldsymbol{i}-\boldsymbol{j})$$

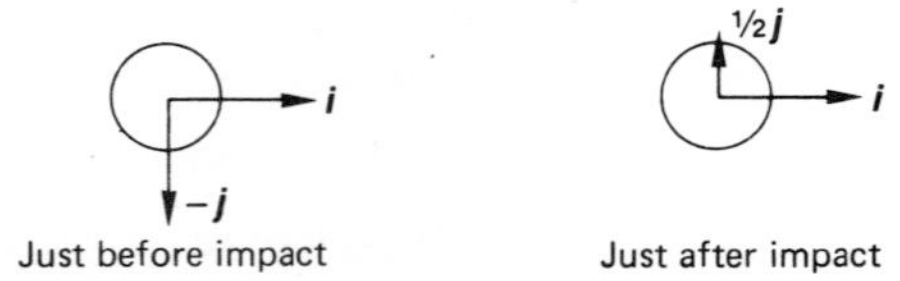

Figure 11.10

The velocity vector after impact (Fig. 11.10) is $\sqrt{(ag)}(\boldsymbol{i}+\frac{1}{2}\boldsymbol{j})$ so there is no change in velocity and therefore no impulse in the $\boldsymbol{i}$-direction. The impulse acts in the $\boldsymbol{j}$-direction. Applying Newton's experimental law in the $\boldsymbol{j}$-direction,

$$\tfrac{1}{2}-0=-e(-1-0)$$

So the coefficient of restitution $e=1/2$ between the ball and the wall.

Now after impact

$$\boldsymbol{r}'=\tfrac{3}{2}a\boldsymbol{k}$$

$$\boldsymbol{v}'=\sqrt{(ag)}(\boldsymbol{i}+\tfrac{1}{2}\boldsymbol{j})$$

and $\boldsymbol{r}'_t=\boldsymbol{r}'+\boldsymbol{v}'t+\frac{1}{2}\boldsymbol{a}t^2$

Therefore

$$r'_t = \tfrac{3}{2}a\mathbf{k} + \sqrt{(ag)}\,t(\mathbf{i} + \tfrac{1}{2}\mathbf{j}) - \tfrac{1}{2}t^2 g\mathbf{k} \qquad (1)$$

The ball meets the floor, $z = 0$, when the coefficient of $\mathbf{k}$ is zero. Therefore

$$0 = \tfrac{3}{2}a - \tfrac{1}{2}gt^2$$

so $\quad t = \sqrt{(3a/g)}$

Substituting in equation (1) for t gives

$$r'_t = \tfrac{3}{2}a\mathbf{k} + \sqrt{(ag)}\sqrt{(3a/g)}(\mathbf{i} + \tfrac{1}{2}\mathbf{j}) - \tfrac{1}{2}(3a/g)g\mathbf{k}$$

$$= a\sqrt{3}(\mathbf{i} + \tfrac{1}{2}\mathbf{j})$$

Therefore

$$\text{OP} = |r'_t| \quad \text{when } t = 0$$

$$= a\sqrt{3}\sqrt{(1 + \tfrac{1}{4})} = \tfrac{1}{2}a\sqrt{15}$$

So the ball meets the floor at a point P when $\text{OP} = \tfrac{1}{2}a\sqrt{15}$.

Summary

(1) The linear momentum of a body is the product of its mass and its velocity, mv.

(2) The impulse $\mathbf{I}$ exerted by a constant force $\mathbf{F}$ over a time t

$$\mathbf{I} = \mathbf{F}t = m(\mathbf{v} - \mathbf{u})$$

If the force is variable

$$\mathbf{I} = \int_0^t \mathbf{F}\,\mathrm{d}t = m(\mathbf{v} - \mathbf{u})$$

(3) The principle of conservation of linear momentum states that if in a specified direction no external force affects the motion of a system, then the total linear momentum remains constant in that direction.

(4) When a light string is jerked the impulsive tension causes a change in momentum to the objects to which the two ends of the string are attached. Perpendicular to the string no impulse acts so momentum is unchanged in this direction.

(5) When two objects collide and coalesce the impact is said to be inelastic. If they collide and bounce the impact is elastic.

(6) Newton's experimental law states that when two bodies made of given substances collide directly then the relative velocity after impact is in a constant ratio to the velocity before impact, and in the opposite direction. For oblique impact the same result holds for the component velocities along the common normal.
The ratio e is the coefficient of restitution for the two bodies concerned, where $0 \leq e \leq 1$. For an inelastic collision $e = 0$ and for an elastic collision $e = 1$.

Direct impact occurs when the bodies are moving along the line of impact before impact and oblique impact occurs when they are not.

Momentum is conserved along the line of impact, since no external force acts, for direct and oblique impact.

Perpendicular to the line of impact or the common normal there is no change in momentum.

12
Simple harmonic motion

Objectives

The student should be able to:

(1) define simple harmonic motion,
(2) quote the equations of motion for simple harmonic motion,
(3) determine when the maximum velocity and acceleration occur,
(4) prove that a simple pendulum moves with simple harmonic motion for small angular displacements,
(5) apply Newton's second law to the tension in an elastic string or the tension or thrust in a spring to show that an attached particle can perform simple harmonic motion and recognise situations in which the oscillations may be incomplete.

Introduction

One important case of variable acceleration that produces oscillatory motion is simple harmonic motion (SHM). When a particle moves so that its acceleration is proportional to the distance x it has moved along its path from a fixed point and is directed towards that point then the particle moves with SHM.

$$\frac{d^2x}{dt^2} = -n^2x$$

using n^2 as a constant of proportionality because it always remains positive.

Simple harmonic motion applies to any path the particle is traversing and not only to motion in a straight line, e.g. the particle may be moving along a curve and the acceleration along the curve may be proportional to the arc length measured from some fixed point on the curve.

Equations of motion

If x is the displacement from a point O then

$$\ddot{x} = v\frac{dv}{dx} = -n^2x$$

where $v = \mathrm{d}x/\mathrm{d}t$. Therefore

$$\int v\,\mathrm{d}v = -n^2 \int x\,\mathrm{d}x$$

$$\tfrac{1}{2}v^2 = -\tfrac{1}{2}n^2x^2 + c$$

or $$v^2 = D - n^2x^2$$

where $D = 2c$ and both c and D are constants.

If $x = a$ when $v = 0$

$$D = n^2a^2$$

Therefore

$$v^2 = n^2(a^2 - x^2)$$

From this equation $v = 0$ when $x^2 = a^2$. Therefore

$$x = \pm a$$

For a real value of v, $a^2 - x^2$ must be positive or zero so SHM is oscillatory between $x = +a$ and $x = -a$ about a point O as the centre or mean position, where a is known as the **amplitude** of the motion (Fig. 12.1). The velocity is a maximum at $x = 0$. The velocity is zero at $x = \pm a$ momentarily.

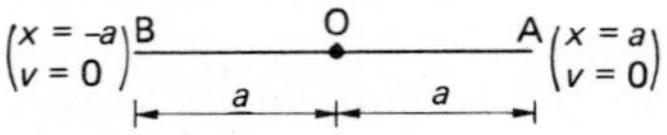

Figure 12.1

$$v = \frac{\mathrm{d}x}{\mathrm{d}t} = n\sqrt{(a^2 - x^2)}$$

$$\int \frac{\mathrm{d}x}{\sqrt{(a^2 - x^2)}} = n \int \mathrm{d}t$$

$$\sin^{-1}(x/a) = C + nt$$

where C is a constant and is determined by the initial conditions. For example:

(1) if t is measured from 0 then $t = 0$ when $x = 0$ and $C = 0$ so

$$x = a \sin nt$$

(2) if t is measured from A then $x = a$ when $t = 0$ and $\sin^{-1} 1 = C = \pi/2$ so

$$x = a \sin(nt + \pi/2) = a \cos nt$$

In general,

$$x = a \sin(nt + \varepsilon)$$

where ε depends on the instant at which we start measuring.

If we substitute $t + 2\pi/n$ for t in the equation for x then

$$x = a \sin[n(t + 2\pi/n) + \varepsilon]$$

i.e. $$x = a \sin(nt + \varepsilon)$$

and similarly for the velocity

$$v = \frac{\mathrm{d}x}{\mathrm{d}t} = an \cos(nt + \varepsilon)$$

we obtain the same value at $t+2\pi/n$ so $2\pi/n$ is the time for a complete oscillation, called the period of the motion T, i.e.

$$T=2\pi/n$$

Differentiating again gives

$$\ddot{x}=\frac{dv}{dt}=-an^2\sin(nt+\varepsilon)$$

i.e. $\ddot{x}=-n^2x$

which is the equation of SHM.

Note If a particle oscillates on a circular arc with angular acceleration which is proportional to the angular displacement along a fixed line and always directed towards that line then the particle is travelling with angular SHM and

$$\ddot{\theta}=-n^2\theta$$

where $\ddot{\theta}$ is the angular acceleration.

Example 12.1

A particle moving with SHM has speeds of 4 and 3 m s^{-1} when its distances from the centre of oscillation are respectively 3 and 4 m. Find:

(a) the period,
(b) the maximum velocity,
(c) the maximum acceleration.

(a) Using $v=n^2(a^2-x^2)$,

$$16=n^2(a^2-9) \quad (1)$$

and $9=n^2(a^2-16)$ (2)

Dividing equation (1) by equation (2),

$$\frac{16}{9}=\frac{(a^2-9)}{(a^2-16)}$$

$$16a^2-16^2=9a^2-9^2$$

$$a^2=175/7$$

so the amplitude $a=5$ m. From equation (2), $n=1$. Therefore the period

$$T=2\pi/1=\underline{2\pi \text{ seconds}}$$

(b) The velocity is greatest when $x=0$. Therefore

$$v_{\max}=na=\underline{5\text{ m s}^{-1}}$$

(c) The acceleration is greatest when x is greatest, i.e. $x=a$. Therefore

$$\ddot{x}_{\max}=na=\underline{5\text{ m s}^{-2}}$$

Relationship of SHM to uniform motion in a circle

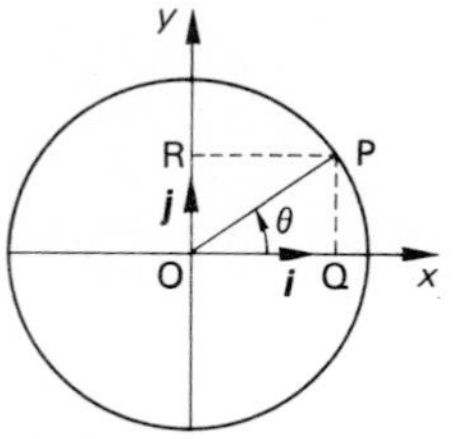

Figure 12.2

Consider a particle P describing a circle of radius a, centre O, with constant angular velocity ω (Fig. 12.2). If $\overrightarrow{OP}$ is the position vector of P then

$$\overrightarrow{OP} = a \cos \omega t \, \boldsymbol{i} + a \sin \omega t \, \boldsymbol{j} = (OQ)\boldsymbol{i} + (OR)\boldsymbol{j}$$

where $\boldsymbol{i}$ and $\boldsymbol{j}$ are unit vectors along Ox and Oy as shown.

So $\dfrac{d}{dt}(\overrightarrow{OP}) = -a\omega \sin \omega t \, \boldsymbol{i} + a\omega \cos \omega t \, \boldsymbol{j}$

and $\dfrac{d}{dt^2}(\overrightarrow{OP}) = -a\omega^2 \cos \omega t \, \boldsymbol{i} - a\omega^2 \sin \omega t \, \boldsymbol{j} = -\omega^2 \overrightarrow{OP}$

The orthogonal projections of OP onto the $\boldsymbol{i}$-axis and the $\boldsymbol{j}$-axis, OQ and OR respectively, move with SHM because

$$\overrightarrow{OQ} = (OQ)\boldsymbol{i} \qquad \overrightarrow{OR} = (OR)\boldsymbol{j}$$

and $\dfrac{d}{dt^2}(\overrightarrow{OQ}) = -\omega^2(\overrightarrow{OQ}) \qquad \dfrac{d}{dt^2}(\overrightarrow{OR}) = -\omega^2(\overrightarrow{OR})$

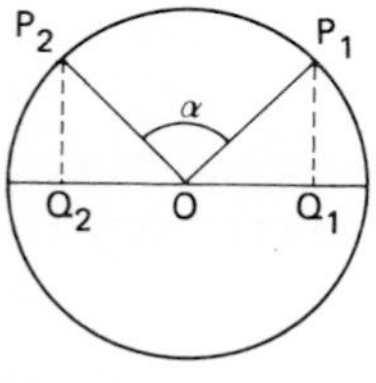

Figure 12.3

So in Fig. 12.3 the time taken to travel from Q_1 to Q_2 with SHM is equal to the time taken to travel from P_1 to P_2 with constant angular velocity ω, i.e. α/ω, where both are measured in radians and

$$\widehat{P_1OP_2} = \alpha$$

Example 12.2

A particle travelling with linear SHM starts from the centre of its path which is of amplitude $3a$. The particle travels for a time $T/3$, where T is the period of the motion. Find its distance from O.

See Fig. 12.4. Let OQ be the distance required and let P_2 be the projection on the associated circle of radius $3a$, where the projection travels with angular velocity ω.

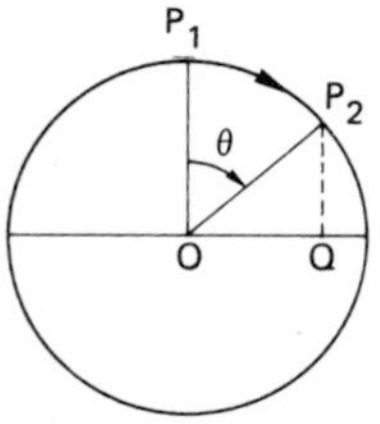

Figure 12.4

$$T = \frac{2\pi}{\omega} \quad \text{or} \quad \omega = \frac{2\pi}{T}$$

$$\theta = \omega t$$

Therefore in time $T/3$

$$\theta = \frac{\omega T}{3} = \frac{2\pi}{T}\frac{T}{3} = \frac{2\pi}{3}$$

or the equation $x = 3a \sin \omega t$ could be used as $x = 0$ when $t = 0$. Therefore

$$\sin^{-1}\left(\frac{x}{3a}\right) = \omega t = \frac{2\pi}{T}\frac{T}{3} = \frac{2\pi}{3}$$

So by either method

$$OQ = x = 3a \sin\left(\frac{2\pi}{3}\right) = \underline{\frac{3\sqrt{3}}{2}a}$$

Simple pendulum

A heavy particle oscillating through a small angle at the end of a light inextensible string, fixed at the other end, is known as the simple pendulum. It is used to demonstrate angular SHM.

Let the particle P in Fig. 12.5 have mass m. The string of length l is fixed at O. OC is vertical and the angle made by the string to the vertical at any time t is θ.

Applying Newton's second law tangentially at P,

$$ml\ddot{\theta} = -mg \sin \theta$$

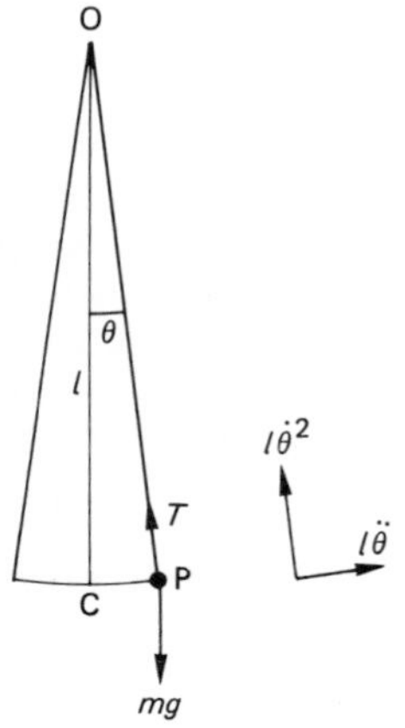

Figure 12.5

because the angular acceleration θ is away from the direction in which θ increases.

For *small angles*

$$\sin \theta \simeq \theta$$

Therefore

$$\ddot{\theta} = \frac{-g}{l}\theta$$

which is the basic equation of angular SHM.

The period $T = 2\pi/n$, where $n^2 = g/l$. Therefore

$$T = 2\pi\sqrt{\left(\frac{l}{g}\right)}$$

Example 12.3

A simple pendulum making small oscillations is released from a position where it makes an angle α with the vertical. Show that the complete period is $2\pi v/g\alpha$, where v is the maximum speed.

For angular SHM

$$\ddot{\theta} = -n^2\theta$$

and for a simple pendulum

$$\ddot{\theta} = \frac{-g}{l}\theta$$

so $n^2 = \dfrac{g}{l}$

Now $\dot{\theta}^2 = n^2(\alpha^2 - \theta^2)$ so the maximum angular velocity

$$\dot{\theta}_{\max} = n\alpha$$

and the maximum speed

$$v = l\dot{\theta}_{\max} = ln\alpha$$

where l is the length of the pendulum.

$$v = ln\alpha = l\sqrt{\left(\frac{g}{l}\right)}\alpha = (gl)\alpha \qquad (1)$$

The period $T=2\pi/n=2\pi\sqrt{(l/g)}$. Substituting for $\sqrt{l}$ from equation (1),

$$T=\frac{2\pi}{\sqrt{g}}\frac{v}{\sqrt{(g\alpha)}}=\frac{2\pi v}{g\alpha}$$

Forces necessary to produce SHM

A force directed towards a fixed point and proportional to its distance x from that point will produce an acceleration proportional to the distance from, and directed towards, a fixed point and so will produce linear SHM. The tension in an elastic string and the tension or thrust in an elastic spring are equal to $\lambda x/L$, with the usual notation, and act so as to reduce x so that a particle attached to an elastic spring or string can perform SHM.

Four cases will now be considered.

(1) A particle on a smooth horizontal plane attached by a spring to a fixed point O in the plane

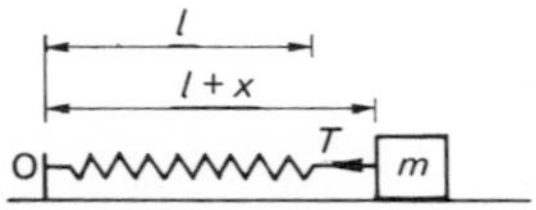

Figure 12.6

Let l be the natural length of the spring, λ the modulus of elasticity of the spring and m the mass of the particle. The spring is extended a distance x as shown in Fig. 12.6 so

$$T=\frac{\lambda x}{l}$$

but $T=-m\ddot{x}$ from Newton's law. Therefore

$$m\ddot{x}=\frac{-\lambda x}{l}$$

so the motion is SHM with period

$$T=2\pi\sqrt{\left(\frac{\lambda}{ml}\right)}$$

about O as a centre.

(2) A particle attached to a string on a smooth horizontal table, the other end of the string being fixed at O

Again

$$\ddot{x}=-\frac{\lambda}{ml}x \quad \text{and} \quad T=2\pi\sqrt{\left(\frac{ml}{\lambda}\right)}$$

so the particle performs SHM with A as a centre until the particle passes through A (Fig. 12.7). At this point $T=0$ and the string becomes slack. No horizontal force acts on the particle and it

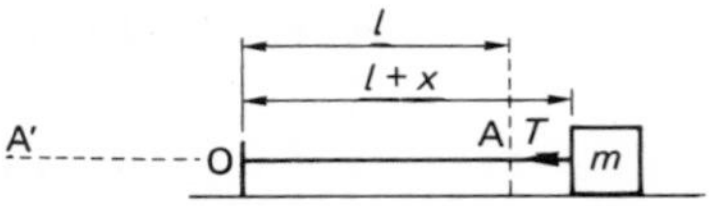

Figure 12.7

will travel with constant speed until it reaches A′, where OA = OA′. The particle then experiences a force $\lambda x/l$ towards A′ and so performs SHM with A′ as a centre.

(3) A particle of mass *m* suspended by a spiral spring from a fixed point A

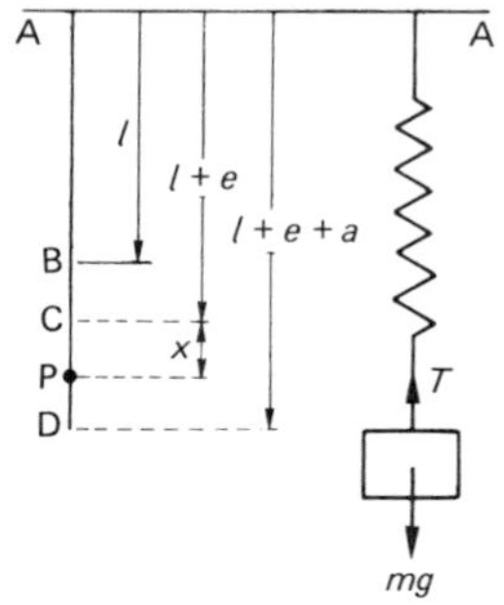

Figure 12.8

Let the natural length AB of the spring $= l$ and let BC $= e$ be the extension of the spring when it is hanging at rest under the action of the weight mg (Fig. 12.8). Therefore

$$T = mg = \frac{\lambda e}{l}$$

The particle is now pulled vertically downwards a distance $a = \text{CD}$ below C and released. Let P be a general position of the particle in the direction of increasing x, then Newton's second law gives

$$mg - T = m\ddot{x}$$

but $T = \dfrac{\lambda(e+x)}{l} = \dfrac{\lambda e}{l} + \dfrac{\lambda x}{l} = mg + \dfrac{\lambda x}{l}$

Therefore

$$mg - mg - \frac{\lambda x}{l} = m\ddot{x}$$

so $\quad \ddot{x} = -\dfrac{\lambda}{ml}x$

and the motion is SHM about C as a centre with $n^2 = \lambda/ml$. Hence the period

$$T = \frac{2\pi}{n} = 2\pi\sqrt{\left(\frac{ml}{\lambda}\right)}$$

Note For a spring, if $a > e$ the motion is still SHM as Hooke's law is the same for the compression as for the extension of a spring.

(4) A particle of mass *m* suspended by a string from a fixed point A

$$\ddot{x} = -\frac{\lambda}{ml}x \quad \text{and} \quad T = 2\pi\sqrt{\left(\frac{ml}{\lambda}\right)}$$

As long as the string is in tension. If the particle rises above the level of B, where AB is the natural length l of the string, the string is no longer stretched and the motion will be free vertical motion under gravity and not SHM.

Example 12.4

A particle of mass 1 kg is attached to one end of a light elastic string of natural length 1 m whose other end is fixed to a point O on a smooth horizontal plane. The string is extended until the particle is at a point B where OB = 1.25 m. The modulus of the string is 5 N find the time taken to travel from B to O after the particle is released from rest at B.

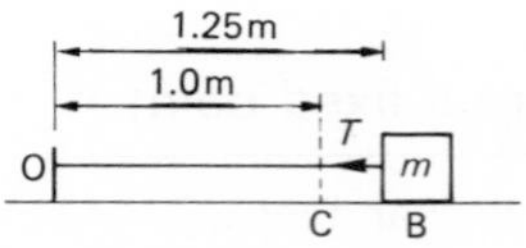

Figure 12.9

See Fig. 12.9. From B to C, where OC = 1 m, the particle travels under SHM about C as a centre.

$$\ddot{x} = \frac{-\lambda}{ml} x$$

$$T = 2\pi\sqrt{\left(\frac{ml}{\lambda}\right)} = 2\sqrt{\left(\frac{1\times 1}{5}\right)} = \frac{2\pi}{\sqrt{5}}\text{ s}$$

The time taken to travel from B to C,

$$t_1 = \frac{T}{4} = \frac{\pi}{2\sqrt{5}} = \frac{\pi\sqrt{5}}{10}\text{ s}$$

At B,

$$v^2 = n^2(a^2 - x^2)$$

where a is the amplitude. At C, $x = 0$ and $n^2 = \lambda/ml$. Therefore

$$v_C^2 = \frac{\lambda}{ml} a^2$$

$$v_C = \sqrt{\left(\frac{\lambda}{ml}\right)} a$$

Since the amplitude $a = 0.25$ m,

$$v_C = \sqrt{\left(\frac{5}{1\times 1}\right)}(0.25)$$

so the speed at C,

$$v_C = \sqrt{5}/4$$

The particle now experiences zero horizontal force from C to O.

velocity = distance/time

so the time to travel from C to O,

$$t_2 = \frac{OC}{v_C} = \frac{1}{\sqrt{5}/4} = \frac{4}{\sqrt{5}}\text{ s}$$

Hence the total time to travel from B to O,

$$t = t_1 + t_2 = \frac{\sqrt{5}}{10}(\pi + 8)\text{ s}$$

Example 12.5

A particle of mass $2mg$ is suspended from a fixed point by an elastic string of natural length l and modulus of elasticity $8mg$. The particle is pulled down a distance $l/2$ below the equilibrium position. Find the time that elapses before the string first goes slack and the greatest height reached.

$$T = \frac{\lambda x}{l}$$

For equilibrium

$$2mg = \frac{8mgx}{l}$$

so the equilibrium extension is $l/4$. From number (4) above,

$$\ddot{x} = -\frac{\lambda}{ml}x$$

$$n^2 = \frac{\lambda}{ml} = \frac{8mg}{2ml} = \frac{4g}{l}$$

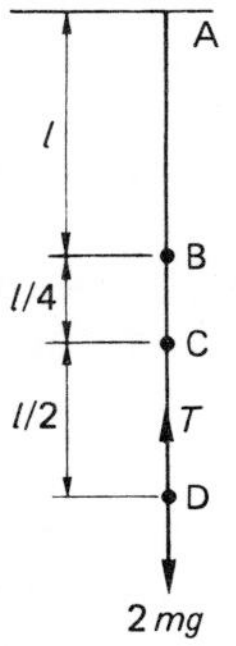

Figure 12.10

The particle travels from D to B under SHM, where AB $= l$ (Fig. 12.10). For $t = 0$ at B when $x = a$,

$$x = a \cos nt \quad \text{and} \quad a = l/2$$

Therefore at B when $x = -l/4$,

$$\frac{-l}{4} = \frac{l}{2}\cos\left[\sqrt{\left(\frac{4g}{l}\right)}t\right]$$

$$\frac{-1}{2} = \cos\left[\sqrt{\left(\frac{4g}{l}\right)}t\right]$$

$$\frac{2\pi}{3} = \sqrt{\left(\frac{4g}{l}\right)}t$$

Hence the time that elapses before the string goes slack at B,

$$\underline{t = \frac{\pi}{3}\sqrt{\left(\frac{l}{g}\right)}\text{ s}}$$

The velocity is given by

$$v^2 = n^2(a^2 - x^2)$$

so at B

$$v^2 = \frac{4g}{l}\left(\frac{l^2}{4} - \frac{l^2}{16}\right) = \frac{12gl}{16}$$

By the conservation of energy, the particle rises until

$$\tfrac{1}{2}mv^2 = mgh$$

or $\quad v^2 = 2gh$

Therefore

$$h = \frac{v^2}{2g} = \frac{12gl}{32g}$$

i.e. $h = \dfrac{3l}{8}$ above B

The particle rises until it is at a height $\underline{5l/8}$ below the point of suspension.

Problem 12.1

A particle P performs simple harmonic oscillations of amplitude 4 cm and period 8 s. Find:

(a) the maximum speed of P,
(b) the maximum magnitude of the acceleration of P,
(c) the speed of P when it is 2 cm from the centre of oscillation.
(AEB J86)

As the motion is given as SHM, the equations of SHM can be applied directly so

$$T=\frac{2\pi}{n} \quad \text{and} \quad n=\frac{2\pi}{T}=\frac{\pi}{4}$$

(a) Use maximum velocity $= na$ to find it equal to $10^{-2}\pi$ m s^{-1}, i.e. π cm s^{-1}.
(b) Use maximum acceleration $= n^2a$ to find it equal to $\pi^2/4$ cm s^{-2}.
(c) Use $v^2 = n^2(a^2 - x^2)$ to find $v^2 = (\pi/16)(16-4)$ and so to find $v = \pi\sqrt{3}/2$ cm s^{-1} at a distance of 2 cm from the centre of oscillation.

Problem 12.2

A horizontal platform is making vertical simple harmonic oscillations of amplitude 0.2 m and period 0.25 s. A particle is placed on the platform when it is instantaneously at rest at its lowest position. Will the particle leave the shelf during the subsequent motion and if so where?

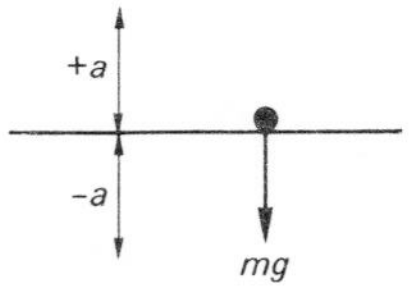

Figure 12.11

(1) Draw a diagram (Fig. 12.11).
(2) The motion is SHM so again use the equation $\ddot{x} = -n^2x$. Hence the force $m\ddot{x} = -n^2mx$.
(3) It is possible for the particle to leave the shelf when it is above the centre of oscillation if $g \leqslant \ddot{x}$. So use the condition $g = \ddot{x} = n^2x$ and

$$n=\frac{2\pi}{T}=\frac{2\pi}{0.25}=8\pi$$

to find that the particle leaves the shelf when it is a distance 0.016 m above the centre of oscillation.

Example 12.6

Particles A and B of masses 0.02 and 0.01 kg respectively are attached, one at each end of a light elastic string. Particle A is held at rest on a rough horizontal rectangular table, the coefficient of friction being 0.51, and the string passes over a smooth pulley P at the edge of the table. The portions AP and BP of the string are both straight and lie in a vertical plane perpendicular to the edge of the table. The particle A is held fixed and B is set in motion. The particle B describes simple harmonic motion, with the centre of oscillation O, along the vertical line through P. (The length of BP is such that B never reaches either P or the floor.) It is given that B is moving with speed 0.15 m s^{-1} when passing through O and with speed 0.12 m s^{-1} when at a distance of 0.03 m from O.

(a) Find the amplitude and period of oscillation.
(b) Show that, when B is at a depth h metres below O, the tension in the string is $(0.1+0.09h)$ N.

The particle A is released when B is moving downwards through O; find

(c) the distance OB when the particle A starts to move,
(d) the time that elapses until A starts to move.

(Take $g=10 \text{ m s}^{-2}$.) (AEB J85)

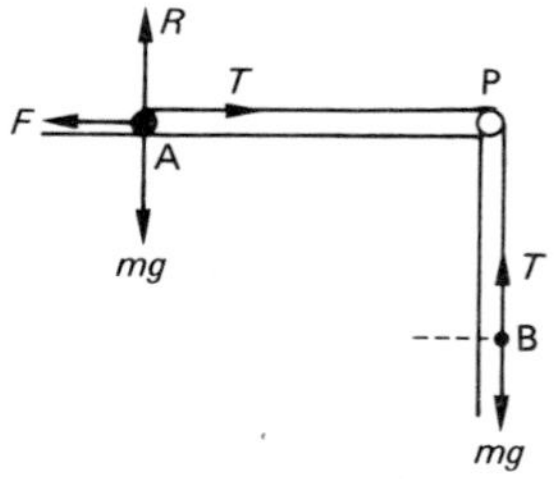

Figure 12.12

See Fig. 12.12. It is given that B moves with SHM so for B,

$$\ddot{x} = -n^2 x$$

and $v^2 = n^2(a^2 - x^2)$

where a is the amplitude of the motion.
When $x=0$, $v=0.15 \text{ m s}^{-1}$. Therefore

$$0.15^2 = n^2 a^2 \tag{1}$$

When $x=0.03$, $v=0.12 \text{ m s}^{-1}$. Therefore

$$0.12^2 = n^2(a^2 - 0.03^2) \tag{2}$$

Subtracting equation (1) from equation (2) gives

$$0.12^2 = 0.15^2 - 0.03^2 n^2$$

$$n^2 = 9$$

$$n = 3 \text{ rad s}^{-1}$$

(a) The period

$$T = 2\pi/n = \underline{2\pi/3 \text{ s}^{-1}}$$

and the amplitude

$$a = 0.15/n = \underline{0.05 \text{ m}}$$

(b) The tension in the string when B is h metres below A is due to the upwards acceleration needed for SHM plus the weight. Therefore

$$T = mn^2h + mg = (9h+g)(0.01)$$

i.e. $T = (0.1+0.09h)$ N

(c) Vertically for A,

$$R = mg = 0.02g$$

$$\text{maximum value of } T = \mu R = 0.51 \times 0.2$$

When the tension in AP = tension in BP = 0.2×0.51 then A will start to move. Therefore OB = h is such that

$$0.1 + 0.09h = 0.2 \times 0.51$$

which gives

$$h = 0.002/0.09 = \underline{1/45 \text{ m}}$$

(d) For SHM with centre O,

$$x = a \sin nt$$

At $h = 1/45$,

$$1/45 = 0.05 \sin 3t$$

$$4/9 = \sin 3t$$

so the time that elapses until A starts to move

$$\underline{t = \tfrac{1}{3} \sin^{-1}(4/9)\ \text{s}}$$

Summary

(1) Simple harmonic motion occurs when a particle moves so that its acceleration is proportional to its displacement x from a fixed point and is directed towards that fixed point.

$$\ddot{x} = -n^2 x$$

where n is a constant.

(2) The velocity v is given by

$v^2 = n^2(a^2 - x^2)$. The displacement x is given by

$$x = a \sin(nt + \varepsilon)$$

so $\quad v = an \cos(nt + \varepsilon)$

where ε depends on the value of x when $t = 0$.

The amplitude a of the motion is the maximum displacement x and occurs when $v = 0$. The period of the motion T is the time for one complete oscillation and is given by

$$T = 2\pi/n$$

(3) The maximum magnitude of velocity occurs when $x = 0$ and equals na.

The maximum magnitude of the acceleration occurs when $x = a$ and equals $n^2 a$.

(4) The orthogonal projections of the position vector of a particle moving in a circle centre $(0, 0)$, with constant angular velocity, onto the x-axis and the y-axis move with SHM.

(5) For small angular displacements a heavy particle oscillating at the end of a light inextensible string in a given vertical plane performs SHM.

$$\ddot{\theta} = -n^2\theta \quad \text{and} \quad n^2 = g/l$$

where l is the length of the pendulum.

(6) The tension in an elastic string and the tension or thrust in an elastic spring produce SHM about the equilibrium position as the centre of oscillation. The amplitude of the motion is the distance from the equilibrium position to the point from which the particle was originally released. If, in an elastic string, the amplitude is greater than the extension to the equilibrium position then incomplete SHM will occur.

13
Differential equations

Objectives

The student should be able to:

(1) set up and solve differential equations of motion for general rectilinear motion where the resulting equations are separable or linear,
(2) recognise the forces causing damped oscillations and set up and solve the equation of motion for damped harmonic motion to determine if the motion is oscillatory, critically damped or overdamped,
(3) set up the equation of motion for forced harmonic motion and obtain a solution with forcing terms $f(t)$ such as At^n, $B\sin(\omega t+\varepsilon)$ or $Ce^{\omega t}$.

Rectilinear motion under the action of known forces

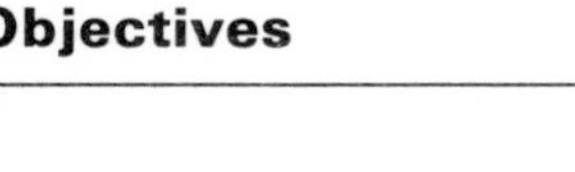

Figure 13.1

Consider the following example: a particle P of constant mass m moving along a straight line Ox in the direction Ox is attracted towards the fixed point O by a force k^2mx and resisted by a force $2km\dot{x}^2$, where $\dot{x}$ is the speed of the particle (Fig. 13.1).
From Newton's second law of motion

$$m\ddot{x} = -k^2mx - 2km\dot{x}^2$$

so $\ddot{x} + 2k\dot{x}^2 + k^2x = 0$ where k is a constant

This is the basic equation of motion of the particle and is a second order differential equation because of the term $\ddot{x}$, it has constant coefficients. A solution of the equation involves two stages of integration and so two constants of integration. A brief description of the method of solution is given later in this chapter when discussing damped SHM.

Given the forces acting on a particle, it is possible to set up the differential equation of motion for the particle and techniques for solutions of the equations can be found in most standard pure mathematics textbooks.

Example 13.1

A car of mass m is moving at $20\ \mathrm{m\,s^{-1}}$ when the brakes are applied with a force equal to vm neutrons, where v is the speed of the car. The resistance to motion between the car and the ground is constant and equal to $10m$ newtons.

(a) Derive the equation of motion of the car.

(b) Find the time taken for the car to stop given that $x=0$ when $t=0$ and $\dot{x}=20\ \mathrm{m\,s^{-1}}$.
(c) Sketch a graph of x against t for the car's motion.

(a) The retarding forces acting on the car are $Vm+10m$. From Newton's second law

$$m\ddot{x}=-10m-m\dot{x}$$

Therefore

$$\underline{\frac{dv}{dt}=-10-v}$$

is the equation of motion of the car.
(b) Separating the variables,

$$\int_{20}^{v}\frac{dv}{10+v}=\int_{0}^{t}-dt$$

$$[\ln(10+v)]_{20}^{v}=-[t]_0^t$$

$$\ln(10+v)-\ln(30)=-t$$

$$\ln\left(\frac{10+v}{30}\right)=-t$$

$$\frac{10+v}{30}=e^{-t}$$

Therefore

$$v=30e^{-t}-10 \tag{1}$$

When $v=0$,

$$30e^{-t}=10$$

$$e^{-t}=1/3$$

Therefore

$$t=\ln 3=\underline{1.1\ \mathrm{s}}$$

(c) Replacing v by dx/dt in equation (1) to find the variation of distance with time,

$$\frac{dx}{dt}=30e^{-t}-10$$

Integrating with respect to time gives

$$\int_0^x dx=\int_0^t(30e^{-t}-10)\,dt$$

$$[x]_0^x=[-30e^{-t}-10t]_0^t$$

Therefore

$$x=-30e^{-t}-10t+30$$

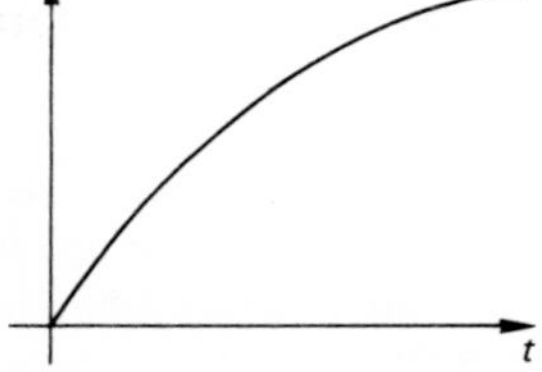

Figure 13.2

and so a graph of x between $t=0$ and $t=1.1$ s when the car stops can be sketched (Fig. 13.2).

Example 13.2

A particle moves along a straight line Ox such that its displacement x from O at a time t is given by the differential equation

$$\ddot{x} + k\dot{x} = 0$$

where k is a constant. Suggest a possible situation which would result in this equation of motion.

If a particle moves horizontally across a level surface against a resistive force R proportional to its speed then $R = A\dot{x}$ and Newton's second law gives $m\ddot{x} = -A\dot{x}$, where A is a constant. Therefore

$$m\ddot{x} + A\dot{x} = 0$$

$$\ddot{x} + \frac{A}{m}\dot{x} = 0$$

Let $A/x = k$, then

$$\ddot{x} + k\dot{x} = 0$$

so such a physical situation can result in this equation of motion.

Problem 13.1

A particle of mass m is projected vertically upwards against gravity in a fluid which offers a resistance to motion of mkv, where v is the speed of the particle and k is a constant. If $v = 2\ \mathrm{m\,s^{-1}}$ when $t = 0$ and $x = 0$ find the time when the particle first comes to rest in terms of k.

(1) Derive the equation of motion using Newton's second law,

$$m\ddot{x} = -mg - mkv$$

(2) Express $\ddot{x}$ as $\mathrm{d}v/\mathrm{d}t$, separate the variables and integrate,

$$\int_2^0 \frac{\mathrm{d}v}{(g/k + v)} = -k\int_0^t \mathrm{d}t$$

to show that

$$t = \frac{1}{k}\ln\left(\frac{g+2k}{g}\right)$$

when $v = 0$.

Damped harmonic motion

Simple harmonic motion is produced by a resultant force acting on a particle that is directed towards a fixed point and proportional to the resultant displacement from that fixed point. The equation of motion of the particle is

$$\frac{\mathrm{d}^2x}{\mathrm{d}t^2} = -n^2x$$

If an additional resisting force exists the nature of the motion may be changed completely or the motion may be damped harmonic. Consider a resisting force Kv proportional to the

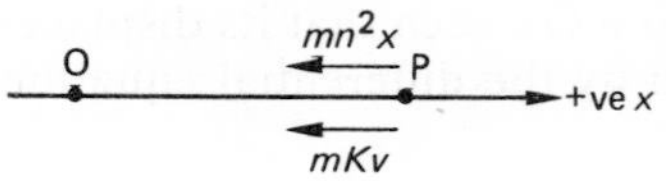

Figure 13.3

speed of the particle P (Fig. 13.3). Then the equation of motion of the particle is given by

$$\frac{d^2x}{dt^2}+K\frac{dx}{dt}+n^2x=0$$

Let $2k=K$. Then

$$\frac{d^2x}{dt^2}+2k\frac{dx}{dt}+n^2x=0 \qquad (1)$$

This is a second order linear differential equation.

Consider the following example. Solve the equation

$$\ddot{x}+6\dot{x}+5x=0$$

Let D stand for d/dt. Then

$$D^2x+6Dx+5x=0$$

or $\quad (D+5)(D+1)x=0$

where D, (D+5) and (D+1) are differential operators. $(D+5)x=0$ is a separable equation with a solution $x=C_1e^{-5t}$ and $(D+1)x=0$ is a separable equation with a solution $x=C_2e^{-t}$. Since the two solutions are linearly independent,

$$x=C_1e^{-5t}+C_2e^{-t}$$

is a general solution of the equation $\ddot{x}+6\dot{x}+5x=0$.

Now consider the following equation:

$$p^2+6p+5=0$$

This is called the **auxiliary equation** for the given differential equation, where p is a constant and must be solved first to solve the differential equation. This method can be applied to equation (1). The auxiliary equation for equation (1) is

$$p^2+2kp+n^2=0$$

and has roots

$$p=-k\pm\surd(k^2-n^2)$$

A solution of the form

$$Ae^{p_1t}+Be^{p_2t}$$

where A, B, p_1 and p_2 are constants, would satisfy the equation provided that p satisfies the auxiliary equation. There are three possible different natures for the roots of the equation.

(1) **Real distinct roots:** $k^2>n^2$

$$p_1=-k+\surd(k^2-n^2) \quad \text{and} \quad p_2=-k-\surd(k^2-n^2)$$

Then

$$x=Ae^{-kt+t\surd(k^2-n^2)}+Be^{-kt-t\surd(k^2-n^2)}$$

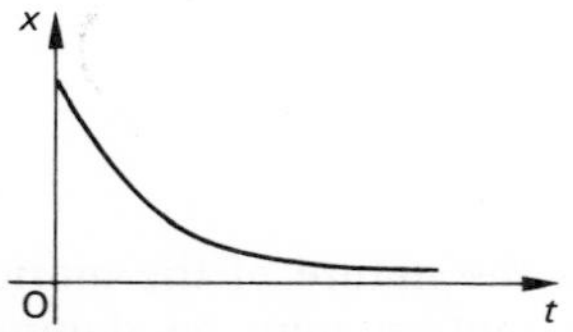

Figure 13.4

The motion will not be oscillatory as there is no value of t for which $x=0$ or $\dot{x}=0$. This is **heavy damping** when the damping term $2km\dot{x}$ dominates the oscillatory term (Fig. 13.4).

(2) **Equal roots:** $k^2 = n^2$

$$p_1 = p_2 = -k \text{ is one solution}$$

A second solution is te^{-kt}, where k is a double root of the auxiliary equation. Therefore

$$x = Ae^{-kt} + Bte^{-kt}$$

or $\quad x = e^{-kt}(A + Bt)$

This motion is not oscillatory since there is only one finite value of t for which $x = 0$ and one finite value of t for which $\dot{x} = 0$. When $x = 0$

$$t = -A/B$$

When $\dot{x} = 0$

$$t = \frac{B - kA}{kB}$$

So again heavy damping occurs, in this case sometimes referred to as **critical damping** (Fig. 13.5).

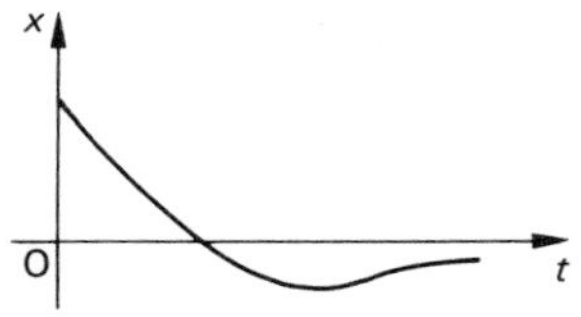

Figure 13.5

(3) **Complex roots:** $k^2 < n^2$

$$p_1 = -k + i\surd(n^2 - k^2) \quad \text{and} \quad p_2 = k + i\surd(n^2 - k^2)$$

The solution is $x = e^{-kt}[A \cos t\surd(n^2 - k^2) + B \sin t\surd(n^2 - k^2)]$

or $\quad x = Ce^{-kt} \cos[t\surd(n^2 - k^2) + \varepsilon]$

This is an oscillatory motion called **damped harmonic motion** (Fig. 13.6). Since $-1 \leqslant \cos \theta \leqslant 1$, then $x = Ce^{-kt}$ and $x = -Ce^{-kt}$ form the upper and lower boundary for the curve so e^{-kt} is called the damping factor.

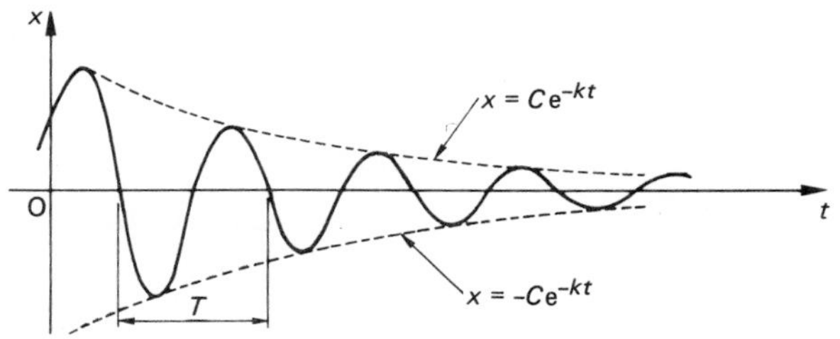

Figure 13.6

Now $x = 0$ when $\cos[t\surd(n^2 - k^2) + \varepsilon] = 0$. Therefore

$$t\surd(n^2 - k^2) + \varepsilon = \frac{\pi}{2}, \frac{3\pi}{2}, \frac{5\pi}{2}, \ldots$$ when the curve cuts the axis as shown.

Hence the period

$$T = \left(\frac{5\pi}{2} - \varepsilon - \frac{\pi}{2} + \varepsilon\right) \frac{1}{\surd(n^2 - k^2)} = \frac{2\pi}{\surd(n^2 - k^2)}$$

and is constant.

The stationary (maximum and minimum) values of x occur when $\dot{x} = 0$ and the amplitudes of successive oscillations decrease with time in a geometric progression of common ratio e^{-T}, where T is the period of the motion.

Example 13.3

A particle of mass m is moving along a straight line and is attracted towards a fixed point O by a force $2m\omega^2x$, where x is the distance of the particle from O at the time t and ω is a constant. In addition, the motion of the particle is resisted by a force of magnitude $2m\omega\dot{x}$, where $\dot{x}$ is the speed of the particle at a time t. Write down a differential equation to determine the motion of the particle and hence show that

$$x = Ce^{-\omega t}\cos(\omega t + \alpha)$$

where C and α are constants.

Given that at $t=0$, $x=a$ and $\dot{x}=(\sqrt{3}-1)a\omega$, where a is a constant, find C and α. Also find the times at which the particle is instantaneously at rest.

Sketch the graph of x against t, showing clearly the behaviour of x as t becomes large. (AEB J86)

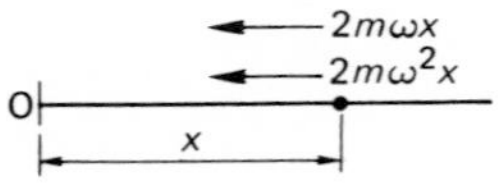

Figure 13.7

See Fig. 13.7. From Newton's second law,

$$m\ddot{x} = -2m\omega\dot{x} - 2m\omega^2x$$

Therefore

$$\ddot{x} + 2\omega\dot{x} + 2\omega^2x = 0 \qquad (1)$$

This is a second order linear differential equation and by comparison with

$$\ddot{x} + 2k\dot{x} + n^2x = 0 \qquad (2)$$

then

$$k = \omega \quad \text{and} \quad n^2 = 2\omega^2$$

so $k^2 < n^2$. The auxiliary equation is

$$p^2 + 2\omega p + 2\omega^2 = 0$$

Therefore

$$p = \frac{-2\omega \pm \sqrt{(4\omega^2 - 8\omega^2)}}{2}$$

so $p_1 = -\omega - i\omega$ and $p_2 = -\omega + i\omega$

A general solution of equation (2) with $k^2 < n^2$ for damped harmonic motion is

$$x = Ce^{-kt}\cos[t\sqrt{(n^2 - k^2)} + \varepsilon]$$

so for equation (1) the solution becomes

$$x = Ce^{-\omega t}\cos[t\sqrt{(2\omega^2 - \omega^2)} + \alpha]$$

i.e. $x = Ce^{-\omega t}\cos(\omega t + \alpha)$

where C and α are constants.

Given that $x = a$ at $t = 0$, then

$$a = C\cos\alpha \qquad (3)$$

In general,

$$\dot{x} = -\omega C e^{-\omega t} \cos(\omega t + \alpha) - \omega C e^{-\omega t} \sin(\omega t + \alpha) \qquad (4)$$

so given that $\dot{x} = (\sqrt{3} - 1)a\omega$ when $t = 0$, then

$$(\sqrt{3} - 1)a\omega = -\omega C \cos \alpha - \omega C \sin \alpha \qquad (5)$$

Dividing equation (5) by equation (3) gives

$$\sqrt{3} - 1 = -1 - \tan \alpha$$

$$\tan \alpha = -\sqrt{3}$$

$$\alpha = \underline{-\pi/3}$$

From equation (3)

$$a = C/2$$

or $C = \underline{2a}$

Therefore

$$x = 2a e^{-\omega t} \cos(\omega t - \pi/3)$$

Using equation (4),

$$\dot{x} = -\omega C e^{-\omega t}[\cos(\omega t + \alpha) + \sin(\omega t + \alpha)]$$

when $\dot{x} = 0$,

$$\cos(\omega t + \alpha) + \sin(\omega t + \alpha) = 0$$

$$\tan(\omega t + \alpha) = -1$$

Therefore, in general,

$$\omega t + \alpha = -\frac{\pi}{4} + n\pi$$

where $n = 1, 2, 3$, etc. As $\alpha = -\pi/3$,

$$\omega t = \frac{\pi}{3} - \frac{\pi}{4} + n\pi$$

The particle is instantaneously at rest at times

$$\underline{t = \frac{\pi}{12\omega} + \frac{n\pi}{\omega}}$$

The graph of x against t is given in Fig. 13.8.

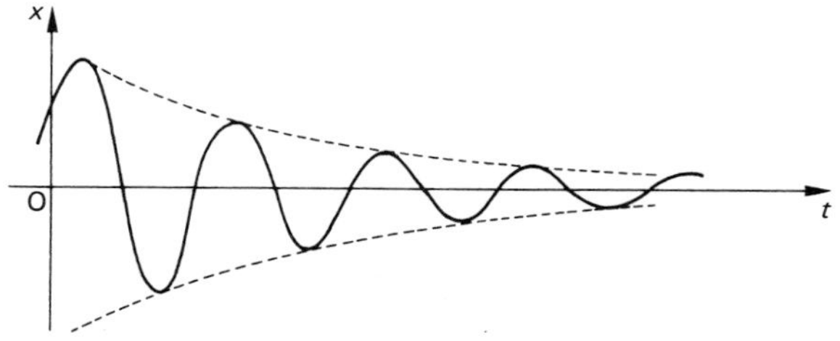

Figure 13.8

Forced harmonic motion

A second order linear differential equation with constant coefficients and zero right-hand side describes free oscillations of a particle. Often the particle is acted upon by a force $mf(t)$, where m is the mass of the particle. The oscillations are then forced and $f(t)$ is often called the forcing function. The equation of motion is

$$\frac{d^2x}{dt^2}+2k\frac{dx}{dt}+n^2x=f(t) \qquad (1)$$

The general solution of the above equation with the right-hand side equal to zero is known, as described in the section on damped harmonic motion: this solution is called the **complementary function.** If we find a particular integral which is a solution of equation (1) and add it to the complementary function then we have the general solution of equation (1). Finding the particular integral involves trying a solution of the form $f(t)$. If $f(t)=at^n$ then we would try

$$At^n+Bt^{n-1}+Ct^{n-2}+\ldots+D$$

If $f(t)=6\sin 2t$ then we would try

$$A\cos 2t+B\sin 2t \quad \text{or} \quad A\sin(\omega t+\varepsilon)$$

If $f(t)=3e^{2t}$ then we would try

$$Ce^t \quad \text{or} \quad Ce^{2t}$$

If $f(t)$ is already in the complementary function then a particular integral of t times the complementary function should be tried. This method of inspection is often sufficient to lead to a solution.

Example 13.4

At time $t=0$ a force given in newtons by $12\sin 5t$, $t\geqslant 0$, is applied to a 6 N weight which hangs in equilibrium at the end of a vertical spring having a modulus of 150 N and a natural length of 1 m. Neglecting damping, find the position of the weight at any time *t*.
See Fig. 13.9.

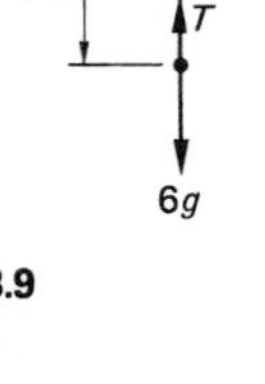

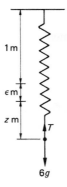

Figure 13.9

Let ε = extension due to the 6 N weight and let z = further extension due to the impressed forced. From Newton's second law

$$m\ddot{z}=-150+12\sin 5t$$

because $T=\lambda z/l$ and is the restoring force while $12\sin 5t$ is the impressed force. Therefore

$$6\ddot{z}+150z=12\sin 5t$$

or $$\ddot{z}+25z=2\sin 5t \qquad (1)$$

We find the complementary function by solving

$$\ddot{z}+25z=0$$

The general solution of this is

$$z=A\cos 5t+B\sin 5t$$

It would do no good to assume a particular solution of the form $z = C_1 \cos 5t + C_2 \sin 5t$ because substitution of this into the left-hand side of equation (1) would lead to zero. Instead we try a particular solution of the form

$$z = t(C_1 \cos 5t + C_2 \sin 5t)$$

Therefore

$$\dot{z} = C_1 \cos 5t + C_2 \sin 5t + t(-5C_1 \sin 5t + 5C_2 \cos 5t)$$

$$\ddot{z} = -5C_1 \sin 5t + 5C_2 \cos 5t - 5C_1 \sin 5t + 5C_2 \cos 5t$$
$$+ t(-25C_1 \cos 5t - 25C_2 \sin 5t)$$

Substituting in equation (1) gives

$$2 \sin 5t = -10C_1 \sin 5t + 10C_2 \cos 5t$$
$$-25t(C_1 \cos 5t + C_2 \sin 5t)$$
$$+25t(C_1 \cos 5t + C_2 \sin 5t)$$

or $\quad 2 \sin 5t = -10C_1 \sin 5t + 10C_2 \cos 5t$

Therefore

$$C_2 = 0 \quad \text{and} \quad C_1 = -\tfrac{1}{5}$$

and the particular integral is

$$z = -\frac{t}{5} \cos 5t$$

Hence the complete solution which is the sum of the complementary function and the particular integral is

$$z = A \cos 5t + B \sin 5t - \frac{t}{5} \cos 5t$$

Using $z = 0$ at $t = 0$,

$$0 = A$$

Using $\dot{z} = 0$ at $t = 0$,

$$\dot{z} = 5B \cos 5t - \frac{1}{5} \cos 5t + \frac{5t}{5} \sin 5t$$

$$0 = 5B - \tfrac{1}{5}$$

$$B = \tfrac{1}{25}$$

and the complete solution is

$$\underline{z = \frac{1}{25} \sin 5t - \frac{t}{5} \cos 5t}$$

As t gets larger, the term $-(t/5) \cos 5t$ increases numerically without bound and physically the spring will break. This demonstrates resonance when the impressed frequency equals the natural frequency of the system.

Problem 13.2

A mass of m kg hung on a vertical string stretches it by 0.1 m. The mass is then pulled down a further 0.3 m and released. Find the position of the mass at any time if a damping force equal to $20m$ times the instantaneous speed is acting. Is the motion oscillatory, critically damped or overdamped? (Take $g = 10\ \text{m s}^{-2}$).

(1) Use $T = \lambda x/l$ to find $\lambda/l = 10mg$.
(2) Then from Newton's second law derive the equation of motion at some extension x below the equilibrium extension of 0.1 m (Fig. 13.10).

$$m\ddot{x} = mg - 10mg(0.1 + x) - 20m\dot{x}$$

i.e. $\ddot{x} + 20\dot{x} + 10gx = 0$

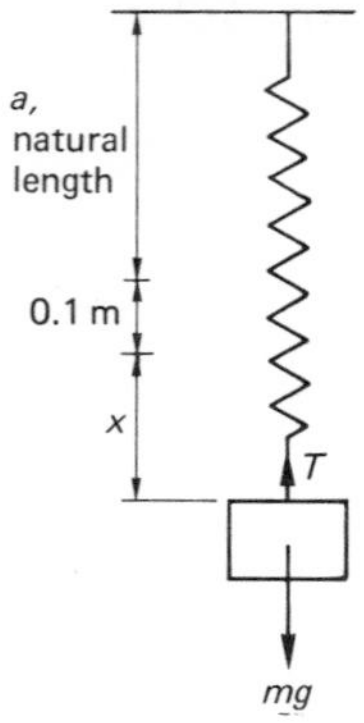

Figure 13.10

(3) Find the auxiliary equation $p^2 + 2kp + n^2 = 0$ and therefore show that $k^2 = n^2$.
(4) So the motion is *critically damped* and the solution is of the form

$$x = e^{-kt}(A + Bt)$$

Now $k = 10$, $t = 0$ at $x = 0.3$ and $\dot{x} = 0$ at $t = 0$, so using these boundary conditions show that $x = e^{-10t}(0.3 + 3t)$.

Problem 13.3

A particle of mass m moves across a smooth horizontal surface along a straight line Ox in the direction Ox under the action of a force of $10mx$ attracting it to O, and through a medium of resistive force $2m\dot{x}$. If x is the distance from O derive the equation of motion of the particle. Given that at $t = 0$, $x = 6$ m and $\mathrm{d}x/\mathrm{d}t = -3\ \text{m s}^{-2}$, find an expression for x in terms of t.
(1) Derive the equation of motion from Newton's second law,

$$m\frac{\mathrm{d}^2x}{\mathrm{d}t^2} + 2m\frac{\mathrm{d}x}{\mathrm{d}t} + 10mx = 0$$

(2) The auxiliary equation $p^2 + 2kp + n^2 = 0$ is $p^2 + 2p + 10 = 0$ so show that $k = 1$ and $n^2 = 10$, i.e. $k^2 < n^2$. Hence the solution is of the form

$$x = e^{-kt}[A \cos t\surd(n^2 - k^2) + B \sin t\surd(n^2 - k^2)]$$

(3) Now use the boundary condition $x = 6$ at $t = 0$ to show that $A = 6$ and $\mathrm{d}x/\mathrm{d}t = -3$ at $t = 0$ to show that $B = 1$. Hence

$$x = e^{-t}(6 \cos 3t + \sin 3t)$$

Example 13.5

A particle P of mass m is moving in a straight line Ox under the action of a force Ft, where t is the time and F is a constant, acting in the same direction as the displacement x from Ox. A resistance of magnitude $5m\dot{x}$ and an attractive force of magnitude $4mx$ and directed towards O also act on the particle. Find an expression for the position at P at any later time t given that $x = 0$ when $t = 0$ and $\dot{x} = 0$ when $t = 0$.

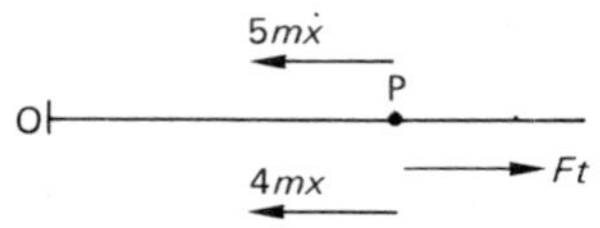

Figure 13.11

See Fig. 13.11. From Newton's second law

$$Ft - 5m\dot{x} - 4mx = m\ddot{x}$$

i.e. $$\ddot{x} + 5\dot{x} + 4x = \frac{F}{m}t \qquad (1)$$

To obtain a general solution of equation (1) first we find the complementary function by solving

$$\ddot{x} + 5\dot{x} + 4x = 0$$

The auxiliary equation

$$p^2 + 2kp + n^2 = 0$$

is $$p^2 + 5p + 4 = 0$$

$$(p+4)(p+1) = 0$$

Therefore

$$p = -4 \quad \text{or} \quad -1$$

so the complementary function is

$$x = Ae^{-4t} + Be^{-t}$$

To find the particular integral we will try a solution of the form

$$x = Ct + D$$

so $\dot{x} = C$

and $\ddot{x} = 0$

Substituting in equation (1),

$$0 + 4Ct + 4D + 5C = \frac{F}{m}t$$

$$4C = \frac{F}{m} \quad \text{or} \quad C = \frac{F}{4m}$$

and $4D = -5C$ so $D = \dfrac{-5F}{16m}$

and the particular integral is

$$x = \frac{F}{4m}t - \frac{5F}{16m}$$

Hence the complete solution which is the sum of the complementary function and the particular integral is

$$x = Ae^{-4t} + Be^{-t} + \frac{F}{4m}t - \frac{5F}{16m}$$

Using $x = 0$ at $t = 0$,

$$0 = A + B - \frac{5F}{16m} \qquad (2)$$

Using $\dot{x}=0$ at $t=0$,

$$\dot{x}=-4Ae^{-4t}-Be^{-t}+\frac{F}{4m} \tag{3}$$

$$0=-4A-B+\frac{F}{4m}$$

Adding equations (2) and (3) gives

$$0=-3A-\frac{5F}{16m}+\frac{F}{4m}$$

$$0=-3A-\frac{F}{16m} \quad \text{or} \quad A=\frac{-F}{48m}$$

so from equation (2)

$$B=\frac{5F}{16m}-A=\frac{16F}{48m}$$

$$\text{so} \quad x=\frac{F}{48m}(-e^{-4t}+16e^{-t}+12t-15)$$

Example 13.6

A light spring AB of natural length $2a$ and of modulus of elasticity $2amn^2$ lies straight, at its natural length and at rest on a smooth horizontal table. The end A is fixed to the table and a particle of mass m is attached to the midpoint of the spring. The end B is then caused to move along the line AB so that after a time t the distance between A and B is $a(2+\sin nt)$. Denoting the distance of P from A by $a+x$, prove that

$$\frac{d^2x}{dt^2}+4n^2x=2n^2a\sin nt$$

Find x in terms of a, b and t. Find also the value of t for which P first comes to rest. (JMB J84)

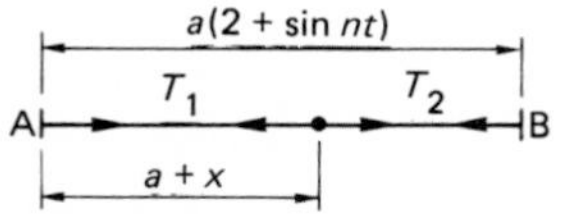

Figure 13.12

See Fig. 13.12. From Hooke's law for AP

$$T_1=\frac{\lambda x}{1}=\frac{2amn^2}{a}x=2mn^2x$$

and for PB

$$\text{extension}=2a+a\sin nt-2a-x$$
$$=a\sin nt-x$$

Therefore

$$T_2=2mn^2(a\sin nt-x)$$

Newton's second law gives $T_2-T_1=m\ddot{x}$. Therefore

$$2mn^2(a\sin nt-x)-2mn^2x=m\ddot{x}$$

$$2n^2a\sin nt-2n^2x-2n^2x=\ddot{x}$$

$$\text{or} \quad \ddot{x}+4n^2x=2n^2a\sin nt \tag{1}$$

To find the complete solution of (1) we must first find the complementary function by solving

$$\ddot{x}+4n^2x=0$$

The solution of this is

$$x=A\sin 2nt+B\cos 2nt$$

where the auxiliary equation is

$$p^2+4n^2p=0$$

We need to find the particular integral for the complete solution so will try the particular solution

$$x=C_1a\sin nt+C_2a\cos nt$$

$$\dot{x}=C_1an\cos nt-C_2an\sin nt$$

$$\ddot{x}=-C_1an^2\sin nt-C_2an^2\cos nt$$

Substituting in equation (1) gives

$$-C_1an^2\sin nt-C_2an^2\cos nt+4n^2C_1a\sin nt$$

$$+4n^2C_2a\cos nt=2n^2a\sin nt$$

Therefore

$$-C_1n^2+4C_1n^2=2n^2$$

$$C_1=2/3$$

and $-C_2n^2+4C_2n^2=0$

$$C_2=0$$

The complete solution is the sum of the complementary function and the particular integral and is given by

$$x=A\sin 2nt+B\cos 2nt+\tfrac{2}{3}a\sin nt$$

where A and B are constants.

The boundary conditions given in the problem are $x=0$ and $\dot{x}=0$ at $t=0$. Using $x=0$ at $t=0$,

$$0=B$$

Using $\dot{x}=0$ at $t=0$,

$$\dot{x}=2An\cos nt+\tfrac{2}{3}an\cos nt$$

$$0=2A+\tfrac{2}{3}a$$

$$A=-\tfrac{1}{3}a$$

So the complete solution is

$$\underline{x=\tfrac{2}{3}a\sin nt-\tfrac{1}{3}a\sin 2nt}$$

$$\dot{x}=\tfrac{2}{3}an\cos nt-\tfrac{2}{3}an\cos 2nt$$

When P comes to rest $\dot{x}=0$.

$$0=\cos nt-\cos 2nt$$

or $$\cos 2nt - \cos nt = 0$$

$$2\cos^2 nt - \cos nt - 1 = 0$$

$$(2\cos nt + 1)(\cos nt - 1) = 0$$

so either $\cos nt = 1$,

$$nt = 0 \quad \text{or} \quad t = 0$$

or $\cos nt = \frac{1}{2}$,

$$nt = 2\pi/3 \quad \text{or} \quad t = 2\pi/3n$$

So P first comes to rest after a time

$$t = \underline{2\pi/3n \text{ s}}$$

Summary

(1) From Newton's second law the sum of the forces acting on a particle $= m\ddot{x}$, where $\ddot{x}$ is the acceleration of the particle. If a particle moves under the action of a force k^2mx proportional to its distance from a fixed point on its line of action and directed towards that point, and a resisting force proportional to its speed squared $2km\dot{x}^2$, then Newton's second law gives

$$m\ddot{x} + 2km\dot{x}^2 + k^2mx = 0$$

where k is a constant.

This is a second order differential equation and so its solution involves two stages of integration and hence two constants of integration. These constants can be found if boundary conditions are known.

(2) The equation of motion for a particle of mass m moving in a straight line under the action of a force mn^2x directed towards a fixed point O and proportional to its distance from that fixed point, and a resisting force $2km\dot{x}$ proportional to its speed $\dot{x}$, is given by

$$m\ddot{x} + 2km\dot{x} + mn^2x = 0$$

or $$\ddot{x} + 2k\dot{x} + n^2 = 0$$

where k and n are constants.

This is a second order linear differential equation and the nature of its solution depends on the roots of the auxiliary equation

$$p^2 + 2kp + n^2 = 0$$

(a) If $k^2 > n^2$ the roots are real and the motion is heavily damped. The solution is of the form

$$x = Ae^{-kt + t\sqrt{(k^2-n^2)}} + Be^{-kt-\sqrt{(k^2-n^2)}}$$

where A and B are constants.

(b) If $k^2 = n^2$ the motion is critically damped. The solution is of the form

$$x = e^{-kt}(A + Bt)$$

(c) If $k^2 < n^2$ the roots are complex and the motion is damped harmonic motion: an oscillatory motion which diminishes with time. The solution is of the form

$$x = Ce^{-kt} \cos[t\sqrt{(n^2 - k^2)} + \varepsilon]$$

or $x = e^{-kt}[A \cos[t\sqrt{(n^2 - k^2)} + B \sin t\sqrt{(n^2 - k^2)}]$

The period $T = 2\pi/\sqrt{(n^2 - k^2)}$ and is constant.

(3) If the particle in addition to the forces described in (2) is acted upon by a further force $mf(t)$ which is a function of time then the equation of motion is

$$\frac{d^2x}{dt^2} + 2k\frac{dx}{dt} + n^2x = f(t)$$

The complementary function of this equation is the equation of damped harmonic motion. To obtain a complete solution a particular integral is found which is a solution of the equation and it is added to the complementary function. Finding the particular integral involves trying a solution of the form $f(t)$ or $tf(t)$ if $f(t)$ is already contained in the complementary function.

14
Relative motion

Objectives

The student should be able to:

(1) draw a vector triangle to represent $\boldsymbol{V}_A$, $-\boldsymbol{V}_B$ and $\boldsymbol{V}_A - \boldsymbol{V}_B$, the velocity of A relative to B, where $\boldsymbol{V}_A$ and $\boldsymbol{V}_B$ are the velocities of objects A and B,
(2) express $\boldsymbol{V}_A$, $\boldsymbol{V}_B$ and $\boldsymbol{V}_A - \boldsymbol{V}_B$ in $\boldsymbol{i}, \boldsymbol{j}$ notation,
(3) draw a scale diagram of the velocity vector triangle,
(4) express the resultant displacement vectors $\overrightarrow{B_tA_t} = \overrightarrow{B_0A_0} + (\boldsymbol{V}_A - \boldsymbol{V}_B)t$, where A_0 and B_0 are the initial positions of A and B and A_t and B_t are their positions at time t,
(5) use the dot or scalar product to find the shortest distance between A and B,
(6) use $t = (d \cos \alpha)/V$ from the velocity vector triangle to find the shortest distance between A and B,
(7) use $\overrightarrow{B_tA_t} = 0$ when interception occurs and $\overrightarrow{A_0B_0}$ is parallel to $t(\boldsymbol{V}_A - \boldsymbol{V}_B)$,
(8) draw two vector triangles to show the line of closest approach.

Relative velocity

If two cars A and B are travelling along a motorway in the same direction and with equal speeds then to an observer in one the other appears to be stationary. To an observer on the roadside both cars appear to be moving with equal velocity. The velocity of a particle is defined as its rate of displacement from a fixed point in a given frame of reference, usually taken as the earth's surface.

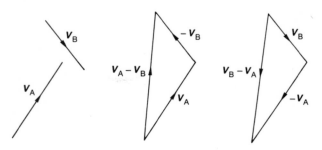

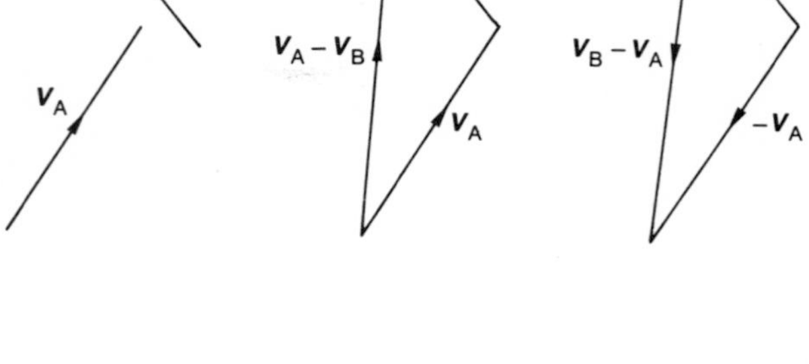

Figure 14.1

If $\boldsymbol{V}_A$ is the velocity of A and $\boldsymbol{V}_B$ is the velocity of B then $\boldsymbol{V}_A - \boldsymbol{V}_B$ is the velocity of A relative to B and $\boldsymbol{V}_B - \boldsymbol{V}_A$ is the velocity of B relative to A (Fig. 14.1) and

$$_A\boldsymbol{V}_B = \frac{d}{dt}(\overrightarrow{BA}) = \frac{d}{dt}(\boldsymbol{r}_A - \boldsymbol{r}_B)$$

Therefore

$$_A\boldsymbol{V}_B = \boldsymbol{V}_A - \boldsymbol{V}_B$$

Resultant velocity

The velocity of a plane in still air or of a boat in still water is often given in problems. The resultant velocity of the plane will be the vector sum of the wind velocity plus the plane velocity and the resultant velocity of the boat will be the vector sum of the current velocity plus the boat velocity in still water.

Common methods of solution of relative velocity problems

(a) Each velocity can be resolved into $\boldsymbol{i}$ and $\boldsymbol{j}$ components.
(b) A velocity triangle can be solved using trigonometry.
(c) A scale diagram of a velocity triangle can be constructed and the magnitude and direction of the relative velocity measured.

Methods (a) and (b) are the quickest and most accurate in examination conditions.

Example 14.1

Cyclist A is riding due east at 5 km h^{-1} and cyclist B is riding due N at 4 km h^{-1}. What is the velocity of B relative to A?

Method (a)

$$\boldsymbol{V}_A = 5\boldsymbol{i} \quad \text{and} \quad \boldsymbol{V}_B = 4\boldsymbol{j}$$

Therefore

$$\boldsymbol{V}_B - \boldsymbol{V}_A = -5\boldsymbol{i} + 4\boldsymbol{j}$$

$$|\boldsymbol{V}_B - \boldsymbol{V}_A| = \sqrt{(25+16)} = \sqrt{41} = \underline{6.4 \text{ km h}^{-1} \text{ at } \theta = \tan^{-1}(4/5)}$$

i.e. $\theta = 39°$N of W or N51°W.

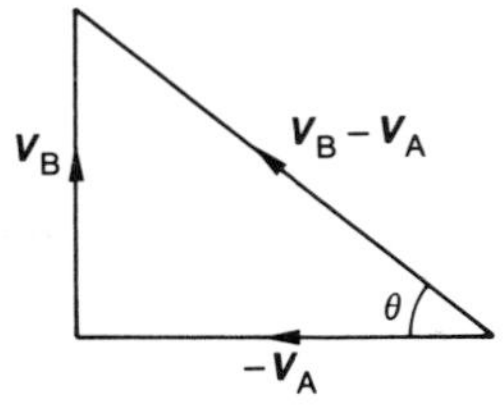

Figure 14.2

Methods (b) and (c)
Draw a scale diagram (Fig. 14.2) and measure $\boldsymbol{V}_B - \boldsymbol{V}_A$ and θ.

Example 14.2

A passenger in a car travelling N45°E at 100 km h^{-1} watches a train travelling on a straight track. The train appears to be travelling S60°W at 50 km h^{-1}. What is the true velocity of the train?

Method (a)

$$\boldsymbol{V}_c = 100\cos 45°\,\boldsymbol{i} + 100\cos 45°\,\boldsymbol{j} = 70.7\boldsymbol{i} + 70.7\boldsymbol{j} \quad (1)$$

$$\boldsymbol{V}_t - \boldsymbol{V}_c = -50\cos 30°\,\boldsymbol{i} - 50\cos 60°\,\boldsymbol{j} = -43.3\boldsymbol{i} - 25\boldsymbol{j} \quad (2)$$

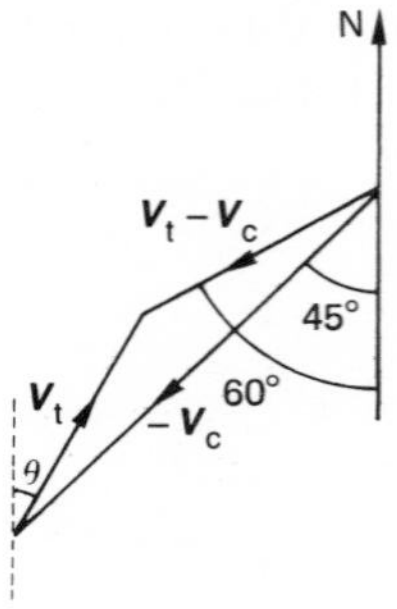

Figure 14.3

Adding equations (1) and (2),

$$\boldsymbol{V}_t - \boldsymbol{V}_c + \boldsymbol{V}_c = 27.4\boldsymbol{i} + 45.7\boldsymbol{j} \tag{3}$$

i.e. $\boldsymbol{V}_t = 27.4\boldsymbol{i} + 45.7\boldsymbol{j}$

Therefore

$$|\boldsymbol{V}_t| = \sqrt{(27.4^2 + 45.7^2)} = \underline{53.3 \text{ km h}^{-1} \text{ at } \theta = \tan^{-1}(45.7/27.4)}$$

i.e. $\theta = \text{N}31°\text{E}$.

Methods (b) and (c)

Draw a scale diagram (Fig. 14.3) and measure $\boldsymbol{V}_t$ and θ.

Relative displacement

When one moving object A is viewed from another moving object B the relative displacement of A from B at a time t depends on:
(1) the initial displacement of A, A_0, and B, B_0,
(2) the velocities of A, $\boldsymbol{V}_A$, and B, $\boldsymbol{V}_B$.
After a time t, A will be at a point A_t, where

$$\overrightarrow{OA_t} = \overrightarrow{OA_0} + t\boldsymbol{V}_A$$

and B will be at a point B_t, where

$$\overrightarrow{OB_t} = \overrightarrow{OB_0} + t\boldsymbol{V}_B$$

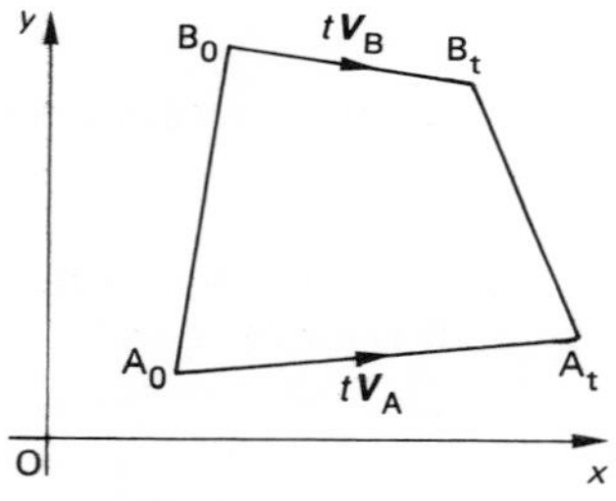

Figure 14.4

In the vector polygon $B_tA_tA_0B_0$ (Fig. 14.4),

$$\overrightarrow{B_tA_t} = \overrightarrow{B_tB_0} + \overrightarrow{B_0A_0} + \overrightarrow{A_0A_t}$$
$$= -t\boldsymbol{V}_B + \overrightarrow{B_0A_0} + t\boldsymbol{V}_A$$

i.e. $$\overrightarrow{B_tA_t} = \overrightarrow{B_0A_0} + t(\boldsymbol{V}_A - \boldsymbol{V}_B) \tag{1}$$

Therefore the displacement vector of A relative to B after a time t is the sum of the initial displacement vector and the product of t with the velocity of A relative to B.

Shortest distance apart

The relative velocities are shown in Fig. 14.5(b) while the displacements in equation (1) are represented by the vector triangle in Fig. 14.5(a).

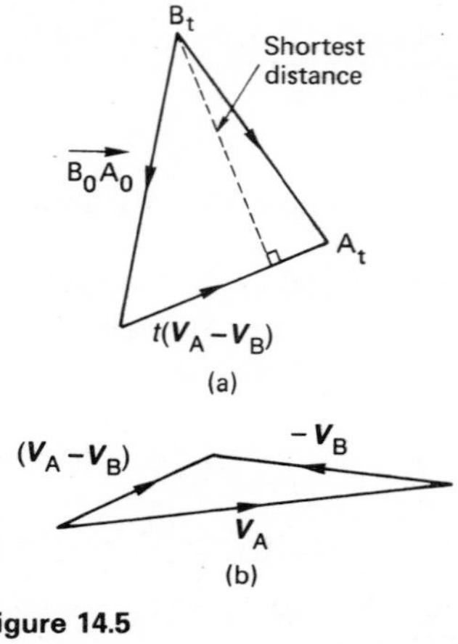

Figure 14.5

Methods of finding the shortest distance apart

(1) The shortest distance between A and B will occur when $\overrightarrow{B_tA_t}$ is at right angles to $(\boldsymbol{V}_A - \boldsymbol{V}_B)t$ so the scalar product of these two vectors is zero, i.e.

$$\overrightarrow{B_tA_t} \cdot (\boldsymbol{V}_A - \boldsymbol{V}_B)t = 0 \tag{2}$$

When $\overrightarrow{B_tA_t}$ is found for the value of time that satisfies this equation then that is the shortest distance apart.

(2) The modulus of $|\overrightarrow{B_tA_t}|$ can be differentiated with respect to time and set equal to zero again to find the time of closest approach, i.e.

$$\frac{d}{dt}|\overrightarrow{B_tA_t}| = 0$$

(3) Let $|\overrightarrow{B_0A_0}| = d$, $|\overrightarrow{B_tA_t}| = l$ and $|\boldsymbol{V}_A - \boldsymbol{V}_B|t = Vt$. By the Sine rule

$$\frac{l}{\sin\alpha} = \frac{d}{\sin\theta}$$

$$l = \frac{d\sin\alpha}{\sin\theta}$$

For minimum l, $\sin\theta = 1$ at the point N (Fig. 14.6). Therefore

$$l = d\sin\alpha$$

and $Vt = d\cos\alpha$

Therefore

$$t = \frac{d\cos\alpha}{V}$$

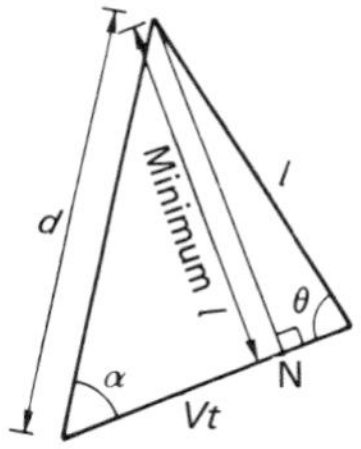

Figure 14.6

for closest approach.

Method (1) is the simplest if $\boldsymbol{i}$, $\boldsymbol{j}$ notation is used. Method (2) is very useful if $|\overrightarrow{B_tA_t}|$ is required at some other part of a problem. Method (3) is useful when the vector triangle has been drawn.

Many people find difficulty drawing the vector triangle initially until they have expressed $\boldsymbol{V}_A - \boldsymbol{V}_B$ in $\boldsymbol{i}, \boldsymbol{j}$ notation. It can be useful to express $\boldsymbol{V}_A$, $\boldsymbol{V}_B$ and $\boldsymbol{V}_A - \boldsymbol{V}_B$ in $\boldsymbol{i}, \boldsymbol{j}$ notation and then to draw the vector triangle from this information.

Interception

Interception occurs when

$$\overrightarrow{B_tA_t} = 0$$

Therefore

$$\overrightarrow{B_0A_0} = -t(\boldsymbol{V}_A - \boldsymbol{V}_B)$$

or $\overrightarrow{A_0B_0} = t(\boldsymbol{V}_A - \boldsymbol{V}_B)$

i.e. $\overrightarrow{A_0B_0}$ and $t(\boldsymbol{V}_A - \boldsymbol{V}_B)$ have the same magnitude and direction so the velocity of A relative to B is parallel to the initial displacement $\overrightarrow{A_0B_0}$ and the time t at which interception occurs is given by

$$t = \frac{\text{initial distance apart}}{\text{relative speed}}$$

Line of closest approach

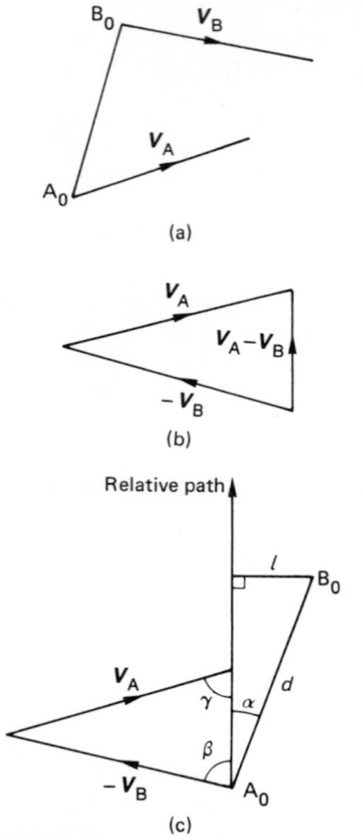

Figure 14.7

The line of closest approach is the direction in which a body with fixed speed but the ability to choose a direction would travel in order to approach as closely as possible to another body travelling with fixed velocity, i.e. chosen direction.

As before, let a particle B move with fixed velocity $\boldsymbol{V}_B$ from B_0 and let a particle A move with fixed speed $|\boldsymbol{V}_A|$ but variable direction from A_0 (Fig. 14.7(a)). The angle α is no longer fixed and the direction of $\boldsymbol{V}_A$ varies so l and γ vary. Figure 14.7(c) illustrates the general case where the relative path makes an angle β with the direction of motion of $\boldsymbol{V}_B$ and γ with the direction of motion of $\boldsymbol{V}_A$. The quantities which are constant are $|\boldsymbol{V}_A|$, $\boldsymbol{V}_B$, $\overrightarrow{A_0B_0}$ and $(\alpha+\beta)$. Since $l = d \sin\alpha$ to minimise l we must minimise $\sin\alpha$. However, $(\alpha+\beta)$ is constant so we must maximise β.

Now,

$$\frac{|\boldsymbol{V}_B|}{\sin\gamma} = \frac{|\boldsymbol{V}_A|}{\sin\beta}$$

so for maximum β

$$\sin\gamma = 1$$

$$\gamma = 90°$$

so the direction of motion of A should be perpendicular to the relative path for A to approach as close as possible to B, i.e

$$\boldsymbol{V}_A \cdot (\boldsymbol{V}_A - \boldsymbol{V}_B) = 0$$

General methods of solution of relative velocity problems

(A) Express $\boldsymbol{V}_A$ and $\boldsymbol{V}_B$ in $\boldsymbol{i}, \boldsymbol{j}$ notation and calculate $\boldsymbol{V}_A - \boldsymbol{V}_B$. Express $\boldsymbol{r}_A$ and $\boldsymbol{r}_B$ in $\boldsymbol{i}, \boldsymbol{j}$ notation and use

$$\overrightarrow{B_tA_t} = \overrightarrow{B_0A_0} + (\boldsymbol{V}_B - \boldsymbol{V}_A)t$$

Solve the scalar product

$$\overrightarrow{B_tA_t} \cdot (\boldsymbol{V}_A - \boldsymbol{V}_B)t = 0$$

for t. Use this value of t to calculate $\overrightarrow{B_tA_t}$, the distance of closest approach.

(B) Draw a velocity triangle to scale and measure $\boldsymbol{V}_A - \boldsymbol{V}_B$ in magnitude and direction. Draw a second scale diagram with the distance apart and $\boldsymbol{V}_A - \boldsymbol{V}_B$ on it from B_0 and construct the perpendicular from A_0 to the line $\boldsymbol{V}_A - \boldsymbol{V}_B$.

(C) Calculate $\boldsymbol{V}_A - \boldsymbol{V}_B$ from the $\boldsymbol{i}, \boldsymbol{j}$ notation method then draw a diagram for A_0, B_0 and $\boldsymbol{V}_A - \boldsymbol{V}_B$ from B_0 as above the calculate or construct the perpendicular distance from A_0 to the line $\boldsymbol{V}_A - \boldsymbol{V}_B$.

Example 14.3

A hovercraft is moving due east at 30 km h^{-1}. Relative to the hovercraft a speedboat is moving on a course of 210° (S30°W) at 50 km h^{-1}. Find the magnitude and direction of the velocity of the speedboat relative to an observer on a clifftop.

At 1600 hours the speedboat is 20 km due east of the hovercraft. If both craft maintain their speeds and courses find:

(a) the time at which the distance between them is least,
(b) their actual distance apart at this instant,
(c) the time at which the speedboat is due south of the hovercraft.

Method (A)
Express $\boldsymbol{V}_s - \boldsymbol{V}_h$ and $\boldsymbol{V}_h$ in $\boldsymbol{i}, \boldsymbol{j}$ notation and add them

$$\boldsymbol{V}_s - \boldsymbol{V}_h = -50 \sin 30° \, \boldsymbol{i} - 50 \cos 30° \, \boldsymbol{j}$$

$$\boldsymbol{V}_h = 30\boldsymbol{i}$$

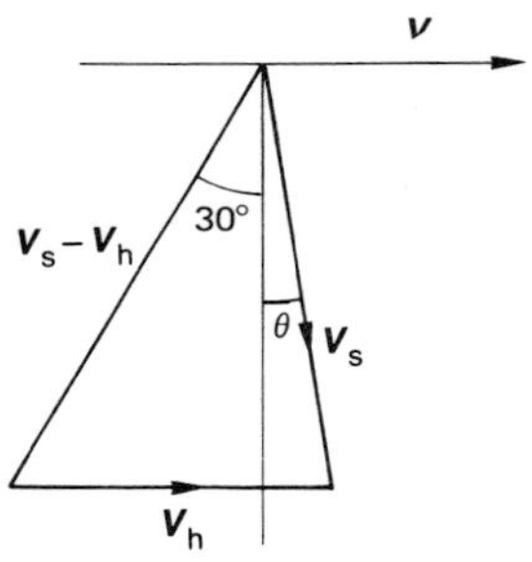

Figure 14.8

Therefore

$$\boldsymbol{V}_s = \boldsymbol{V}_s - \boldsymbol{V}_h + \boldsymbol{V}_h = 5\boldsymbol{i} - 25\sqrt{3}\boldsymbol{j}$$

$$|\boldsymbol{V}_s| = \sqrt{(5^2 + 3 \times 25^2)}$$

$$= 43.6 \text{ km h}^{-1} \text{ at } \tan^{-1}(5/25\sqrt{3}) \text{ E of S}$$

i.e. $|\boldsymbol{V}_s| = \underline{43.6 \text{ km h}^{-1} \text{ at } 173.4°}$

Method (B)
A scale diagram can be drawn as in Fig. 14.8 and $\boldsymbol{V}_s$ can be measured in magnitude and direction on the velocity vector triangle.

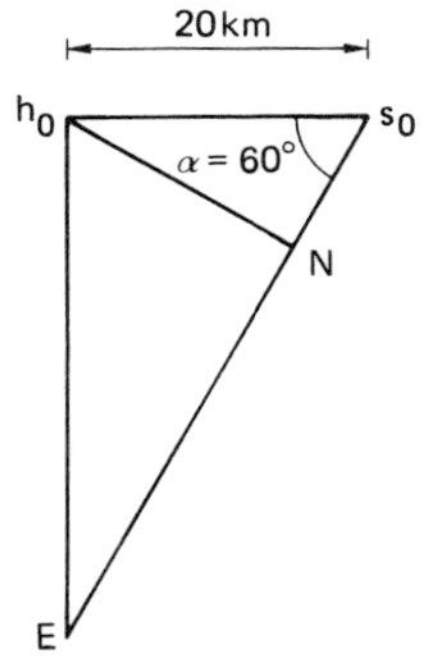

Figure 14.9

(a) A second diagram, Fig. 14.9, should now be drawn showing the initial distance between the craft and their relative velocity then their nearest distance apart, h_0N is found from

$$t = \frac{d \cos \alpha}{V}$$

$$t = \frac{h_0 s_0 \cos 60°}{50} = \frac{20 \cos 60°}{50}$$

i.e. $t = 0.2 \text{ h} = 12 \text{ minutes}$

Hence the time at which the distance between them is least is <u>1612 h</u>.
(b) The distance apart at 1612 h is given by

$$h_0N = 20 \sin 60° = \underline{17.32 \text{ km}}$$

The answers to (a) and (b) can be measured on Fig. 14.9 if it is drawn accurately to scale.

(c) The speedboat is due south at E, $s_0E = 20/(\cos 60°)$. Therefore

$$\text{time to reach E} = \frac{\text{distance } s_0E}{\text{relative velocity}} = \frac{20 \times 60}{\cos 60° \times 50}$$

i.e. time to reach E = 48 minutes

Hence the time at which the speedboat is due south of the hovercraft is 1648 h.

In this problem either method is suitable for calculating $\boldsymbol{V}_s$. A scale diagram is the simplest method for the distance of closest approach. Method (A) could be used to find the time as follows.

$$\overrightarrow{h_0s_0} = 20\boldsymbol{i}$$

$$\overrightarrow{h_ts_t} = \overrightarrow{h_0s_0} + (\boldsymbol{V}_s - \boldsymbol{V}_h)t$$

Therefore

$$\overrightarrow{h_ts_t} = 20\boldsymbol{i} + (-50 \sin 30°\, \boldsymbol{i} - 50 \cos 30°\, \boldsymbol{j})t$$

Closest approach occurs when

$$\overrightarrow{h_ts_t} \cdot (\boldsymbol{V}_s - \boldsymbol{V}_h)t = 0$$

Therefore

$$0 = [\boldsymbol{i}(20 - 50t \sin 30°) + \boldsymbol{j}(-50t \cos 30°)] \cdot [\boldsymbol{i}(-50t \sin 30°) + \boldsymbol{j}(-50t \cos 30°)]$$

$$= 1000 \times \tfrac{1}{2} + 50^2 t \times \tfrac{1}{4} + 50^2 t \times \tfrac{3}{4}$$

Therefore

$$t = \tfrac{500}{2500} = 0.2 \text{ h} = 12 \text{ minutes}$$

as in Method (3).

Example 14.4

At time $t = 0$ a ship A is at the point O and a ship B is at the point with position vector $10\boldsymbol{j}$ nautical miles referred to O. The velocities of the two ships are constant. Ship A sails at 17 knots, where 1 knot is 1 nautical mile per hour, in the direction of the vector $8\boldsymbol{i} + 15\boldsymbol{j}$ and ship B sails at 15 knots in the direction of the vector $3\boldsymbol{i} + 4\boldsymbol{j}$. Write down:

(a) the velocity vector of each ship,
(b) the velocity of B relative to A,
(c) the position vector of B relative to A at time t hours.

Given that the visibility is 5 nautical miles, show that the ships are within sight of each other for $\sqrt{6}$ hours. (UL J83)

(a) See Fig. 14.10. Calculate the unit vectors $\hat{\boldsymbol{V}}_A$ and $\hat{\boldsymbol{V}}_B$ and multiply by the magnitudes V_A and V_B

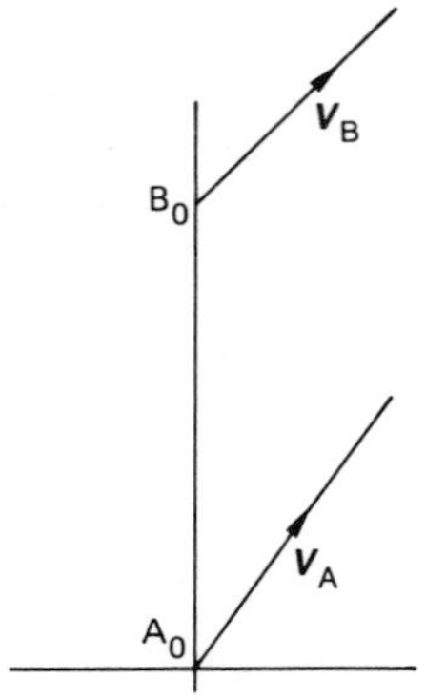

Figure 14.10

$$\hat{\boldsymbol{V}}_A = \tfrac{8}{17}\boldsymbol{i} + \tfrac{15}{17}\boldsymbol{j}$$

$$\boldsymbol{V}_A = 17\hat{\boldsymbol{V}}_A = \underline{8\boldsymbol{i} + 15\boldsymbol{j}}$$

Therefore

$$\hat{\boldsymbol{V}}_B = \tfrac{3}{5}\boldsymbol{i} + \tfrac{4}{5}\boldsymbol{j}$$

$$\boldsymbol{V}_B = 15\hat{\boldsymbol{V}}_B = \underline{9\boldsymbol{i} + 12\boldsymbol{j}}$$

Therefore

(b) $\boldsymbol{V}_B - \boldsymbol{V}_A = 9\boldsymbol{i} + 12\boldsymbol{j} - 8\boldsymbol{i} - 15\boldsymbol{j} = \underline{\boldsymbol{i} - 3\boldsymbol{j}}$

(c) $\overrightarrow{A_tB_t} = \overrightarrow{A_0B_0} + (\boldsymbol{V}_B - \boldsymbol{V}_A)t$

Therefore

$$\overrightarrow{A_tB_t} = 10\boldsymbol{j} + (\boldsymbol{i} - 3\boldsymbol{j})t = \underline{t\boldsymbol{i} + (10 - 3t)\boldsymbol{j}}$$

Now $|\overrightarrow{A_tB_t}|$ is 5 nautical miles.

Therefore

$$|\overrightarrow{A_tB_t}|^2 = 25 = t^2 + (10 - 3t)^2$$

$$2t^2 - 12t + 15 = 0$$

i.e. $t = \dfrac{12 \pm \sqrt{24}}{4}$

The length of time for visibility will be the difference between these two limits, so

$$t_1 - t_2 = \left(\frac{12 + \sqrt{24}}{4}\right) - \left(\frac{12 - \sqrt{24}}{4}\right) = \sqrt{6}\ \text{h}$$

Problem 14.1

Find the time of closest approach of the two ships in Example 14.4 above.

Use $\overrightarrow{A_tB_t} \cdot (\boldsymbol{V}_B - \boldsymbol{V}_A)t = 0$ to solve for t and find $t = 3$ h.

Note Both Example 14.4 and Problem 14.1 were solved very simply by method (A) as they were given in ***i, j*** notation.

Example 14.5

A river flows at a constant speed of 5 ms^{-1} between straight parallel banks which are 240 m apart. A boat crosses the river travelling relative to the water at a constant speed of 12 m s^{-1}. A man cycles at a constant speed of 4 m s^{-1} along the edge of one bank of the river in the direction opposite to the direction of flow of the river. At the instant when the boat leaves a point O on the opposite bank, the cyclist is 80 m downstream of O. The boat is steered relative to the water in a direction perpendicular to the banks. Taking $\boldsymbol{i}$ and $\boldsymbol{j}$ to be perpendicular horizontal unit vectors downstream and across the river from O respectively, express, in terms of $\boldsymbol{i}$ and $\boldsymbol{j}$, the velocities and the position vectors relative to O of the boat and the cyclist t seconds after the boat leaves O. Hence, or otherwise, calculate the time when the distance between the boat and the cyclist is least, giving this least distance.

If, instead, the boat were to be steered so that it crosses the river from O to a point on the other bank directly opposite to O, show that this crossing would take approximately 22 seconds. (UL J83)

On the river the velocity of the boat

$$\boldsymbol{V}_B = 5\boldsymbol{i} + 12\boldsymbol{j}$$

from Fig. 14.11(b) and the velocity of the cyclist

$$\boldsymbol{V}_C = -4\boldsymbol{i}$$

Therefore the distance of the cyclist from O,

$$\overrightarrow{OC_t} = (80-4t)\boldsymbol{i} + 240\boldsymbol{j}$$

and the distance of the boat from O,

$$\overrightarrow{OB_t} = 5t\boldsymbol{i} + 12t\boldsymbol{j}$$

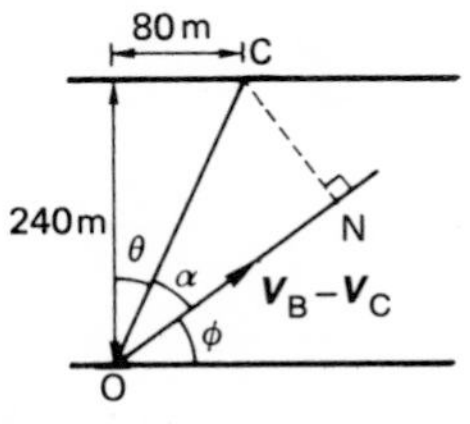

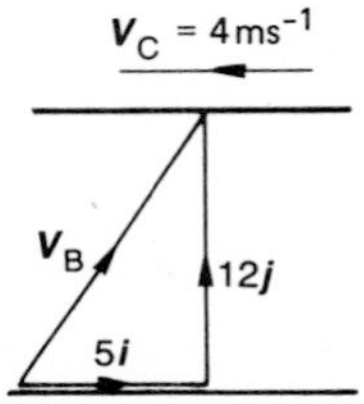

Figure 14.11

The velocity of the boat relative to the cyclist,

$$\boldsymbol{V}_B - \boldsymbol{V}_C = 9\boldsymbol{i} + 12\boldsymbol{j}$$

The displacement vector from the cyclist to the boat,

$$\overrightarrow{C_tB_t} = \overrightarrow{OB_t} - \overrightarrow{OC_t} = 5t\boldsymbol{i} + 12t\boldsymbol{j} - (80-4t)\boldsymbol{i} - 240\boldsymbol{j}$$

i.e. $\overrightarrow{C_tB_t} = (9t-80)\boldsymbol{i} + (12t-240)\boldsymbol{j}$

The least distance occurs when

$$\overrightarrow{C_tB_t} \cdot (\boldsymbol{V}_B - \boldsymbol{V}_C)t = 0$$

Therefore

$$[(9t-80)\boldsymbol{i} + (12t-240)\boldsymbol{j}] \cdot [9\boldsymbol{i} + 12\boldsymbol{j}] = 0$$

$$81t - 9\times 80 + 144t - 240\times 12 = 0$$

i.e. $t = \underline{16 \text{ s}}$

Then

$$\overrightarrow{C_tB_t} = (9\times 16-80)\boldsymbol{i} + (12\times 16-240)\boldsymbol{j} = 64\boldsymbol{i} - 48\boldsymbol{j}$$

i.e. $|\overrightarrow{C_tB_t}| = \underline{80 \text{ m}}$

The problem could be solved by methods (B) or (C) using the diagram in Fig. 14.11(a) and calculating $\theta = 18.43°$, $\phi = 53.1°$, and $\alpha = 18.49°$ and then CN = 80 m.

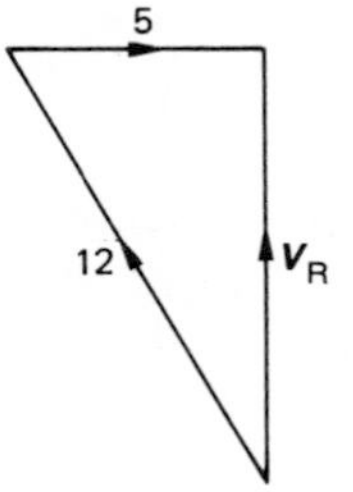

Figure 14.12

In the second part the boat is steered so that the resultant velocity is in the $\boldsymbol{j}$-direction as shown in Fig. 14.12.

$$\boldsymbol{V}_R = \sqrt{(12^2 - 5^2)} = 10.9 \text{ km h}^{-1}$$

$$\text{time} = \frac{\text{distance}}{\text{velocity}} = \frac{240}{10.9} = 22 \text{ s}$$

Example 14.6

A swimmer B sets off due east across a lake at 10 m s^{-1}. He is 60 m due north of a second swimmer A whose maximum speed is 6 m s^{-1}. Show that swimmer A cannot catch swimmer B and find his distance of closest approach.

Swimmer A cannot catch swimmer B because even when travelling due east

$$\boldsymbol{V}_B - \boldsymbol{V}_A = 4 \text{ m s}^{-1}$$

Swimmer A will come as close as possible to swimmer B when $\boldsymbol{V}_A$ is perpendicular to $\boldsymbol{V}_A - \boldsymbol{V}_B$ as in Fig. 14.13(a). Then from Fig. 14.13(b)

$$\sin \beta = 6/10 = 3/5 = 0.6$$

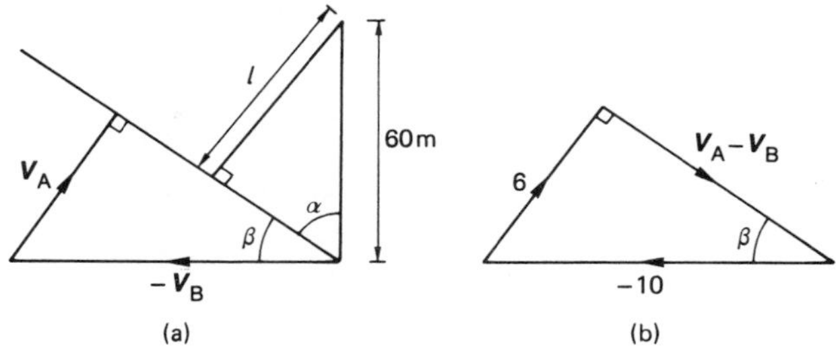

Figure 14.13

Hence, from Fig. 14.13(a), the shortest distance l is given by

$$l = 60 \cos \beta = 60 \times 4/5 = \underline{48 \text{ m}}$$

Problem 14.2

A ship A detects on her radar a ship B 20 km due east of A. Ship B is sailing at 20 km h^{-1} on a course of 150° and ship A is sailing on a course of $(90+\theta)°$ at 40 km h^{-1}. Using vectors $\boldsymbol{i}$ and $\boldsymbol{j}$ pointing east and north, find the velocity of A relative to B. Show that the ships will meet if θ is the acute angle $\sin^{-1}(\sqrt{3}/4)$ and that this will occur after $(1+\sqrt{13})/12$ h.

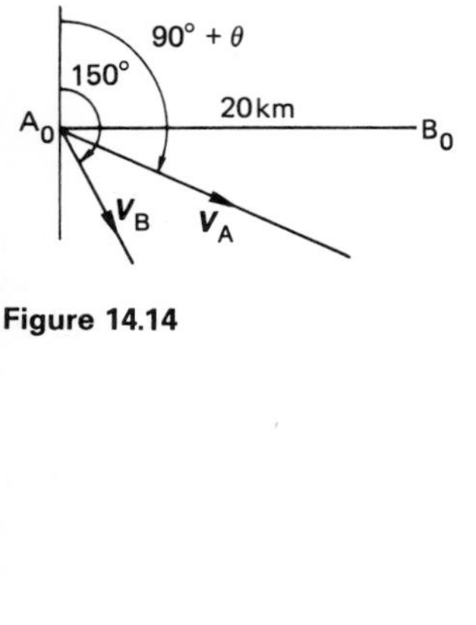

Figure 14.14

(1) Draw a diagram showing the distances apart of A and B at $t = 0$ s and the directions of the velocities $\boldsymbol{V}_A$ and $\boldsymbol{V}_B$ (Fig. 14.14).

(2) Show that

$$\boldsymbol{V}_A = 40 \cos \theta\, \boldsymbol{i} - 40 \sin \theta\, \boldsymbol{j}$$

$$\boldsymbol{V}_B = 20 \cos 60°\, \boldsymbol{i} - 20 \sin 60°\, \boldsymbol{j}$$

and $\boldsymbol{V}_A - \boldsymbol{V}_B = (40 \cos \theta - 10)\boldsymbol{i} + (10\sqrt{3} - 40 \sin \theta)\boldsymbol{j}$

(3) $\overrightarrow{B_0A_0} = -10\boldsymbol{i}$

Therefore show that

$$\overrightarrow{B_tA_t} = (-10 + 40 \cos \theta\, t - 10t)\boldsymbol{i} + (10\sqrt{3} - 40 \sin \theta)t\boldsymbol{j}$$

(4) When $\overrightarrow{B_tA_t} = 0$ the ships collide so use this as follows: set the coefficient of $\boldsymbol{j}$ to zero to show that

$$\sin \theta = \sqrt{3}/4$$

and set the coefficient of $\boldsymbol{i}$ to zero to show that

$$t = 1/(\sqrt{13} - 1) = (1 + \sqrt{13})/12 \text{ h}$$

There is no need to draw the vector triangle for this problem and it is more easily solved using method (A). Interception occurs when $\boldsymbol{V}_A - \boldsymbol{V}_B$ is parallel to $\overline{A_0B_0}$ and the problem could be solved by method (C) using this fact.

Summary

Note Several methods are available to solve relative velocity problems.

(1) The velocities $\boldsymbol{V}_A$ and $\boldsymbol{V}_B$ of the objects A and B can be expressed in $\boldsymbol{i}, \boldsymbol{j}$ notation. The velocity of A relative to B, $\boldsymbol{V}_A - \boldsymbol{V}_B$, can be calculated. Knowing the initial positions A_0 and B_0, the relative displacement at a time t can be found from

$$\overrightarrow{B_tA_t} = \overrightarrow{B_0A_0} + t(\boldsymbol{V}_A - \boldsymbol{V}_B) \qquad (1)$$

The shortest distance apart occurs when

$$\overrightarrow{B_tA_t} \cdot (\boldsymbol{V}_A - \boldsymbol{V}_B)t = 0$$

This can be used to find the time corresponding to this distance. Substitution in equation (1) then gives the distance.

Interception occurs when $\overrightarrow{B_tA_t} = 0$, i.e.

$$\overrightarrow{A_0B_0} = t(\boldsymbol{V}_A - \boldsymbol{V}_B)$$

and this can be used to find the time of interception.

The line of closest approach is given by

$$\boldsymbol{V}_A \cdot (\boldsymbol{V}_A - \boldsymbol{V}_B) = 0$$

for A to B, where A has fixed speed but may vary direction and B has fixed velocity, and occurs where A chooses the direction to be perpendicular to the relative path.

(2) A velocity triangle can be drawn consisting of $\boldsymbol{V}_A$, $-\boldsymbol{V}_B$ and $\boldsymbol{V}_A - \boldsymbol{V}_B$ from which $\boldsymbol{V}_A - \boldsymbol{V}_B$ can be calculated. The time of closest approach can be found from

$$t = \frac{d \cos \alpha}{V}$$

Interception occurs when $t(\boldsymbol{V}_A - \boldsymbol{V}_B)$ is parallel to $\overrightarrow{A_0B_0}$.

(3) The diagram in method (2) can be drawn to scale so that $\boldsymbol{V}_A - \boldsymbol{V}_B$ can be measured in magnitude and direction. A second diagram can be drawn to scale comprising the points A_0 and B_0 and the line $t(\boldsymbol{V}_A - \boldsymbol{V}_B)$ from B_0. The perpendicular from A_0 to the line $t(\boldsymbol{V}_A - \boldsymbol{V}_B)$ can be constructed and measured.

(4) The simplest method depends on the question and can be a combination, e.g. calculating $\boldsymbol{V}_A - \boldsymbol{V}_B$ from method (1), then drawing a diagram and using $t = (d \cos \alpha)/V$ to calculate t from method (2).

15
Centres of gravity and mass

Objectives

The student should be able to:

(1) define the centre of gravity of a body,
(2) define the centre of mass of a body,
(3) state the position vectors of the centre of mass and centre of gravity of a body and the conditions under which they are coincident,
(4) define the centroid of a body,
(5) calculate the position of the centre of gravity for composite bodies using the principle of moments,
(6) derive the position of the centre of gravity of some standard bodies,
(7) compare situations in which a body may topple or slide.

Centre of gravity

The centre of gravity of a body is that point from which the weight of the body may be considered to be acting. A solid body may be considered to be made of a set of particles having masses $m_1, m_2, m_3, \ldots, m_n$ with position vectors $\boldsymbol{r}_1, \boldsymbol{r}_2, \boldsymbol{r}_3, \ldots, \boldsymbol{r}_n$, where

$$\boldsymbol{r}_1 = x_1\boldsymbol{i} + y_1\boldsymbol{j}$$

$$\boldsymbol{r}_2 = x_2\boldsymbol{i} + y_2\boldsymbol{j}$$

etc. The weight of the body is the algebraic sum of the weight of its constituent particles

$$W = \sum_{i=1}^{i=n} m_i g$$

and acts vertically downwards through a fixed point called the centre of gravity of the body. The sum of the moments of the weights of the constituent particles of the body about any axis equals the moment of the resultant weight about that axis.

Supposing the (x, y) plane is horizontal so that the weights act perpendicularly to it (Fig. 15.1). Then taking moments about Oy,

$$(m_1 + m_2 + m_3 + \ldots + m_n)g\bar{x}$$

$$= m_1gx_1 + m_2gx_2 + m_3gx_3 + \ldots + m_ngx_n$$

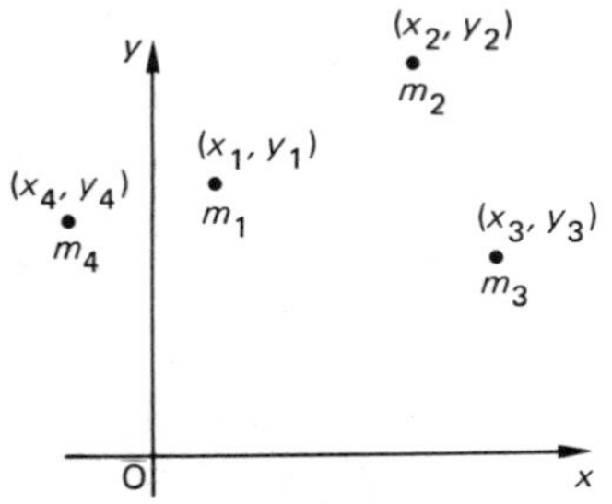

Figure 15.1

i.e. $\bar{x}\sum_i m_i = \sum_i m_i x_i$

or $$\bar{x} = \frac{\Sigma_i m_i x_i}{\Sigma_i m_i}$$

Similarly taking moments about Ox,

$$\bar{y} = \frac{\Sigma_i m_i y_i}{\Sigma_i m_i}$$

and the position vector of the centre of gravity G of the body is $\bar{x}\boldsymbol{i} + \bar{y}\boldsymbol{j}$, where $\boldsymbol{i}$ and $\boldsymbol{j}$ are unit vectors along Ox and Oy respectively and i is a subscript denoting which particle from 1 to n is under consideration.

Centre of mass

The centre of mass of a system is defined as the point with position vector

$$\boldsymbol{r}_{\mathrm{m}} = \frac{\Sigma_i m_i \boldsymbol{r}_i}{\Sigma_i m_i}$$

so the centre of mass and the centre of gravity are coincident in a uniform gravitational field. The centroid of a body is the geometric centre, i.e. the point about which the area for a lamina or the volume for a solid is uniformly distributed.

Example 15.1

Find the centre of gravity of masses of 2, 5 and 8 kg at position vectors $2\boldsymbol{i}+\boldsymbol{j}$, $3\boldsymbol{i}-4\boldsymbol{j}$ and $-6\boldsymbol{i}+\boldsymbol{j}$ respectively.

$$\bar{x} = \frac{\Sigma mx}{\Sigma m} = \frac{(2\times 2)+(5\times 3)-(8\times 6)}{15} = \frac{-29}{15}$$

$$\bar{y} = \frac{\Sigma my}{\Sigma m} = \frac{(2\times 1)-(5\times 4)+(8\times 1)}{15} = \frac{-10}{15}$$

Therefore G is at position vector $\underline{\frac{-29}{15}\boldsymbol{i}\frac{-10}{15}\boldsymbol{j}}$.

Uniform bodies

A uniform body has the same mass per unit area, length or volume over its entire body so it will have mass equally distributed about any line of symmetry, therefore the centre of gravity of a uniform body lies on each line of symmetry of that body. Hence the centre of gravity of a uniform rod lies at its midpoint, of a circle at its centre and of a parallelogram at the intersection of the diagonals.

Consider a *uniform triangular lamina* ABC (Fig. 15.2). It may be divided into a series of rods parallel to the side BC. Each rod is uniform so its centre of gravity lies at its midpoint on the median AM and therefore the centre of gravity of the triangular lamina must lie on the line joining the midpoints of the rod. Similarly for•rods parallel to AC the centre of gravity must lie

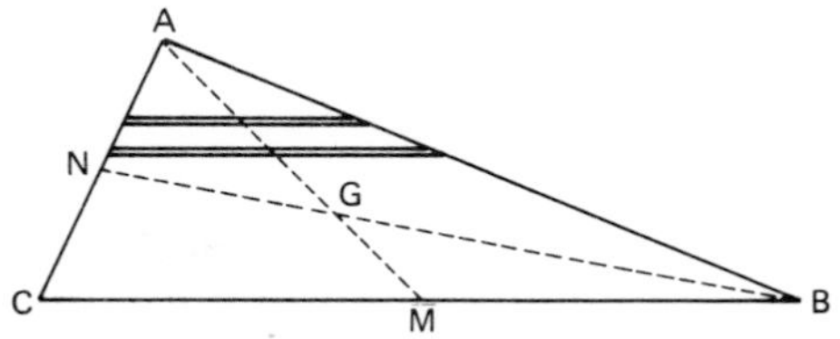

Figure 15.2

on the median BN. Hence the centre of gravity of a uniform triangular lamina is at the *intersection of its medians* (two-thirds of the length of each from a vertex).

Composite bodies

If a body is made up of several parts, each of which has a known weight and centre of gravity, then from the principle of moments

> moment of the weight of the whole body about a given axis = sum of the moments of the weight of the composite parts of the body about the same axis

If part of a body is removed

> moment of the weight of the remainder about a given axis = (moment of the weight of the whole body − moment of the weight of the part removed) about the axis

Example 15.2

Consider a uniform lamina made up of a rectangle ABDE, where AB = 4 m, and two triangles BCD and AEF, where BC = AF = 4 m and FC = 8 m. Find the position of the centre of gravity of the lamina.

By symmetry the centre of gravity lies on a line joining the midpoints of AB and ED, i.e. 4 m from FY (Fig. 15.3). Let w = weight per unit area. Then the following table can be derived.

Body	Weight	Distance of centre of gravity from FC
Rectangle, ABDE	$4\sqrt{12}w$	$\sqrt{12}/2$ (by intersection of the diagonals)
Triangle, AEF	$\sqrt{12}w$	$\sqrt{12}/3$ (BG : GM = 2 : 1, so by similar triangles BOG and BDM, OD = $\sqrt{12}/3$)
Triangle, BCD	$\sqrt{12}w$	$\sqrt{12}/3$ (BO : OD = 2 : 1, therefore OD = $\sqrt{12}/3$)
Whole, ABCF	$6\sqrt{12}w$	$\bar{y}$

moment of whole = sum of moments of the parts

Taking moments about FC,

$$6\sqrt{12}w\bar{y} = 4\sqrt{2}\times\frac{\sqrt{12}}{2}w + 2\times\sqrt{12}\times\frac{\sqrt{12}}{3}w$$

$$\underline{\bar{y} = \frac{4\sqrt{12}}{9}\text{ m from FC}}$$

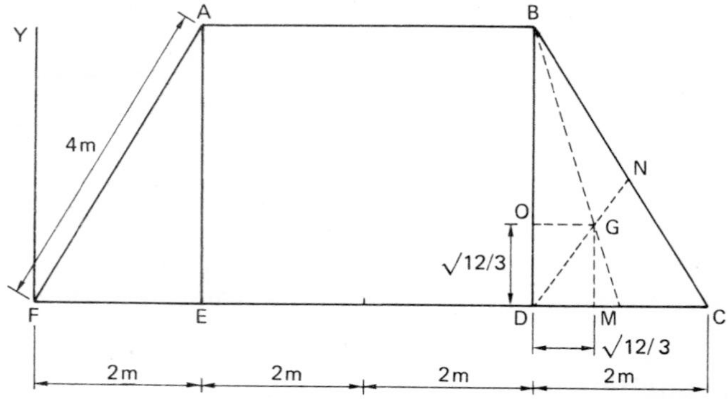

Figure 15.3

Example 15.3

A frustum is cut from a solid right circular cone of height h by a plane parallel to its base and distance $2h/3$ from it. Find the distance of the centre of gravity from the base.

By symmetry all the centres of gravity lie on the axis VO of the cone (Fig. 15.4).

$$VG_1=\frac{3}{4}\times\frac{h}{3}=\frac{h}{4} \quad \text{and} \quad VG=\frac{3h}{4} \qquad \text{(proof follows)}$$

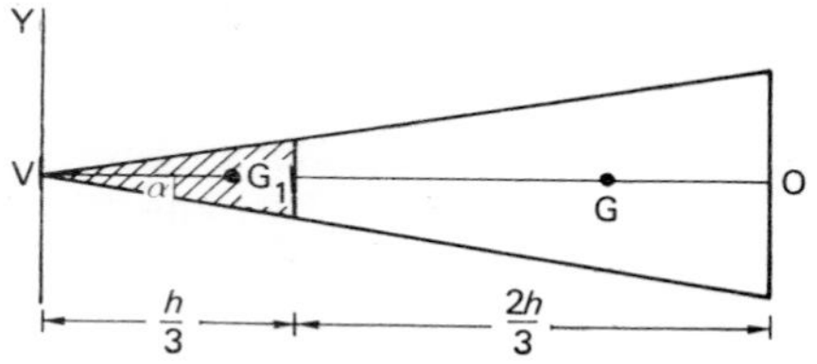

Figure 15.4

Let w = weight per unit volume. Then the following table can be derived.

Body	Weight	Distance of centre of gravity from VY	Relative weight
Whole cone	$\pi w\frac{1}{3}h^2\tan^2\alpha\, h$	$\frac{3h}{4}$	27
Small cone	$\pi w\frac{1}{3}\frac{h^2}{9}\tan^2\alpha\frac{h}{3}$	$\frac{3}{4}\times\frac{h}{3}=\frac{h}{4}$	1
Remainder	$\pi w\frac{1}{3}\frac{26h^2}{27}\tan^2\alpha\, h$	$\bar{x}$	26

moment of remainder
= moment of whole − moment of part removed

Taking moments about VY,

$$26\bar{x}=27\times\frac{3h}{4}-1\times\frac{h}{4}$$

$$\bar{x}=\underline{\frac{20}{26}h}$$

Centre of gravity by integration

A body may be divided into a very large number of very small parts whose weights and centres of gravity are known. Each elemental part has the same shape reflecting the shape of the whole body. The position of the centre of gravity of the body can be found by taking moments about suitable axes and the summation of the moments found by integration.
Some standard results follow.

Uniform lamina in the form of a sector of a circle

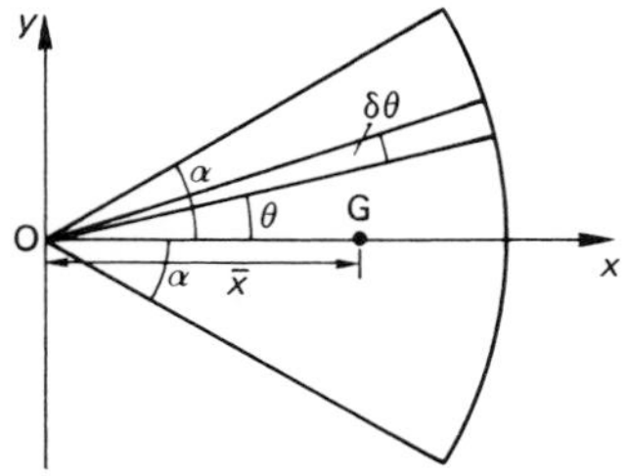

Figure 15.5

Let the lamina be of radius r, subtending an angle of 2α at the centre (Fig. 15.5). The centre of gravity lies on the line Ox by symmetry. Divide the lamina into a set of sectors.

A sector inclined at an angle θ to O subtends an angle $\delta\theta$ at O. It is approximately a triangle with centre of gravity $2r/3$ from O. Let w = weight per unit area. Then the following table can be derived.

Body	Weight	Distance of centre of gravity from OY
Whole sector	$w \times \pi r^2 \times \frac{\alpha}{\pi}$	$\bar{x}$
Elemental sector	$w \times \pi r^2 \times \frac{\delta\theta}{2\pi}$	$\frac{2r}{3} \cos\theta$

Taking moments about OY,

$$w\pi r^2 \frac{\alpha}{\pi} \bar{x} = \sum \left(w\pi r^2 \frac{\delta\theta}{2\pi} \cos\theta \frac{2r}{3} \right)$$

In the limit as $\delta\theta \to 0$,

$$\frac{\alpha}{\pi} \bar{x} = \int_{-\alpha}^{\alpha} \frac{r}{3\pi} \cos\theta \, d\theta$$

$$\alpha\bar{x} = \frac{r}{3} [\sin\theta]_{-\alpha}^{\alpha}$$

i.e. $$\bar{x} = \frac{2r\sin\alpha}{3\alpha}$$

If $\alpha = \pi/2$, i.e. for a semicircle,

$$\bar{x} = \frac{4r}{3\pi}$$

Uniform solid hemisphere

Let the hemisphere be of radius r (Fig. 15.6). The centre of gravity lies on the line Ox by symmetry. Divide the hemisphere into a set of discs where each disc is of thickness δ_2.

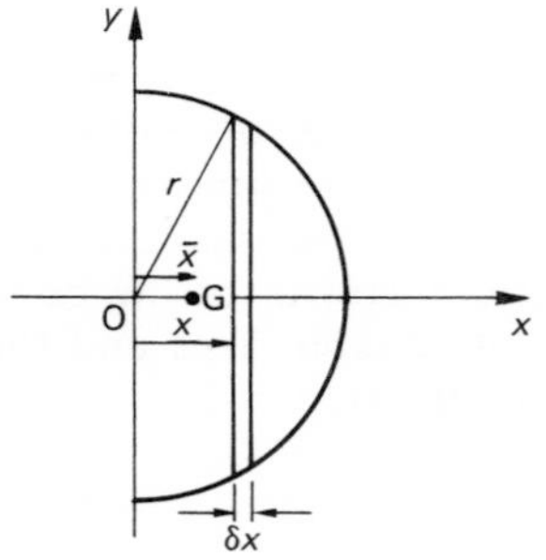

Figure 15.6

Consider the disc a distance x from the line O_2. Let w = weight per unit volume. Then

Body	Weight	Distance of centre of gravity from OY
Hemisphere	$\frac{2}{3}\pi r^3 w$	$\bar{x}$
Disc	$\doteqdot \pi w(r^2 - x^2)\delta x$	x

Taking moments about OY,

$$w(\tfrac{2}{3}\pi r^2 \bar{x}) = \sum w\pi(r^2 - x^2)x\,\delta x$$

In the limit as $\delta x \to 0$,

$$\tfrac{2}{3}r^3\bar{x} = \int_0^r (r^2 x - x^3)\,dx = \left[\frac{r^2x^2}{2} - \frac{x^4}{4}\right]_0^r$$

i.e. $\frac{2}{3}r^3\bar{x} = \dfrac{r^4}{4}$

Therefore

$$\bar{x} = \frac{3r}{8} \text{ from the base}$$

Uniform solid tetrahedron

Let the tretrahedron be of height h with a base area of A (Fig. 15.7). The centre of gravity lies on the line joining the vertex O to the centroid of the base by symmetry so this is chosen as the x-axis.

Divide the tetrahedron into a set of triangular laminas each with its plane parallel to the base, each of thickness δx and a distance x from the base. Let w = weight per unit volume. From similar triangles, the area of the elemental triangular lamina

$$A' = A\frac{x^2}{h^2}$$

Then the following table can be derived where w is the weight per unit volume.

Body	Weight	Distance of centre of gravity from OY
Tetrahedron	$w\frac{1}{3}Ah$	$\bar{x}$
Triangular lamina	$w\frac{Ax^2}{h^2}\delta x$	x

Taking moments about OY,

$$w\frac{1}{3}Ah\bar{x} = \sum\left(w\frac{Ax^2}{h^2}x\,\delta x\right)$$

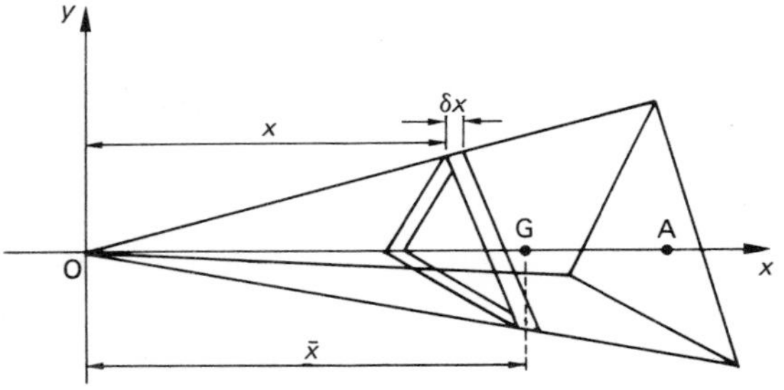

Figure 15.7

In the limit as $\delta x \to 0$,

$$\frac{h\bar{x}}{3} = \int_0^h \frac{x^3}{h^2}\,dx = \frac{1}{h^2}\left[\frac{x^4}{4}\right]_0^h$$

i.e. $\dfrac{h\bar{x}}{3} = \dfrac{h^2}{4}$

Therefore

$$\bar{x} = \frac{3h}{4} \text{ from the vertex}$$

Note A pyramid can be split into tetrahedrons with a common vertex and as the number of sides of the base of a pyramid increases to infinity then the pyramid tends to become a cone. Hence the result can be applied to *a pyramid or a cone.*

Thin hollow hemisphere

Let the hemisphere be of radius r (Fig. 15.8). The centre of gravity lies on Oy by symmetry.

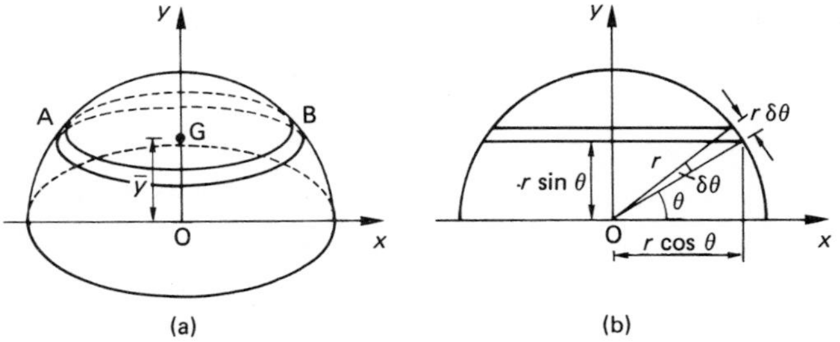

Figure 15.8

Divide the hemisphere into a set of rings parallel to the base AB as in Fig. 15.8(a). Each ring is approximately a cylinder of thickness $r\,\delta\theta$ and radius $r\cos\theta$ so its surface area is $2\pi r^2 \cos\theta\,\delta\theta$. Let w = weight per unit area. Then the following table can be derived.

Body	Weight	Distance of centre of gravity from OY
Uniform hollow hemisphere	$2\pi r^2 w$	$\bar{y}$
Ring element	$2\pi r^2 \cos\theta\,\delta\theta\,w$	$r\sin\theta$

Taking moments about Ox,

$$2\pi r^2 \bar{x} w = \sum (2\pi r^2 \cos\theta\, \delta\theta\, r \sin\theta)$$

In the limit as $\delta\theta \to 0$,

$$2\pi r^2 w\bar{w} = 2\pi w r^3 \int_0^{\pi/2} \sin\theta \cos\theta \, \mathrm{d}\theta$$

$$= 2\pi w r^3 \left[\frac{\sin^2\theta}{2}\right]_0^{\pi/2}$$

i.e. $2\pi r^2 w\bar{x} = \pi w r^3$

Therefore

$$\bar{x} = \frac{r}{2} \text{ from the base of a hollow uniform hemisphere}$$

Note The technique used in deriving the centre of gravity of standard bodies can be applied to other figures. The elemental section shown must be capable of summation to the whole body so it must reflect the symmetry of the whole body.

Example 15.4

A uniform thin rod is bent into the form of an arc of a circle of radius r subtending an angle 2α at the centre of the circle. Find the position of its centre of gravity.

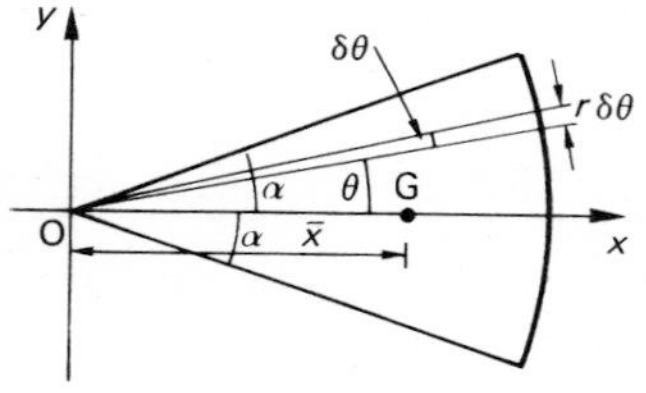

Figure 15.9

The centre of gravity lies on the line Ox by symmetry (Fig. 15.9). Let w = weight per unit length of the rod. Divide the rod into a set of small arcs δx subtending an angle $\delta\theta$ at the centre O and displaced an angle θ from the centre as shown in the figure. Then the following table can be derived.

Body	Weight	Distance of centre of gravity from OY
Whole arc	$2\alpha r w$	$\bar{x}$
Elemental arc	$r\,\delta\theta\, w$	$r\cos\theta$

Taking moments about Oy,

$$2\alpha r w\bar{x} = \sum (r\delta\theta\, w r \cos\theta)$$

In the limit as $\delta\theta \to 0$,

$$2\alpha r w\bar{x} = \int_{-\alpha}^{\alpha} r^2 w \cos\theta \, \mathrm{d}\theta$$

$$2\alpha\bar{x} = r[\sin\theta]_{-\alpha}^{\alpha} = 2r\sin\alpha$$

Therefore

$$\bar{x} = \frac{r\sin\alpha}{\alpha}$$

Note For a semicircular arc $\alpha = \pi/2$. Therefore

$$\bar{x} = \frac{2r}{\pi}$$

Bodies hanging freely from a point

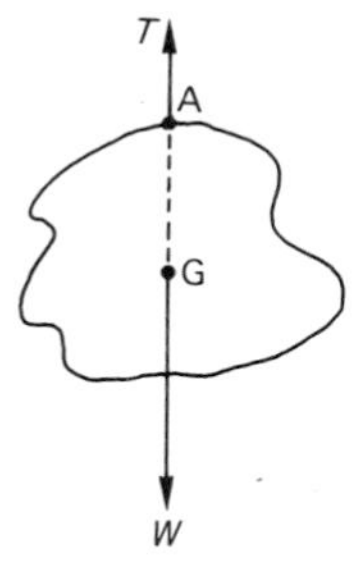

Figure 15.10

Consider a body freely suspended from a point A (Fig. 15.10). The only forces acting on the body are the tension T in the string and the weight W of the body. If the body is in equilibrium then $T = W$ and, as there will then be no torque, AG must be vertical.

Problems involving toppling and sliding

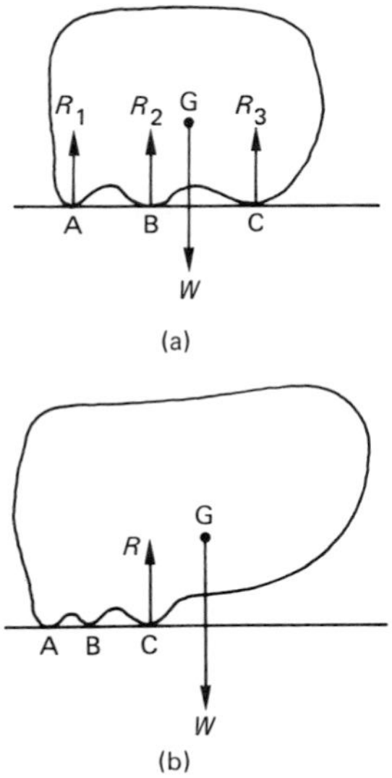

Figure 15.11

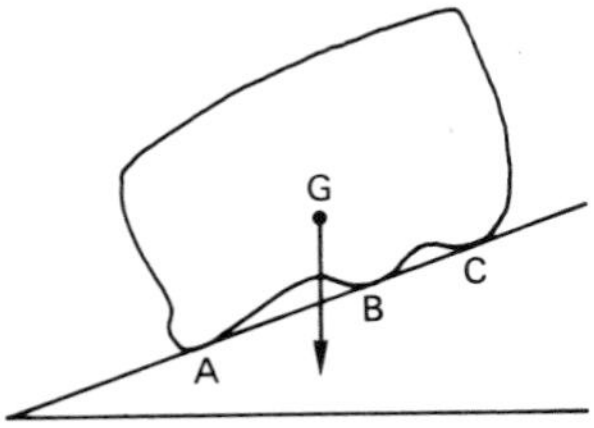

Figure 15.12

Consider a body resting on a horizontal plane (Fig. 15.11(a)). The forces acting on the body are its weight W and the normal reaction forces R_1, R_2 and R_3 at the points of contact between the body and the plane. The reaction forces are vertical and parallel so the resultant normal reaction force must lie between A and C, the extreme points of contact with the plane. If the body is in equilibrium the resultant normal reaction must be equal and opposite to the weight of the body and act in the same vertical line. If the centre of gravity falls outside AC then, as shown in Fig. 15.11(b), there will be a turning effect about A or C and the body will topple.

Similarly on a rough inclined plane if the only forces acting on the body are the normal reaction, the frictional force and the weight of the body then again the vertical through G must fall between A and C to prevent toppling (Fig. 15.12). On a rough inclined plane the possibility of sliding instead of toppling occurs unless the plane is perfectly rough.

Example 15.5

A uniform cylinder of height $2h$ and radius $h/2$ is placed on a rough inclined plane, the coefficient of friction between the plane and the cylinder being $1/3$. The inclination of the plane is gradually increased. Find whether equilibrium is broken by sliding or toppling.

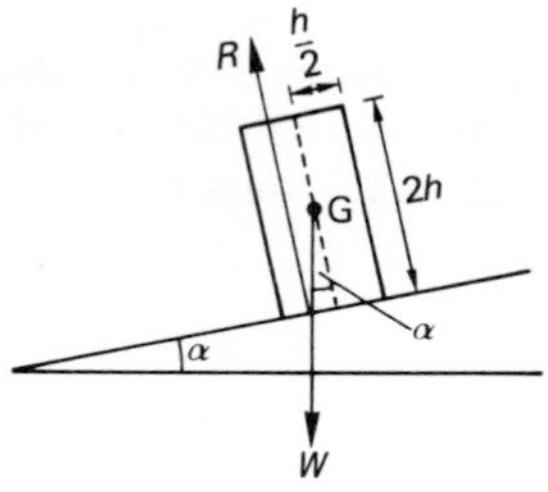

Figure 15.13

Let W be the weight of the cylinder and α be the inclination of the plane in the limiting position, when $F = \mu R$ and sliding is about to occur (Fig. 15.13). Then resolving perpendicular to the plane,

$$R = W \cos \alpha_1$$

and resolving parallel to the plane,

$$\mu R = F = W \sin \alpha_1$$

Therefore

$$\mu W \cos \alpha_1 = W \sin \alpha_1$$

$$\tan \alpha_1 = \mu = 1/3 \text{ on the point of sliding}$$

If equilibrium is to be broken by toppling then the normal reaction will act through A, the bottom edge of the cylinder. Then taking moments about A,

$$W \sin \alpha_2 \times h = W \cos \alpha_2 \times \frac{h}{2}$$

$$\tan \alpha_2 = 1/2$$

Since $1/3 < 1/2$ the cylinder will slide before it topples.

Example 15.6

A toy top is constructed by joining, at their circular rims, the bases of a solid uniform hemisphere of base radius a and a solid uniform right circular cone of base radius a and height h. The density of the hemisphere is b times that of the cone.

(a) Show that the centre of gravity of the top is at a distance

$$\frac{3h^2 + b(3a^2 + 8ah)}{4(h + 2ab)}$$

from the vertex of the cone.

(b) The top, when suspended from a point on the rim of the base of the cone, rests in equilibrium with the axis of the cone inclined at an acute angle, α, to the downward vertical. Find $\tan \alpha$.

(c) For the case $h = 4a$ determine the range of values of b such that the top cannot rest in equilibrium with the slant surface of the cone in contact with a smooth horizontal plane. (AEB J82)

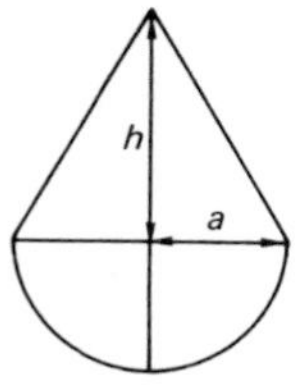

Figure 15.14

Let w be the density of the cone (Fig. 15.14).

(a) Derive the following table.

Body	Weight	Distance of centre of gravity from vertex
Hemisphere	$W_1 = \frac{2}{3}\pi a^3 bw$	$h + \frac{3a}{8}$
Cone	$W_2 = \frac{1}{3}\pi a^2 hw$	$\frac{3h}{4}$
Top	$(\frac{2}{3}\pi a^3 b + \frac{1}{3}\pi a^2 h)w$	$\bar{y}$

Taking moments about the vertex,

$$w\bar{y}\left(\frac{2}{3}\pi a^3 b+\frac{1}{3}\pi a^2 h\right)=\frac{2}{3}\pi a^3 bw\left(h+\frac{3a}{8}\right)+\frac{1}{3}\pi a^2 hw\frac{3h}{4}$$

Dividing by $\pi a^2 w/3$,

$$(2ab+h)\bar{y}=2ab\left(h+\frac{3a}{8}\right)+\frac{3h^2}{4}$$

and multiplying by 4,

$$(8ab+4h)\bar{y}=8abh+3a^2b+3h^2$$

i.e. $$\bar{y}=\frac{3h^2+b(3a^2+8ah)}{4(h+2ab)}$$

(b) When suspended the centre of gravity G lies directly below the point of suspension O. Consider the triangle OGN, enlarged in Fig. 15.15. The angle $\alpha=\widehat{\text{OGN}}$, ON $=a$ and GN $=h-\bar{y}$. Therefore

$$\tan\alpha=\frac{a}{|h-\bar{y}|}$$

and is positive for an acute angle.

$$\tan\alpha=\frac{a}{\left|h-\left(\frac{b(3a^2+8ah)+3h^2}{4(h+2ab)}\right)\right|}$$

i.e. $$\tan\alpha=\frac{4a(h+2ab)}{|h^2-3a^2b|}$$

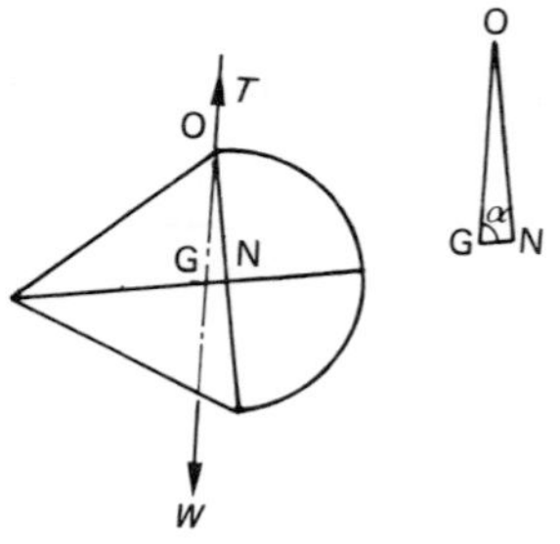

Figure 15.15

(c) See Fig. 15.16. The top cannot rest in equilibrium with the slant surface of the cone in contact with a smooth horizontal plane if, on taking moments about X (the point on the rim of the base)

moment of the hemisphere about X > moment of the cone about X

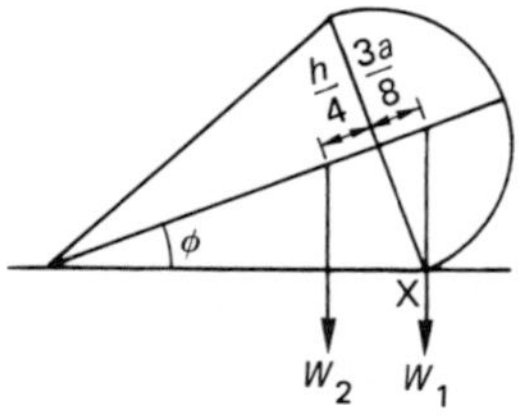

Figure 15.16

Therefore

$$\frac{2}{3}\pi a^3 bw\left(\frac{3a}{8}a\cos\phi-a\sin\phi\right)$$

$$>\frac{1}{3}\pi a^2 hw\left(\frac{h}{4}\cos\phi+a\sin\phi\right)$$

Substituting $h=4a$ and dividing by $\cos\phi$,

$$2ab\left(\frac{3a}{8}-a\tan\phi\right)>4a(a+a\tan\phi)$$

Now $\tan\phi=1/4$, so

$$2ab\left(\frac{3a}{8}-\frac{a}{4}\right)>4a\left(a+\frac{a}{4}\right)$$

i.e. $$b>\underline{20}$$

Example 15.7

Show, without using any result quoted in a book of formulae, that the centre of gravity of a uniform triangular lamina lies at the point of intersection of the medians.

A lamina ABCD, in the form of a rhombus, consists of two uniform triangular laminae, ABC and ADC, joined along AC. Both triangles are equilateral of side $2a$, ABC is of mass $2m$ and ADC is of mass m. Determine the perpendicular distance of the centre of gravity G of the rhombic lamina from AC and from AB.

The rhombic lamina is then suspended by a string attached to A. Determine:

(a) the tangent of the angle between AC and the vertical,
(b) the tension in the string when a mass is attached at D so that AC is vertical. (AEB J84)

The proof is given previously in this chapter (see Uniform bodies, p. 173).

By symmetry the centre of gravity of the body lies on BD (Fig. 15.17). Let M be the midpoint of AC. Then the following table can be derived.

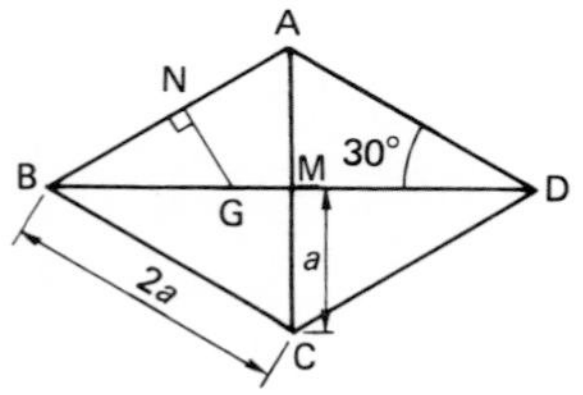

Figure 15.17

Body	Weight	Distance of centre of gravity from AC
ABC	$2mg$	$BM/3=\sqrt{3}a/3$
ADC	mg	$BM/3=\sqrt{3}a/3$
ABCD	$3\,mg$	$\bar{x}$

Taking moments about AC,

$$3mg\bar{x} = 2mg\frac{\sqrt{3}a}{3} - mg\frac{\sqrt{3}a}{3}$$

i.e. $\bar{x} = \dfrac{a}{3\sqrt{3}}$

Let N be the perpendicular from G, the centre of gravity of ABCD, to AB so the distance required for G from AB is NG.

$$\widehat{ABM} = 30°$$

$$NG = BG\sin 30° = \left(\sqrt{3}a - \frac{a}{3\sqrt{3}}\right) \times \frac{1}{2}$$

i.e. $NG = \underline{\dfrac{4a}{3\sqrt{3}}}$

(a) See Fig. 15.18(a).

$$\tan\theta = \frac{GM}{AM}$$

but $GM = \bar{x}$. Therefore

$$\tan\theta = \frac{a/3\sqrt{3}}{a}$$

i.e. $\tan\theta = \underline{1/3\sqrt{3}}$

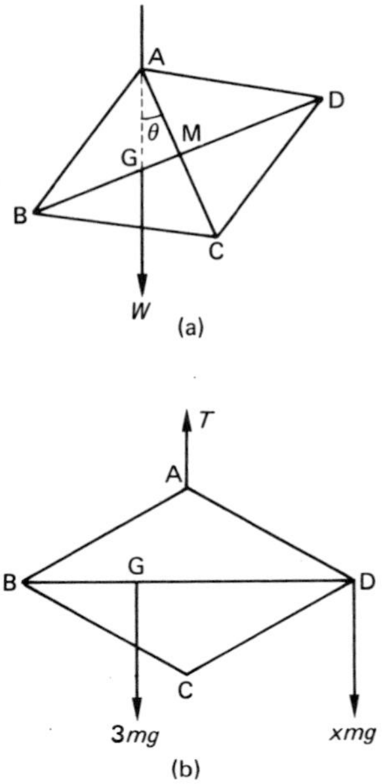

Figure 15.18

(b) See Fig. 15.18(b).

$T = (3+x)mg$

Taking moments about M,

$$3mg\frac{a}{3\sqrt{3}} = xmg\sqrt{3}a$$

i.e. $x = 1/3$

Hence the tension in the string

$T = \underline{10mg/3}$

Problem 15.1

A square portion of side x metres is cut from a square of side a metres by removing a length x metres long from two sides adjacent to one corner. Show that the remainder can stand on the remaining part of the cut side if $x = 0.6a$ but not if $x = 0.7a$.

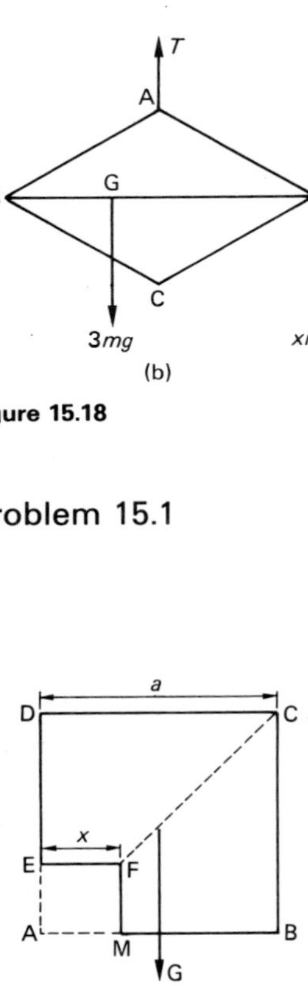

Figure 15.19

(1) Draw a diagram (Fig. 15.19). If the line of action of the centre of gravity falls between A and M the lamina will topple.
(2) Let w = weight per unit area. Then complete the following table.

Value of x	Body	Weight	Distance of centre of gravity from AD
$0.6a$	ABCD	a^2w	$a/2$
	EFAM	$(0.6)^2wa^2$	$0.3a$
	MBCDE	$w(a^2-0.6^2a^2)$	$\bar{x}$
$0.7a$	As above		

(3) For $x = 0.6a$, take moments about AD to show that

$$\bar{x} = \frac{a^3-(0.6a)^3}{2(a^2-(0.6a)^2)} = 0.61a$$

Therefore $\bar{x}$ lies between M and B and the lamina *will not* topple.
(4) Repeat step (3) for $x = 0.7a$ to show that $\bar{x} = 0.67a$. Therefore $\bar{x}$ lies between A and M and the lamina *will* topple.

Summary

(1) The positions of the centres of gravity of some standard bodies are tabulated below.

Uniform body	Position of centre of gravity on the axis of symmetry
Sector subtending an angle 2α at the centre	$\dfrac{2r \sin \alpha}{3\alpha}$
Semicircular lamina	$\dfrac{4r}{3\pi}$
Solid hemisphere	$\dfrac{3r}{8}$
Solid $\left\{\begin{array}{l}\text{pyramid}\\ \text{cone}\\ \text{tetrahedron}\end{array}\right\}$	$\dfrac{3h}{4}$ from the vertex
Hollow hemisphere	$\dfrac{r}{2}$ from plane face
Arc subtending an angle $2a$ at the centre	$\dfrac{r \sin \alpha}{\alpha}$

(2) The centre of gravity of a body is that point from which the weight of the body acts vertically downwards.

(3) The centre of mass of a body is defined as the point with position vector

$$\boldsymbol{r}_m = \frac{\Sigma_i m_i \boldsymbol{r}_i}{\Sigma_i m_i}$$

(4) The position vector of the centre of gravity of a body is given by

$$\bar{x}\boldsymbol{i} + \bar{y}\boldsymbol{j}$$

where

$$\bar{x} = \frac{\Sigma_i m_i x_i}{\Sigma m_i} \quad \text{and} \quad \bar{y} = \frac{\Sigma_i m_i y_i}{\Sigma m_i}$$

and the body consists of n particles $m_1, m_2, \ldots, m_n$, each with position vector $\boldsymbol{r}_1, \boldsymbol{r}_2, \ldots, \boldsymbol{r}_n$ respectively, where $\boldsymbol{r}_i = x_i\boldsymbol{i} + y_i\boldsymbol{j}$. The subscript i varies from 1 to n and indicates which particle is denoted.

(5) The centre of mass and centre of gravity of a body are thus coincident in a uniform gravitational field.

(6) The centroid of a body is the geometric centre and is that point about which the area for a lamina and the volume for a solid are uniformly distributed.

The centroid and the centre of mass are coincident for a body with uniformly distributed mass and the centre of gravity lies on each line of symmetry of a uniform body.

(7) From the principle of moments

moment of the weight of the whole body about a given axis = sum of the moments of the weight of the parts of the body about that axis

(8) When a body is suspended from a point it rests in equilibrium with its centre of gravity directly below the point of suspension. When a body rests on a plane it will not topple if the vertical through its centre of gravity falls inside the extreme points of contact of the body with the plane. Equilibrium may be broken by sliding or toppling on a rough plane depending on the geometry of the figure and the angle of inclination of the plane and the coefficient of friction between the plane and the body.

16
Frameworks

Objectives

The student should be able to:

(1) define a framework,
(2) define a light rod as a strut or a tie depending on the direction of the forces in the rod,
(3) use the state of equilibrium for the body as a whole and at each joint to determine the forces in the members of the framework and any external reactions of forces at the joints.

Definitions

If a fra·nework of light rods, smoothly jointed together at their ends to form a rigid construction, is in equilibrium, then for each rod the only forces acting upon it are applied at the ends. For the forces to balance they must be directed along the rod so that equal and opposite forces can act. The stress in a light (i.e. weightless) rod acted upon by forces at the ends only must therefore consist of a thrust or tension along the length of the rod. A rod which prevents the framework from collapse is described as a **strut** and is said to be in thrust or in compression (Fig. 16.1). A rod which prevents the framework coming apart in a state of tension is said to be a **tie** (Fig. 16.2).

Figure 16.1

Figure 16.2

Problem solving

When solving problems some rods can be marked immediately as in thrust or in tension; others are not obvious and need to be calculated. In the latter case let the rod be in thrust, then if the force calculated in the rod is negative it will be in tension. The usual first step is to mark in the external forces. These must be in equilibrium as the internal forces acting along the rods occur in equal and opposite pairs. The next step is to take moments about an axis in the framework to calculate one or more of the external forces. The stresses in the light rods can then be found, usually by resolving horizontally and vertically at individual joints in the framework. Sometimes it is preferable to take moments about another point and the sequence of steps depends on the problem.

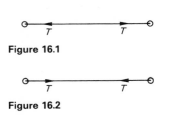

Example 16.1

A smoothly jointed framework ABCDEF consists of eight light rods in equilibrium in a vertical plane smoothly hinged to a vertical wall at A and B and carrying a load of 200 N at D. AF is of length 2 m and all the other rods are of length 4 m. The rods AF, FE, BC and CD are horizontal. Find the reaction at A and the forces in the rods CD, CE, CF and BC stating which are in compression.

See Fig. 16.3. The angles in the triangles FBC, FEC and ECD are all 60°. Resolving at D, E, C and F gives the direction of action of the tensions in the rods.

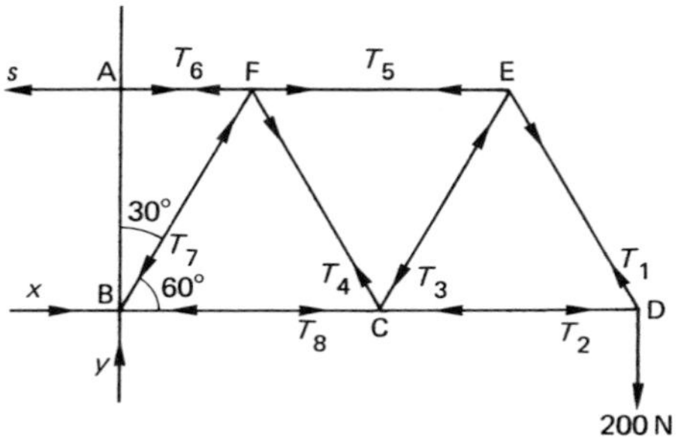

Figure 16.3

At D,

$\uparrow$D, T_1 must act up and, $\rightarrow$D, T_2 must act towards D

At E,

$\uparrow$E, T_3 must act towards E and, $\rightarrow$E, T_5 must act away from E

At C,

$\uparrow$C, T_4 must act up and, $\rightarrow$C, T_8 must act towards C

At F,

$\uparrow$F, T_7 must act up and, $\rightarrow$F, T_6 must act away from F

Therefore at A,

T_6 must act away from A and the reaction at A, s, must act away from A

Hence at B for external forces,

x must act towards B and y must act up

Note It is not always possible to indicate directions on all rods in a framework in this way.

Taking moments about B, to find the reaction at A,

$200 \times 8 = s \times 4 \cos 30°$

i.e. $\underline{s = 800/\sqrt{3} \text{ N acting along FA}}$

At D,

$\uparrow$D, $T_1 \cos 30° = 200$, i.e. $T_1 = 400/\sqrt{3}$ N in ED in tension and $\rightarrow$D, $T_1 \cos 60° = T_2$, i.e. $T_2 = 200/\sqrt{3}$ N in DC in compression

At E,

$\uparrow$E, $T_3 \cos 30° = T_1 \cos 30°$, i.e. $T_3 = 400/\sqrt{3}$ N in CE in compression

At C,

$\uparrow$C, $T_4 \cos 30° = T_3 \cos 30°$, i.e. $T_4 = 400/\sqrt{3}$ N in CF in tension

and $\rightarrow$C, $T_8 = T_2 + (T_4 + T_3) \cos 60° = \dfrac{200}{\sqrt{3}} + \dfrac{400}{\sqrt{3}} = \dfrac{600}{\sqrt{3}}$ in BC in compression

Rods CD, CE and CF are in compression.

Note It is often useful to give the answers in a table if there are several as they can be tabulated clearly.

Example 16.2

Seven light rods AB, AC, BC, BD, CD, CE and DE are smoothly jointed to form a framework as shown in Fig. 16.4. The rods

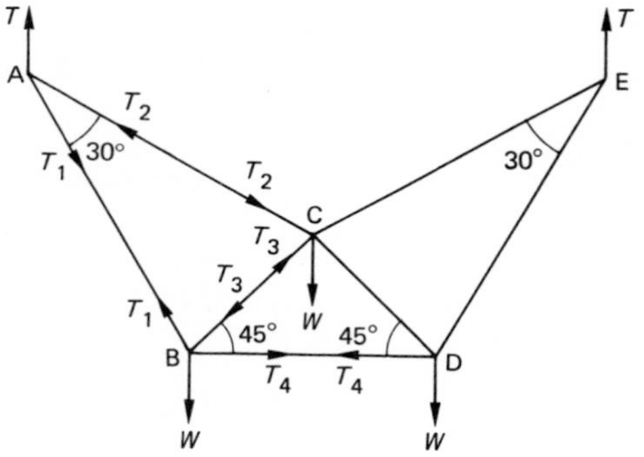

Figure 16.4

AB, AC, CE and DE are equal in length and angle BAC = angle CED = 30°. Triangle BCD is isosceles with angle BCD = 90°. The framework is suspended in a vertical plane from A and E so BD is horizontal. Equal weights W are attached at B, C and D. Show that the force in AB is of magnitude $3\sqrt{3}W/2$. Calculate the forces in (a) AC and (b) BD. The weights at B and D are each increased to $4W$ without changing either the shape or the size of the structure and BD is still horizontal. Determine the forces in (c) AB and (d) CE stating for each whether it is a tension or a compression. (AEB J83)

Triangles ABC and BCD are both isosceles. Therefore

$$\widehat{ABC} = \widehat{ACB} = 75°$$

and $\widehat{CBD} = \widehat{CDB} = 45°$

By symmetry the tensions at A and E acting upwards are equal. Resolving vertically for the system,

$$2T = 3W \quad \text{or} \quad T = \frac{3W}{2}$$

At A, one tension must act towards A and one away in rods AB and AC.

$$\rightarrow \text{A}, \ T_1 \cos 60° = T_2 \cos 30°, \text{ i.e. } T_1 = \sqrt{3}\, T_2$$

As $T_1 > T_2$,

$$\uparrow A, \ T_1 \cos 30° = T_2 \cos 60° + T$$

Therefore

$$\frac{\sqrt{3}\, T_1}{2} = \frac{T_1}{2\sqrt{3}} + \frac{3W}{2}$$

i.e. $$T_1 = \frac{3\sqrt{3}\, W}{2} \text{ in AB}$$

and $$\underline{T_2 = \frac{3W}{2} \text{ in AC in tension}}$$

Let BC act as a strut.

$$\uparrow \text{B}, \ W + T_3 \cos 45° = T_1 \cos 30° = \frac{3\sqrt{3}\, W}{2} \frac{\sqrt{3}}{2}$$

i.e. $$T_3 = \frac{5\sqrt{2}\, W}{4} \text{ in BC}$$

(positive, so it is a strut)

T_4 must act away from B to balance the component of T_1 and T_3 horizontally.

$$\rightarrow \text{B}, \ T_4 = T_3 \cos 45° + T_1 \cos 60°$$

i.e. $$\underline{T_4 = \frac{5W}{4} + \frac{3\sqrt{3}\, W}{4} \text{ in BD in tension}}$$

The weights are increased to $4W$ so T changes to T'. Then resolving vertically for the system,

$$2T' = 9W \quad \text{or} \quad T^1 = 9W/2$$

$$\uparrow \text{A}, \ T^1 + T_2' \cos 60° = T_1' \cos 30°$$

As before, $T_1' = \sqrt{3}\, T_2'$, therefore

$$\underline{T_1' = \frac{9\sqrt{3}\, W}{2} \text{ in AB in tension}}$$

and $$\underline{T_2' = \frac{9W}{2} \text{ in CE in compression}}$$

Example 16.3

Figure 16.5 shows a framework of nine light freely jointed rods AB, BC, CD, DE, EF, FA, BF, BD and FD. The first six named rods form a regular hexagon. Vertical loads of $2W$ and W are

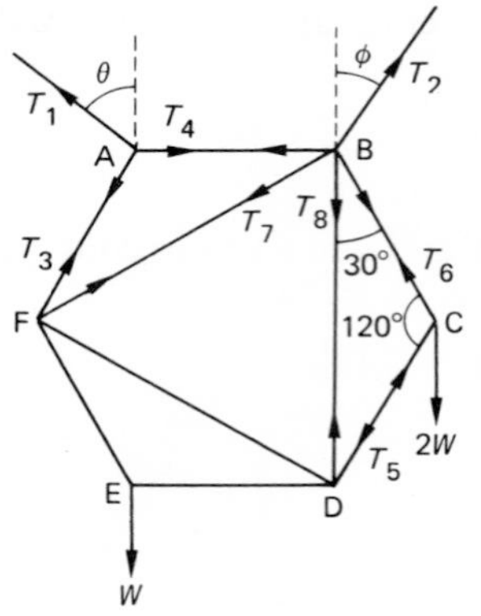

Figure 16.5

applied to C and E respectively. The framework is suspended in equilibrium in a vertical plane by strings attached to A and B with AB horizontal. The inclinations of the strings to the vertical are θ and ϕ in the senses shown with $0 \leqslant \theta \leqslant 90°$ and $0 \leqslant \phi \leqslant 90°$. Assuming the string at A is not slack, show that $\theta = 90°$. For the particular case when $\phi = 60°$ determine:

(a) the tensions in the strings,
(b) the forces in the rods AF, AB, BC, BF and BD stating whether the latter rods are in tension or compression.

(AEB N83)

Let the hexagon sides $= 2a$. Resolving vertically for the system,

$$T_1 \cos\theta + T_2 \cos\phi = 3W$$

and horizontally,

$$T_1 \sin\theta = T_2 \cos\phi$$

Taking moments about B,

$$W2a - 2W2a \cos 60° + T_1 \cos\theta \, a = 0$$

As $T_1 \neq 0$,

$$\cos\theta = 0$$
$$\theta = 90°$$

(a) The angle $\phi = 60°$. Taking moments about A,

$$T_2 \cos\phi \; 2a = 2W(2a + 2a \cos 60°)$$

i.e. $\quad T_2 = \underline{6W}$

$$T_1 = T_2 \cos 30° = \underline{3\sqrt{3}\,W}$$

(b) At A,

$\uparrow A$, $0 = T_3 \cos 30°$, i.e. $T_3 = \underline{0 \text{ in AF}}$

and $\rightarrow A$, $T_1 = T_4$, i.e. $T_4 = \underline{3\sqrt{3}\,W \text{ in AB in tension}}$

At C,

$$\rightarrow C,\; T_5 \cos 60° = T_6 \cos 60°$$

Therefore $T_5 = T_6$ and must act in opposite directions horizontally: T_5 must act towards C and T_6 away from C.

$\uparrow C$, $(T_5 + T_6) \cos 30° = 2W$, i.e. $T_6 = \underline{2W\sqrt{3} \text{ in BC in tension}}$

Let BF be in thrust.

$$\rightarrow B,\; T_4 - T_2 \cos 30° - T_6 \cos 60° + T_7 \cos 30° = 0$$

$$3\sqrt{3}\,W - 3\sqrt{3}\,W - \frac{2W}{\sqrt{3}} \times \frac{1}{2} = T_7 \cos 30°$$

i.e. $T_7 = \underline{-2W/3 \text{ in BF, i.e. BF is in tension}}$

Let BD be in thrust.

$$\uparrow B,\ T_2 \cos 60° - T_7 \cos 60° - T_6 \cos 30° + T_8 = 0$$

i.e. $T_8 = -5W/3$ in BD, i.e. BD is in tension

Summarising, the forces in the rods are as tabulated below.

Rod	Force	State
AF	0	—
AB	$3\sqrt{3}W$	In tension
BC	$2W/\sqrt{3}$	In tension
BF	$2W/\sqrt{3}$	In tension
BD	$5W/3$	In tension

Problem 16.1

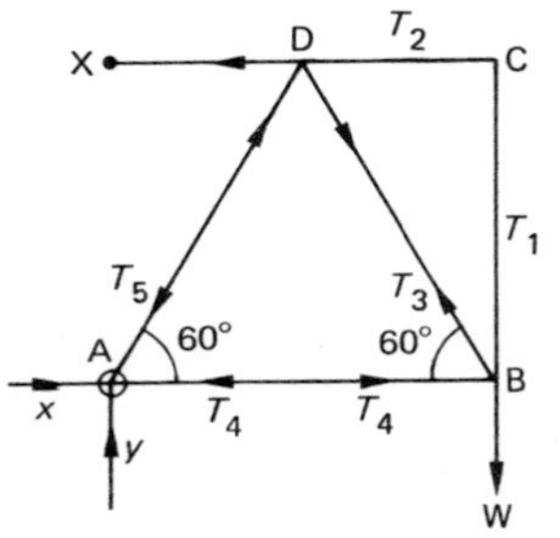

Figure 16.6

Figure 16.6 shows a framework of five light freely jointed rods AB, BC, CD, DB and DA smoothly hinged to a wall at A, where AB = BD = DA = $2a$ and DC = a. A weight W is hung at B. Find the horizontal external force required at X to keep the framework in equilibrium and determine the forces in all the rods stating which are in compression.

(1) Mark in the angles.
(2) Take moments about A to find $x = 2W/\sqrt{3}$.
(3) Resolve ↑ and → at C to show that $T_2 = T_1 = 0$.
(4) Now the force in DB at B must act upwards and the force in AB at B must act towards B. Resolve ↑B to show that $T_3 = 2W/\sqrt{3}$ and →B to show that $T_4 = W/\sqrt{3}$.
(5) The force in AD at D must act upwards. Resolve ↑D to show that $T_3 = T_5 = 2W/\sqrt{3}$.
(6) Tabulate the results, as below.

Rod	Force	State
AB	$W/\sqrt{3}$	In compression
BC	0	—
CD	0	—
DB	$2W/\sqrt{3}$	—
DA	$2W/\sqrt{3}$	In compression

Note The external forces acting at the joint A are $y = W$ acting upwards and $x = W/\sqrt{3}$ acting at A along AB. They are not required in this question.

Problem 16.2

Figure 16.7 shows seven equal smoothly jointed light rods AB, BC, CD, DE, EA, EB and BD. The framework is in a vertical plane with AB, BC and DE horizontal and is simply supported at A and C. It carries vertical loads of 400 N and 80 N at E and D respectively. Calculate the reactions at R and S and the forces in all the members of the framework.

(1) Let AB = a. Resolve ↑ and take moments about A to find $R = 320$ N and $S = 160$ N.
(2) ↑A to find $T_1 = 640/\sqrt{3}$ N in AE in compression. ↑C to find $T_2 = 320/\sqrt{3}$ N in DC in compression.

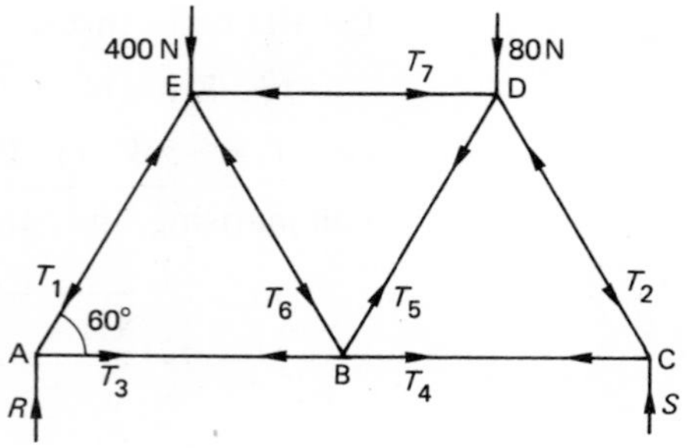

Figure 16.7

(3) →A to find $T_3 = 320/\sqrt{3}$ N in AB in tension. →C to find $T_4 = 160/\sqrt{3}$ N in BC in tension.
(4) Let EB and BD be in thrust ↑E to find $T_3 = 160/\sqrt{3}$ N in EB in compression. ↑D to find $T_5 = -160/\sqrt{3}$ N in DB in tension (and is shown in tension in Fig. 16.7).
(5) Then →E or →D to find $T_7 = 240/\sqrt{3}$ N in ED in tension. Use the other joint to check for the same value of T_7.

Summary

(1) A framework is a set of light rods smoothly jointed at their ends to form a rigid construction.

(2) A rod which prevents a framework from collapse is a strut and is in thrust or compression.

(3) A rod which prevents a framework coming apart is in a state of tension and is said to be a tie.

(4) If a framework is in equilibrium then:

(a) the external forces acting on the framework are in equilibrium,
(b) the sum of the moments about any point is zero,
(c) the forces acting at each joint are in equilibrium.

These three conditions can be used to produce independent equations to calculate the external reactions at a joint, the external forces at a joint and the forces in any given rod where these occur in a framework.

17
Equilibrium of forces in three dimensions

Objectives

The student should be able to:

(1) define and use the vector moment of a force about a point,
(2) define and use the vector moment of a couple,
(3) determine resultants of systems of forces in three dimensions.

Vector moment of a force about a point

The moment of a force is the turning effect of the force about an axis passing through a point and perpendicular to the plane containing the point and the force. It is commonly abbreviated to the 'moment of a force about a point' although the whole definition should be used.

Consider a force $\boldsymbol{F}$ acting about a point P, where AB is the axis passing through P and is perpendicular to the plane containing $\boldsymbol{F}$ (Fig. 17.1). Let $\boldsymbol{r}$ be the position vector to any point on the line of action of $\boldsymbol{F}$ from P. The magnitude of the moment of $\boldsymbol{F}$ about P is

$$dF = r \sin \theta\, F = |\boldsymbol{r} \times \boldsymbol{F}|$$

The vector $\boldsymbol{r} \times \boldsymbol{F}$ is parallel to AB, i.e. directed along the axis of rotation in the sense of a right-handed screw turned from $\boldsymbol{r}$ to $\boldsymbol{F}$ and is equal in magnitude to dF so $\boldsymbol{r} \times \boldsymbol{F}$ is the vector moment of $\boldsymbol{F}$ about P.

If the vector moment of $\boldsymbol{F}$ about P is $\boldsymbol{a}$ then $\boldsymbol{r} \times \boldsymbol{F} = \boldsymbol{a}$ is a vector equation of the line of action of $\boldsymbol{F}$.

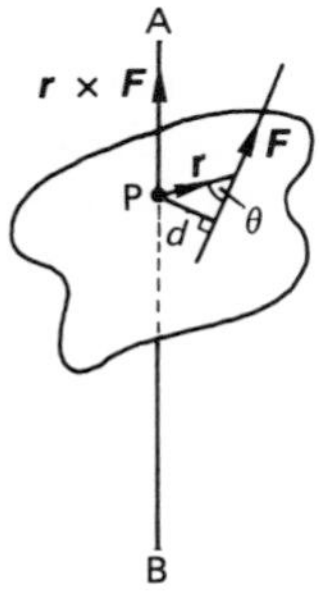

Figure 17.1

Example 17.1

A force $\boldsymbol{F} = 2\boldsymbol{i} + \boldsymbol{j} - \boldsymbol{k}$ acts through a point A with position vector $\boldsymbol{i} + 2\boldsymbol{j}$. Find the vector moment of $\boldsymbol{F}$:

(a) about the origin,
(b) about a point B with position vector $-2\boldsymbol{i} - \boldsymbol{j}$.

Find also the vector equation of the axis CD through B.

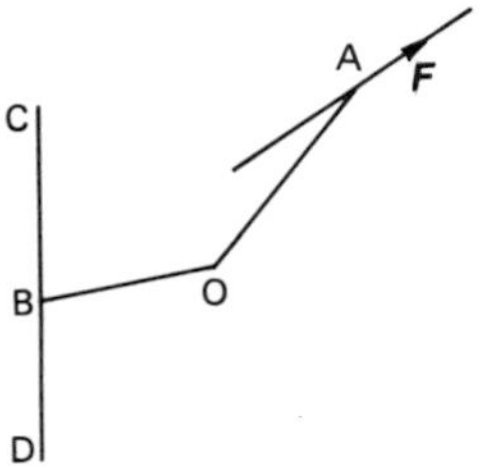

Figure 17.2

See Fig. 17.2.

(a) moment of $\boldsymbol{F}$ about $\mathrm{O} = \boldsymbol{r} \times \boldsymbol{F} = \overrightarrow{\mathrm{OA}} \times \boldsymbol{F} = \begin{vmatrix} \boldsymbol{i} & \boldsymbol{j} & \boldsymbol{k} \\ 1 & 2 & 0 \\ 2 & 1 & -1 \end{vmatrix}$

$$= \underline{-2\boldsymbol{i} + \boldsymbol{j} - 3\boldsymbol{k}}$$

(b) moment of $\boldsymbol{F}$ about B $= \overrightarrow{BA} \times \boldsymbol{F}$

and $\overrightarrow{BA} = 3\boldsymbol{i} + 3\boldsymbol{j}$

therefore

$$\text{moment of } \boldsymbol{F} \text{ about B} = \begin{vmatrix} \boldsymbol{i} & \boldsymbol{j} & \boldsymbol{k} \\ +3 & +3 & 0 \\ 2 & 1 & -1 \end{vmatrix} = \underline{-3\boldsymbol{i} + 3\boldsymbol{j} - 3\boldsymbol{k}}$$

The direction of $\overrightarrow{BA} \times \boldsymbol{F}$ is parallel to the axis through B. Therefore

$$\boldsymbol{r} = \overrightarrow{OB} + \lambda(\overrightarrow{BA} \times \boldsymbol{F})$$

i.e. $\boldsymbol{r} = \underline{-2\boldsymbol{i} - \boldsymbol{j} + \lambda(-\boldsymbol{i} + \boldsymbol{j} - \boldsymbol{k})}$

is the vector equation of the axis CD through B.

Vector moment of a couple

A pair of parallel forces $\boldsymbol{F}$ and $-\boldsymbol{F}$ with separate lines of action is a couple. Let A and B be two points on the lines of action of $\boldsymbol{F}$ and $-\boldsymbol{F}$ and let P be a point on the plane of the couple so $\boldsymbol{a}$ and $\boldsymbol{b}$ are the position vectors of the two points A and B (Fig. 17.3). The vector moment of the couple about P is given by

$$\boldsymbol{G} = \boldsymbol{b} \times (-\boldsymbol{F}) + \boldsymbol{a} \times \boldsymbol{F} = (\boldsymbol{a} - \boldsymbol{b}) \times \boldsymbol{F}$$

$$= \overrightarrow{BA} \times \boldsymbol{F} = \overrightarrow{BA}\, F \sin\theta\, \hat{\boldsymbol{n}}$$

i.e. $\boldsymbol{G} = Fd\hat{\boldsymbol{n}}$

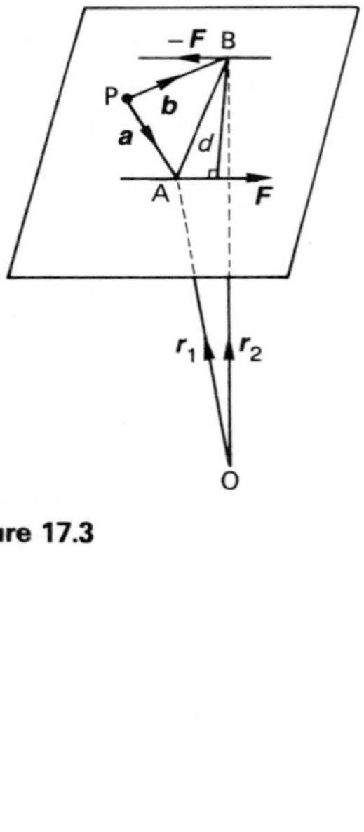

Figure 17.3

Its magnitude equals the magnitude of the moment of the couple and its direction is perpendicular to the plane of the couple in the sense of the motion of a right-handed screw from $\overrightarrow{BA}$ to $\boldsymbol{F}$.

The point O is not in the plane of the couple. Let $\boldsymbol{r}_1$ and $\boldsymbol{r}_2$ be the position vectors of the points A and B from O. The vector moment of the couple about O is given by

$$\boldsymbol{G} = \boldsymbol{r}_1 \times \boldsymbol{F} + \boldsymbol{r}_2 \times (-\boldsymbol{F}) = (\boldsymbol{r}_1 - \boldsymbol{r}_2) \times \boldsymbol{F}$$

$$= \overrightarrow{BA} \times \boldsymbol{F} \qquad \text{(i.e. the same)}$$

(1) The vector moment of a couple is constant about any point and independent of that point because $\overrightarrow{BA}$ is independent of the point, O or P.

(2) $\boldsymbol{G} = \overrightarrow{BA} \times \boldsymbol{F}$ is perpendicular to the plane of the couple.

(3) $|\overrightarrow{BA} \times \boldsymbol{F}| = Fd = G$ which is the magnitude of the moment of the couple.

Two couples are equivalent if their vector moment is equal so they must act in parallel planes as $\boldsymbol{G}$ is perpendicular to the planes.

The resultant vector moment of a system of forces is the sum of the vector moments of the individual forces. Consider a set of forces $\boldsymbol{F}_1, \boldsymbol{F}_2, \boldsymbol{F}_3, \ldots,$ with position vectors $\boldsymbol{r}_1, \boldsymbol{r}_2, \boldsymbol{r}_3, \ldots$ of points on the lines of action of the forces respectively, relative

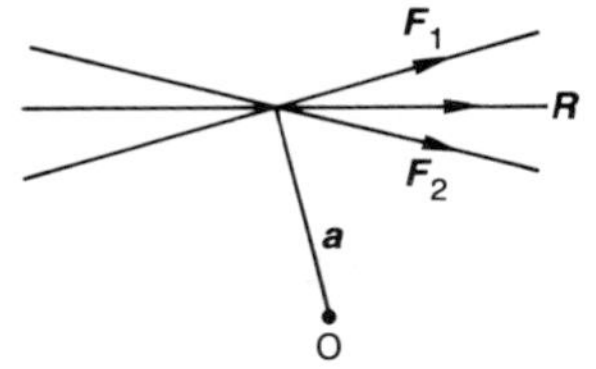

Figure 17.4

to P. The resultant vector moment about the point P is given by

$$G = (r_1 \times F_1) + (r_2 \times F_2) + (r_3 \times F_3) + \cdots$$

Consider a simple set of two non-parallel forces equivalent to a single force $R = F_1 + F_2$ (Fig. 17.4). Their lines of action must intersect as they have a single resultant. Therefore about the point O

$$\text{moment of } F_1 + \text{moment of } F_2 =$$

$$a \times F_1 + a \times F_2 = a \times (F_1 + F_2)$$

This argument can be generalised to state that if a set of forces reduces to a single force then the vector sum of the moments of all the forces about a point is equal to the moment of the resultant force R about that point, i.e.

$$\sum (r \times F) = a \times R$$

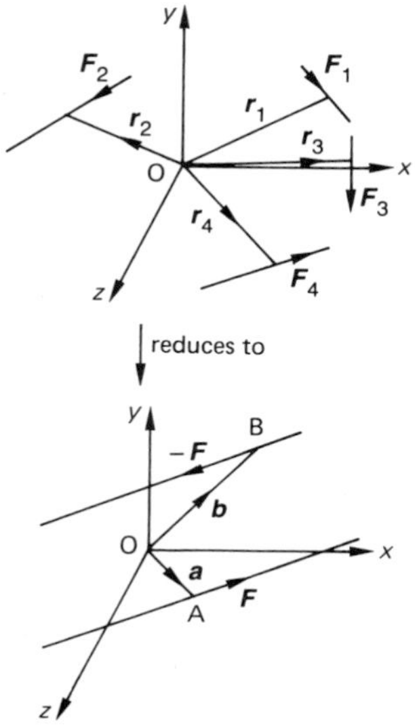

Figure 17.5

Now consider a set of forces which is equivalent to a couple of moment G. In its simplest form it reduces to two parallel forces F and $-F$. Let A be a point on F and B a point on $-F$ with position vectors a and b respectively. The vector sum of the moments of F and $-F$ about O is given by

$$G = a \times F + b \times (-F) = (b - a) \times F$$

Thus if a system of forces reduces to a couple then the vector sum of the moments of all the forces about a point is equal to the vector moment of the couple and the vector sum of the forces is zero. The system reducing to a couple is illustrated in Fig. 17.5.

Example 17.2

A force $F = 3i + 2j + k$ acts through a point with position vector $i - j$ and a second unlike parallel force $-F$ acts through a point with position vector $2i + j + k$. Find the vector moment of the couple and hence a unit vector in a plane perpendicular to the plane of the couple.

Let $\overrightarrow{OA} = i - j$ and $\overrightarrow{OB} = 2i + j + k$. Then

$$\overrightarrow{BA} = -i - 2j - k$$

The vector moment of the couple,

$$G = \overrightarrow{BA} \times F = \begin{vmatrix} i & j & k \\ -1 & -2 & -1 \\ 3 & 2 & 1 \end{vmatrix} = \underline{0i - 2j + 4k}$$

$$\text{and } \hat{G} = \frac{-2}{\sqrt{20}} j + \frac{4}{\sqrt{20}} k = \underline{\frac{-1}{\sqrt{5}} j + \frac{2}{\sqrt{5}} k}$$

Resultant of systems of forces in three dimensions

As discussed in Chapter 4, two systems of forces are equivalent if their effect on a body is the same in all respects. An original set of forces is said to *reduce* to its resultant system, where the resultant system is the simplest equivalent system.

A set of coplanar forces is equivalent to a single force or to a couple or the system is in equilibrium because a force $\boldsymbol{F}$ plus a couple $\boldsymbol{G}$ is equivalent to a coplanar force displaced through G/F. If forces in three dimensions are considered a fourth possibility exists because there may be two forces whose lines of action are skew. Such a pair of forces cannot be in equilibrium and cannot reduce to either a single force or a couple. The resultant of such a system of two forces will involve a combination of linear motion and rotation and may be reduced to a couple and a single non-coplanar force. Thus a set of non-coplanar forces $\boldsymbol{F}_1, \boldsymbol{F}_2, \boldsymbol{F}_3, \ldots$, acting through points with position vectors $\boldsymbol{r}_1, \boldsymbol{r}_2, \boldsymbol{r}_3, \ldots$, either:

(a) reduces to a single force $\boldsymbol{R}$ acting through the point $\boldsymbol{a}$ then

$$\sum \boldsymbol{F} = \boldsymbol{R} \quad \text{and} \quad \sum \boldsymbol{r} \times \boldsymbol{F} = \boldsymbol{a} \times \boldsymbol{R}$$

the latter equation can be used to find $\boldsymbol{a}$ and then the equation of the line of action of $\boldsymbol{R}$,

$$\boldsymbol{r} = \boldsymbol{a} + \lambda \boldsymbol{R}$$

or (b) reduces to a couple $\boldsymbol{G}$ then

$$\sum \boldsymbol{F} = 0 \quad \text{and} \quad \sum \boldsymbol{r} \times \boldsymbol{F} = \boldsymbol{G}$$

or (c) is in equilibrium

$$\sum \boldsymbol{F} = 0 \quad \text{and} \quad \sum \boldsymbol{r} \times \boldsymbol{F} = 0$$

or (d) reduces to a combination of a couple and a non-coplanar force $\boldsymbol{F}$.

Conversely to show that a system of forces reduces to equilibrium it is necessary to show that both $\Sigma\, \boldsymbol{F} = 0$ and $\Sigma\, \boldsymbol{r} \times \boldsymbol{F} = 0$ because $\Sigma\, \boldsymbol{F} = 0$ for a system reducing to a couple and $\Sigma\, \boldsymbol{r} \times \boldsymbol{F} = 0$ for a system reducing to a single force whose line of action passes through the origin.

To prove that a system of forces reduces to a couple it is necessary to show that both $\Sigma\, \boldsymbol{F} = 0$ and $\Sigma\, \boldsymbol{r} \times \boldsymbol{F}$ is non-zero.

If $\Sigma\, \boldsymbol{F}$ is non-zero a system of forces could reduce to either a single force or a combination of a couple and a non-coplanar force. If the lines of action of the forces are concurrent then the vector sum of the moments of the forces about the point of intersection is zero so the system must reduce to a single force. Also if the forces are coplanar the resultant system acts in one plane so eliminating the possibility of a non-coplanar couple.

Problem 17.1

A force $\boldsymbol{F}_1 = 2\boldsymbol{i} - \boldsymbol{j} + \boldsymbol{k}$ acts through the point $3\boldsymbol{i} + 2\boldsymbol{k}$, a force $\boldsymbol{F}_2 = 3\boldsymbol{i} + 4\boldsymbol{j} - 4\boldsymbol{k}$ acts through the point $4\boldsymbol{i} + 5\boldsymbol{j} - 3\boldsymbol{k}$, and a force $\boldsymbol{F}_3 = -5\boldsymbol{i} - 3\boldsymbol{j} + 3\boldsymbol{k}$ acts through the point $-4\boldsymbol{i} - 2\boldsymbol{j} + 4\boldsymbol{k}$. Prove that the system of forces is in equilibrium.

(1) Show that $\Sigma\, \boldsymbol{F} = 0 = \boldsymbol{F}_1 + \boldsymbol{F}_2 + \boldsymbol{F}_3$.

(2) Show that

$$\sum(\boldsymbol{r}\times\boldsymbol{F})=0=(3\boldsymbol{i}+2\boldsymbol{k})\times(2\boldsymbol{i}-\boldsymbol{j}+\boldsymbol{k})$$
$$+(4\boldsymbol{i}+5\boldsymbol{j}-3\boldsymbol{k})\times(3\boldsymbol{i}+4\boldsymbol{j}-4\boldsymbol{k})$$
$$+(-4\boldsymbol{i}-2\boldsymbol{j}+4\boldsymbol{k})\times(-5\boldsymbol{i}-3\boldsymbol{j}+3\boldsymbol{k})$$

$$\text{i.e. } \sum(\boldsymbol{r}\times\boldsymbol{F})=\begin{vmatrix}\boldsymbol{i} & \boldsymbol{j} & \boldsymbol{k}\\ 3 & 0 & 2\\ 2 & -1 & 1\end{vmatrix}+\begin{vmatrix}\boldsymbol{i} & \boldsymbol{j} & \boldsymbol{k}\\ 4 & 5 & -3\\ 3 & 4 & -4\end{vmatrix}+\begin{vmatrix}\boldsymbol{i} & \boldsymbol{j} & \boldsymbol{k}\\ -4 & -2 & +4\\ -5 & -3 & +3\end{vmatrix}$$

$$=0\boldsymbol{i}+0\boldsymbol{j}+0\boldsymbol{k}$$

Hence the system is in equilibrium.

(3) For a system of three forces if $\Sigma\,\boldsymbol{F}=0$ and the forces cross at a point they are in equilibrium so an alternative to step (2) is to solve the following three equations for μ, λ and ρ to show that they are coincident.

$$\boldsymbol{r}_1=3\boldsymbol{i}+2\boldsymbol{k}+\lambda(2\boldsymbol{i}-\boldsymbol{j}+\boldsymbol{k})$$
$$\boldsymbol{r}_2=4\boldsymbol{i}+5\boldsymbol{j}-3\boldsymbol{k}+\mu(3\boldsymbol{i}+4\boldsymbol{j}-4\boldsymbol{k})$$
$$\boldsymbol{r}_3=-4\boldsymbol{i}-2\boldsymbol{j}+4\boldsymbol{k}+\rho(-5\boldsymbol{i}-3\boldsymbol{j}+3\boldsymbol{k})$$

where these are the vector equations of the lines of action of $\boldsymbol{F}_1$, $\boldsymbol{F}_2$ and $\boldsymbol{F}_3$ respectively. Solution gives $\lambda=\mu=\rho=-1$.

Problem 17.2

The forces $\boldsymbol{F}_1=2\boldsymbol{i}+\boldsymbol{j}-\boldsymbol{k}$, $\boldsymbol{F}_2=-\boldsymbol{i}+\boldsymbol{j}-\boldsymbol{k}$ and $\boldsymbol{F}_3=-\boldsymbol{i}-2\boldsymbol{j}+2\boldsymbol{k}$ act through the points A (1, 0, 1), B (0, 1, 1) and C (1, 1, 1) respectively. Show that this system of forces reduces to a couple and find its vector moment.

(1) Show that $\Sigma\,\boldsymbol{F}=\boldsymbol{F}_1+\boldsymbol{F}_2+\boldsymbol{F}_3=0$ and $\Sigma(\boldsymbol{r}\times\boldsymbol{F})\neq 0$.
(2) Then show that

$$\boldsymbol{G}=\sum(\boldsymbol{r}\times\boldsymbol{F})=(\boldsymbol{i}+\boldsymbol{k})\times(2\boldsymbol{i}+\boldsymbol{j}-\boldsymbol{k})$$
$$+(\boldsymbol{j}+\boldsymbol{k})\times(-\boldsymbol{i}+\boldsymbol{j}-\boldsymbol{k})$$
$$+(\boldsymbol{i}+\boldsymbol{j}+\boldsymbol{k})\times(-\boldsymbol{i}-2\boldsymbol{j}+2\boldsymbol{k})$$

$$\text{i.e. } \boldsymbol{G}=\begin{vmatrix}\boldsymbol{i} & \boldsymbol{j} & \boldsymbol{k}\\ 1 & 0 & 1\\ 2 & 1 & -1\end{vmatrix}+\begin{vmatrix}\boldsymbol{i} & \boldsymbol{j} & \boldsymbol{k}\\ 0 & 1 & 1\\ -1 & 1 & -1\end{vmatrix}+\begin{vmatrix}\boldsymbol{i} & \boldsymbol{j} & \boldsymbol{k}\\ 1 & 1 & 1\\ -1 & -2 & 2\end{vmatrix}$$

(3) Hence show that $\boldsymbol{G}=\boldsymbol{i}-\boldsymbol{j}+\boldsymbol{k}$ is the vector moment of the system about the origin.

Example 17.3

A car in a fairground ride moves along a continuous track. At the time t the position vector of the car relative to an origin O at horizontal ground level is

$$\boldsymbol{r}(t)=[40\sin 2\omega t\,\boldsymbol{i}+40\cos\omega t\,\boldsymbol{j}+10(1-\cos\omega t)\boldsymbol{k}]\ m$$

where $\omega=1/10\ \text{s}^{-1}$ and k points vertically upwards.

(a) How long does each lap take?
(b) Find the maximum height of the car above ground level and determine its velocity and acceleration at this point.

(c) Calculate the vector $\dot{\boldsymbol{r}}(0)\times\dot{\boldsymbol{r}}(t)$ and hence show that the car's velocity is always perpendicular to $\boldsymbol{j}+4\boldsymbol{k}$.
(d) Deduce that the motion takes place in a plane and given that $\boldsymbol{i}$, $\boldsymbol{j}$ and $\boldsymbol{k}$ are unit vectors along axes Ox, Oy and Oz respectively, find the cartesian equation of this plane. (AEB J84)

(a) The initial position vector at $t=0$,

$$\boldsymbol{r}(0)=40\boldsymbol{j}$$

so when a lap is completed at time T,

$$\boldsymbol{r}(T)=40\boldsymbol{j}$$

and the coefficients of $\boldsymbol{i}$ and $\boldsymbol{k}$ are zero. Then for $\boldsymbol{k}$

$$1-\cos\omega T=0$$

$$\cos\omega T=1$$

i.e. $\omega T=0, 2\pi, \ldots, \omega=1/10\ \mathrm{s}^{-1}$

$$T/10=2\pi \text{ for one lap}$$

$$T=\underline{20\pi \text{ s for one lap}}$$

(b) During a lap the height of the car above the ground varies according to the coefficient of $\boldsymbol{k}$. For a maximum or minimum

$$\frac{\mathrm{d}}{\mathrm{d}t}(1-\cos\omega t)=0$$

so $\quad 0+\sin\omega t=0$

$$\omega t=0 \text{ or } \pi \text{ during one lap}$$

Therefore

$$\text{height}=10(1-\cos\omega t)=0 \text{ or } 20\ \text{m}$$

So the maximum height of the car above ground level is $\underline{20\ \text{m at } \omega t=\pi}$.

Now

$$\dot{\boldsymbol{r}}(t)=80\omega\cos 2\omega t\,\boldsymbol{i}-40\omega\sin\omega t\,\boldsymbol{j}+10\omega\sin\omega t\,\boldsymbol{k}$$

with $\omega t=\pi$ and $\omega=1/10\ \mathrm{s}^{-1}$. At 20 m, $t=\pi/\omega$ and

$$\dot{\boldsymbol{r}}(10\pi)=\underline{8\boldsymbol{i}\ \mathrm{m\,s^{-1}}}$$

$$\ddot{\boldsymbol{r}}(t)=-160\omega^2\sin 2\omega t\,\boldsymbol{i}-40\omega^2\cos\omega t\,\boldsymbol{j}+10\omega^2\cos\omega t\,\boldsymbol{k}$$

At 20 m, $t=\pi/\omega$ and

$$\ddot{\boldsymbol{r}}(10\pi)=\underline{(0.4\boldsymbol{j}-0.1\boldsymbol{k})\ \mathrm{m\,s^{-2}}}$$

(c) $\dot{\boldsymbol{r}}(0)=8\boldsymbol{i}$

$$\dot{\boldsymbol{r}}(0)\times\dot{\boldsymbol{r}}(t)=\begin{vmatrix}\boldsymbol{i} & \boldsymbol{j} & \boldsymbol{k}\\ 8 & 0 & 0\\ 8\cos 2\omega t & -4\sin\omega t & \sin\omega t\end{vmatrix}$$

$$=0\boldsymbol{i}-8\sin\omega t\,\boldsymbol{j}-32\sin\omega t\,\boldsymbol{k}$$

i.e. $\dot{\boldsymbol{r}}(0)\times\dot{\boldsymbol{r}}(t)=\underline{-8\sin\omega t(\boldsymbol{j}+4\boldsymbol{k})}$

where $\dot{\boldsymbol{r}}(0)$ is the initial velocity of the car and $\dot{\boldsymbol{r}}(t)$ is any future velocity of the car at a time t. The cross product

$$\dot{\boldsymbol{r}}(0) \times \dot{\boldsymbol{r}}(t) = r(0)\, r(t) \sin\theta\, \hat{\boldsymbol{n}}$$

where θ is the angle between the vectors $\dot{\boldsymbol{r}}(0)$ and $\dot{\boldsymbol{r}}(t)$ and $\hat{\boldsymbol{n}}$ is a unit vector perpendicular to the plane containing both of them and acts along $\boldsymbol{j}+4\boldsymbol{k}$. Hence $\boldsymbol{j}+4\boldsymbol{k}=\boldsymbol{n}$ is a vector that is always perpendicular to the plane containing $\dot{\boldsymbol{r}}(0)$ and $\dot{\boldsymbol{r}}(t)$ and so is always perpendicular to the car's velocity.

(d) As a constant vector is always perpendicular to the plane containing the car's velocity from $t=0$ to $t=t$, the motion takes place in a plane where the equation of the plane is

$$\boldsymbol{r}_p \cdot \boldsymbol{n} = D$$

and $\dot{\boldsymbol{r}}(0) \times \dot{\boldsymbol{r}}(t) \cdot \boldsymbol{n} = 0$

where $\boldsymbol{n} = \boldsymbol{j}+4\boldsymbol{k}$. Now a point in the plane is $\boldsymbol{r}(0) = 40\boldsymbol{j}$. Therefore

$$40\boldsymbol{j} \cdot (\boldsymbol{j}+4\boldsymbol{k}) = D = 40$$

so the vector equation of the plane is

$$\boldsymbol{r} \cdot (\boldsymbol{j}+4\boldsymbol{k}) = 40$$

If $\boldsymbol{r}_{\mathrm{P}} = x\boldsymbol{i}+y\boldsymbol{j}+z\boldsymbol{k}$ is the position vector of a general point P on the plane then

$$(x\boldsymbol{i}+y\boldsymbol{j}+z\boldsymbol{k}) \cdot (\boldsymbol{j}+4\boldsymbol{k}) = 40$$

i.e. $\underline{y+4z=40}$

is the cartesian equation of the plane.

Example 17.4

The vertices of a triangle ABC have position vectors $3\boldsymbol{i}+\boldsymbol{j}+2\boldsymbol{k}$, $\boldsymbol{i}+5\boldsymbol{j}+6\boldsymbol{k}$ and $4\boldsymbol{i}-\boldsymbol{j}+4\boldsymbol{k}$ respectively relative to an origin O. Forces $\boldsymbol{F}_1$, $\boldsymbol{F}_2$ and $\boldsymbol{F}_3$ act along the sides $\overrightarrow{\mathrm{AB}}$, $\overrightarrow{\mathrm{BC}}$ and $\overrightarrow{\mathrm{CA}}$ respectively. Given that $|\boldsymbol{F}_1| = 18$ N, $|\boldsymbol{F}_2| = 14$ N and $|\boldsymbol{F}_3| = 6$ N, find $\boldsymbol{F}_1$, $\boldsymbol{F}_2$ and $\boldsymbol{F}_3$ in terms of $\boldsymbol{i}$, $\boldsymbol{j}$ and $\boldsymbol{k}$. Show that the resultant of these forces is $-2\boldsymbol{i}+4\boldsymbol{j}+4\boldsymbol{k}$ and find the total moment of the forces about the origin O.

A force $\boldsymbol{F}_4 = \lambda(-\boldsymbol{i}+3\boldsymbol{j}+2\boldsymbol{k})$, where λ is a constant, is now added to the system. Given that $\boldsymbol{F}_4$ acts through the point with position vector $7\boldsymbol{j}$ relative to O, find the value of λ such that the total moment of all the forces about O is zero and find the resultant of all the forces in this case. (AEB J82)

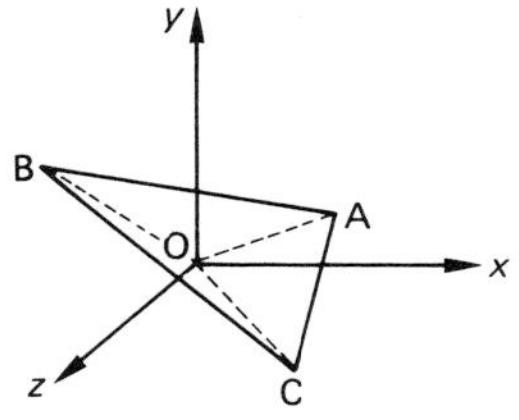

Figure 17.6

See Fig. 17.6.

$$\boldsymbol{F}_1 = 18\widehat{\mathrm{AB}} \quad \boldsymbol{F}_2 = 14\widehat{\mathrm{BC}} \quad \boldsymbol{F}_3 = 6\widehat{\mathrm{CA}}$$

First calculate $\overrightarrow{\mathrm{AB}}$, $\widehat{\mathbf{AB}}$, $\overrightarrow{\mathrm{BC}}$, $\widehat{\mathbf{BC}}$ and $\overrightarrow{\mathrm{CA}}$ and $\widehat{\mathbf{CA}}$.

$$\overrightarrow{\mathrm{OA}} = 3\boldsymbol{i}+\boldsymbol{j}+2\boldsymbol{k}$$

$$\overrightarrow{\mathrm{OB}} = \boldsymbol{i}+5\boldsymbol{j}+6\boldsymbol{k}$$

and $\overrightarrow{\mathrm{OC}} = 4\boldsymbol{i}-\boldsymbol{j}+4\boldsymbol{k}$

$$\overrightarrow{\mathrm{AB}} = \overrightarrow{\mathrm{OB}} - \overrightarrow{\mathrm{OA}} = -2\boldsymbol{i}+4\boldsymbol{j}+4\boldsymbol{k}$$

and $\widehat{\mathbf{AB}}=\frac{1}{6}(-2\boldsymbol{i}+4\boldsymbol{j}+4\boldsymbol{k})$

$\overrightarrow{\mathrm{BC}}=3\boldsymbol{i}-6\boldsymbol{j}-2\boldsymbol{k}$

and $\widehat{\mathbf{BC}}=\frac{1}{7}(3\boldsymbol{i}-6\boldsymbol{j}-2\boldsymbol{k})$

$\overrightarrow{\mathrm{CA}}=-\boldsymbol{i}+2\boldsymbol{j}-2\boldsymbol{k}$

and $\widehat{\mathbf{CA}}=\frac{1}{3}(-\boldsymbol{i}+2\boldsymbol{j}-2\boldsymbol{k})$

Therefore

$$\boldsymbol{F}_1=18\widehat{\mathbf{AB}}=(-6\boldsymbol{i}+12\boldsymbol{j}+12\boldsymbol{k})\ \mathrm{N}$$

$$\boldsymbol{F}_2=14\widehat{\mathbf{BC}}=(6\boldsymbol{i}-12\boldsymbol{j}-4\boldsymbol{k})\ \mathrm{N}$$

and $\boldsymbol{F}_3=6\widehat{\mathbf{CA}}=(-2\boldsymbol{i}+4\boldsymbol{j}-4\boldsymbol{k})\ \mathrm{N}$

The resultant $\boldsymbol{R}=\boldsymbol{F}_1+\boldsymbol{F}_2+\boldsymbol{F}_3$, i.e.

$$\boldsymbol{R}=-2\boldsymbol{i}+4\boldsymbol{j}+4\boldsymbol{k}$$

The total moment of the forces about O, $\boldsymbol{G}$, is given by

$$\begin{aligned}\boldsymbol{G}&=\sum(\boldsymbol{r}\times\boldsymbol{F})\\&=\overrightarrow{\mathrm{OA}}\times\boldsymbol{F}_1+\overrightarrow{\mathrm{OB}}\times\boldsymbol{F}_2+\overrightarrow{\mathrm{OC}}\times\boldsymbol{F}_3\\&=\begin{vmatrix}\boldsymbol{i}&\boldsymbol{j}&\boldsymbol{k}\\3&1&2\\-6&12&12\end{vmatrix}+\begin{vmatrix}\boldsymbol{i}&\boldsymbol{j}&\boldsymbol{k}\\1&5&6\\6&-12&-4\end{vmatrix}+\begin{vmatrix}\boldsymbol{i}&\boldsymbol{j}&\boldsymbol{k}\\4&-1&4\\-2&4&-4\end{vmatrix}\\&=(12-24)\boldsymbol{i}-(36+12)\boldsymbol{j}+(36+6)\boldsymbol{k}+(-20+72)\boldsymbol{i}\\&\quad-(-4-36)\boldsymbol{j}+(-12-30)\boldsymbol{k}\\&\quad+(4-16)\boldsymbol{i}-(-16+8)\boldsymbol{j}+(16-2)\boldsymbol{k}\end{aligned}$$

i.e. $\boldsymbol{G}=\underline{(28\boldsymbol{i}+14\boldsymbol{k})\ \mathrm{N\,m}}$

Now $\boldsymbol{F}_4=\lambda(-\boldsymbol{i}+3\boldsymbol{j}+2\boldsymbol{k})$ acts through $7\boldsymbol{j}$. Therefore

$$\boldsymbol{G}'=\boldsymbol{r}\times\boldsymbol{F}_4=7\boldsymbol{j}\times(-\boldsymbol{i}+3\boldsymbol{j}+2\boldsymbol{k})\lambda=\lambda\begin{vmatrix}\boldsymbol{i}&\boldsymbol{j}&\boldsymbol{k}\\0&7&0\\-1&3&2\end{vmatrix}$$

i.e. $\boldsymbol{G}'=\lambda(14\boldsymbol{i}+0\boldsymbol{j}+7\boldsymbol{k})$

Therefore

$$\boldsymbol{G}+\boldsymbol{G}'=0 \quad \text{when} \quad \lambda=-2$$

and $\boldsymbol{F}_4=+2\boldsymbol{i}-6\boldsymbol{j}-4\boldsymbol{k}$

The resultant of all the forces $\boldsymbol{R}_{\mathrm{A}}$ is given by

$$\boldsymbol{R}_{\mathrm{A}}=\boldsymbol{F}_1+\boldsymbol{F}_2+\boldsymbol{F}_3+\boldsymbol{F}_4=\boldsymbol{R}+\boldsymbol{F}_4=\underline{-2\boldsymbol{j}}$$

Example 17.5

A tripod consists of three light rigid legs AL, BL and CL which are freely pinned at their base points A, B and C and at their apex L. The position vectors of the points A, B, C and L with respect to some origin are

$$2\boldsymbol{i}-\boldsymbol{j}-3\boldsymbol{k}$$

$$3\boldsymbol{i}+2\boldsymbol{j}+2\boldsymbol{k}$$

$$\boldsymbol{j}+\boldsymbol{k}$$

and $2\boldsymbol{i}+\boldsymbol{j}+3\boldsymbol{k}$

respectively, where $\boldsymbol{k}$ points vertically upwards.

The tripod supports a camera of weight 2 N at L. Calculate the magnitudes of the resultant forces in the legs of the tripod. (AEB N82)

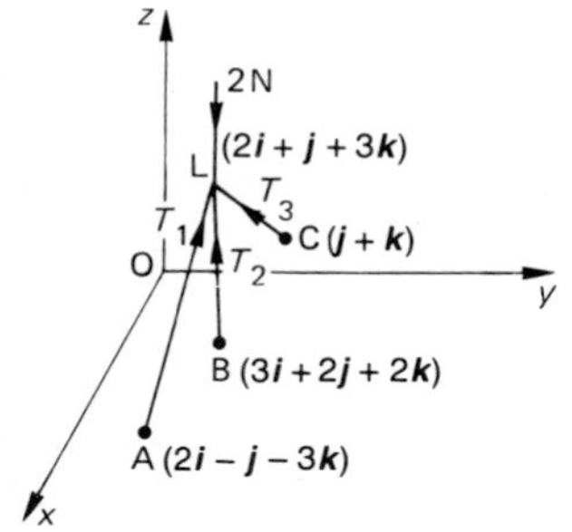

Figure 17.7

Draw a diagram (Fig. 17.7).

The 2 N force acts vertically downwards. Let T_1, T_2 and T_3, be the magnitudes of the forces acting along the light rods AL, BL and CL towards L at L respectively.

For equilibrium the sums of the resolved components of the forces parallel to Ox, Oy and Oz are separately zero.

$$\boldsymbol{T}_1 = T_1\,\widehat{\mathbf{AL}} \quad \boldsymbol{T}_2 = T_2\,\widehat{\mathbf{BL}} \quad \boldsymbol{T}_3 = T_3\,\widehat{\mathbf{CL}}$$

$$\overrightarrow{\mathrm{AL}} = +2\boldsymbol{j}+6\boldsymbol{k}$$

and $\widehat{\mathbf{AL}} = \dfrac{1}{\sqrt{40}}(2\boldsymbol{j}+6\boldsymbol{k})$

$$\overrightarrow{\mathrm{BL}} = -\boldsymbol{i}-\boldsymbol{j}+\boldsymbol{k}$$

and $\widehat{\mathbf{BL}} = \dfrac{1}{\sqrt{3}}(-\boldsymbol{i}-\boldsymbol{j}+\boldsymbol{k})$

$$\overrightarrow{\mathrm{CL}} = 2\boldsymbol{i}+2\boldsymbol{k}$$

and $\widehat{\mathbf{CL}} = \dfrac{1}{\sqrt{8}}(2\boldsymbol{i}+2\boldsymbol{k})$

The components of $\boldsymbol{T}_1$, $\boldsymbol{T}_2$ and $\boldsymbol{T}_3$ parallel to Oz are $\boldsymbol{T}_1 \cdot \boldsymbol{k}$, $\boldsymbol{T}_2 \cdot \boldsymbol{k}$ and $\boldsymbol{T}_3 \cdot \boldsymbol{k}$ respectively. Therefore resolving parallel to Oz,

$$2 = \frac{T_1}{\sqrt{40}}(2\boldsymbol{j}+6\boldsymbol{k})\cdot\boldsymbol{k} + \frac{T_2}{\sqrt{3}}(-\boldsymbol{i}-\boldsymbol{j}+\boldsymbol{k})\cdot\boldsymbol{k} + \frac{T_3}{\sqrt{8}}(2\boldsymbol{i}+2\boldsymbol{k})\cdot\boldsymbol{k}$$

i.e. $$2 = \frac{6T_1}{\sqrt{40}} + \frac{T_2}{\sqrt{3}} + \frac{2T_3}{\sqrt{8}} \qquad (1)$$

Similarly resolving parallel to Oy,

$$0 = \frac{T_1}{\sqrt{40}}(2\boldsymbol{j}+6\boldsymbol{k})\cdot\boldsymbol{j} + \frac{T_2}{\sqrt{3}}(-\boldsymbol{i}-\boldsymbol{j}+\boldsymbol{k})\cdot\boldsymbol{j} + \frac{T_3}{\sqrt{8}}(2\boldsymbol{i}+\boldsymbol{k})\cdot\boldsymbol{j}$$

$$= \frac{2T_1}{\sqrt{40}} - \frac{T_2}{\sqrt{3}}$$

$$\frac{T_1}{\sqrt{10}} = \frac{T_2}{\sqrt{3}}$$

$$T_2 = T_1\sqrt{\frac{3}{10}} \qquad (2)$$

and resolving parallel to Ox,

$$0=\frac{T_1}{\sqrt{40}}(2\boldsymbol{j}+6\boldsymbol{k})\cdot\boldsymbol{i}+\frac{T_2}{\sqrt{3}}(-\boldsymbol{i}-\boldsymbol{j}+\boldsymbol{k})\cdot\boldsymbol{i}+\frac{T_3}{\sqrt{8}}(2\boldsymbol{i}+\boldsymbol{k})\cdot\boldsymbol{i}$$

$$=-\frac{T_2}{\sqrt{3}}+\frac{2T_3}{\sqrt{8}}$$

$$\frac{T_2}{\sqrt{3}}=\frac{T_3}{\sqrt{2}}$$

$$T_3=T_2\sqrt{\frac{2}{3}} \qquad (3)$$

Substituting in equation (1) for T_1 and T_3 from equations (2) and (3),

$$2=\frac{6}{\sqrt{40}}T_2\sqrt{\frac{10}{3}}+\frac{T_2}{\sqrt{3}}+\frac{2}{\sqrt{8}}T_2\sqrt{\frac{2}{3}}$$

$$=\frac{3T_2}{\sqrt{3}}+\frac{T_2}{\sqrt{3}}+\frac{T_2}{\sqrt{3}}=\frac{5T_2}{\sqrt{3}}$$

Hence

$$\text{magnitude of the force in BL}=\underline{\frac{2\sqrt{3}}{5}\text{ N}}$$

$$\text{magnitude of the force in AL}=\underline{\frac{2\sqrt{10}}{5}\text{ N}}$$

$$\text{and magnitude of the force in CL}=\underline{\frac{2\sqrt{2}}{5}\text{ N}}$$

Summary

(1) If a force $\boldsymbol{F}$ has a position vector $\boldsymbol{r}$ with respect to a point P then $\boldsymbol{r}\times\boldsymbol{F}$ is the vector moment of $\boldsymbol{F}$ about an axis perpendicular to the plane containing the point P and passing through P. The magnitude of $\boldsymbol{r}\times\boldsymbol{F}$ is the magnitude of its moment about P and its direction is perpendicular to a plane containing $\boldsymbol{r}$ and $\boldsymbol{F}$ in the sense of the motion of a right-handed screw from $\boldsymbol{r}$ to $\boldsymbol{F}$.

(2) A couple consists of two equal unlike forces $\boldsymbol{F}$ and $-\boldsymbol{F}$ with separate lines of action. If B is any point on the line of action of $\boldsymbol{F}$ and A is any point on the line of action of $-\boldsymbol{F}$ then the vector moment of the couple is given by $\overrightarrow{BA}\times\boldsymbol{F}$. Thus the vector moment of the couple:

(a) is a vector perpendicular to the plane of the couple,
(b) is constant and independent of the point about which moments are taken.

Two couples are equivalent if their vector moment is equal so they must act in parallel planes.

(3) An original system of forces reduces to a resultant system where the resultant system is the simplest equivalent system that

has the same effect on the body in all respects as the original system.

A system of forces in three dimensions may:
(a) reduce to equilibrium in which case

$$\sum \boldsymbol{F}=0 \quad \text{and} \quad \sum (\boldsymbol{r}\times \boldsymbol{F})=0$$

(b) reduce to a couple $\boldsymbol{G}$ in which case

$$\sum \boldsymbol{F}=0 \quad \text{and} \quad \sum (\boldsymbol{r}\times \boldsymbol{F})\neq 0$$

(c) reduce to a single resultant force $\boldsymbol{R}$—now $\Sigma \boldsymbol{F}=\boldsymbol{R}$ and if $\boldsymbol{R}$ acts through the point $\boldsymbol{a}$ then

$$\sum (\boldsymbol{r}\times \boldsymbol{F})=\boldsymbol{a}\times \boldsymbol{R}$$

and this equation can be used to find $\boldsymbol{a}$ and so the equation of the line of action of $\boldsymbol{R}$,

$$\boldsymbol{r}=\boldsymbol{a}+\lambda \boldsymbol{R}$$

which can be found directly if $\boldsymbol{R}$ and $\boldsymbol{a}$ are known,
(d) reduce to a combination of a couple $\boldsymbol{G}$ and a single non-coplanar force $\boldsymbol{R}$, where $\Sigma \boldsymbol{F}=\boldsymbol{R}$ and the sum of the moments about any point will not be zero but will not, in general, be constant.

18 Motion of the centre of mass. Stability

Objectives

The student should be able to:

(1) define the position of the centre of mass of a system of particles,
(2) relate:

(a) the acceleration,
(b) the change in resultant momentum,
(c) the work done and so the change in kinetic energy,

of the centre of mass of a system of particles to that of a particle whose mass is the total mass of the system, at the centre of mass of the system, acted upon by the resultant of the forces acting upon the system,
(3) define stable, unstable and neutral equilibrium,
(4) apply the condition

$$\frac{\mathrm{d}}{\mathrm{d}\theta}(\mathrm{PE}) = 0$$

to find the positions of equilibrium and determine whether the equilibrium is stable or unstable.

Centre of mass

The centre of mass of a system of n particles, whose masses m_1, m_2, $m_3, \ldots, m_p, \ldots, m_n$ are at points with position vectors $\boldsymbol{r}_1, \boldsymbol{r}_2, \boldsymbol{r}_3, \ldots, \boldsymbol{r}_p, \ldots, \boldsymbol{r}_n$, is the point whose position vector $\boldsymbol{r}_\mathrm{m}$ is given by

$$\boldsymbol{r}_\mathrm{m} = \frac{\sum_{p=1}^{p=n} m_p \boldsymbol{r}_p}{\sum_{p=1}^{p=n} m_p}$$

and its position is independent of the origin chosen. As we saw in Chapter 15, the positions of the centre of mass and centre of gravity are coincident in a uniform gravitational field.

Motion of the centre of mass

Acceleration

$$\boldsymbol{r}_\mathrm{m} = \frac{\sum m_p \boldsymbol{r}_p}{\sum m_p} \qquad (1)$$

Differentiating with respect to time,

$$\boldsymbol{v}_{\mathrm{m}} = \frac{\mathrm{d}\boldsymbol{r}_{\mathrm{m}}}{\mathrm{d}t} = \frac{\Sigma\, m_p \dfrac{\mathrm{d}\boldsymbol{r}_p}{\mathrm{d}t}}{\Sigma\, m_p} \tag{2}$$

and again,

$$\frac{\mathrm{d}^2\boldsymbol{r}_m}{\mathrm{d}t^2}\sum m_p = \sum m_p \frac{\mathrm{d}^2\boldsymbol{r}_p}{\mathrm{d}t^2} \tag{3}$$

Let $\boldsymbol{F}_{\mathrm{p}}$ be a force acting on a particle P of mass m_{p} and position vector $\boldsymbol{r}_{\mathrm{p}}$ at a time t. Let $\boldsymbol{v}_{\mathrm{p}}$ be the velocity vector of the particle and $\boldsymbol{v}_{\mathrm{m}}$ the velocity vector of the centre of mass, similarly $\boldsymbol{a}_{\mathrm{m}}$ and $\boldsymbol{r}_{\mathrm{m}}$ are the acceleration and position vectors of the centre of mass at time t, and $\boldsymbol{V}_{\mathrm{p}}$, $\boldsymbol{V}_{\mathrm{m}}$, $\boldsymbol{A}_{\mathrm{m}}$ and $\boldsymbol{R}_{\mathrm{m}}$ their values at $t=0$. As

$$\boldsymbol{F}_{\mathrm{p}} = m_{\mathrm{p}} \frac{\mathrm{d}^2\boldsymbol{r}_{\mathrm{p}}}{\mathrm{d}t^2}$$

from Newton's second law, equation (3) can be written

$$\boldsymbol{a}_{\mathrm{m}} \sum m_{\mathrm{p}} = \sum m_{\mathrm{p}}\boldsymbol{a}_{\mathrm{p}}$$

so $\quad \boldsymbol{a}_{\mathrm{m}} \sum m_{\mathrm{p}} = \sum \boldsymbol{F}_{\mathrm{p}}$

where $\Sigma\, \boldsymbol{F}_{\mathrm{p}}$ is the vector sum of the external forces acting on the system since the summation of any internal forces will be zero.

Thus the acceleration of the centre of mass of a system of particles is the same as that of a particle whose mass is the total mass of the system acted upon by all the external forces exerted on the system.

Momentum

The right-hand side of equation (3) can be written

$$\sum \boldsymbol{F}_{\mathrm{p}} = \sum m_{\mathrm{p}} \frac{\mathrm{d}^2\boldsymbol{r}}{\mathrm{d}t^2} = \sum \left(\frac{\mathrm{d}}{\mathrm{d}t}(m\boldsymbol{v})\right)$$

or $\quad \sum \boldsymbol{F}_{\mathrm{p}} = \dfrac{\mathrm{d}}{\mathrm{d}t}(\sum m\boldsymbol{v})$

If $\sum \boldsymbol{F}_{\mathrm{p}} = 0$ this gives

$$\frac{\mathrm{d}}{\mathrm{d}t}(\sum m\boldsymbol{v}) = 0$$

so $\quad \sum (m\boldsymbol{v}) = \text{constant}$

This is the principle of conservation of linear momentum, that the total momentum of a system remains constant if the vector sum of the external forces acting on the system is zero.

If we consider the impulse $\boldsymbol{I}_{\mathrm{p}}$ acting on each particle

$$\boldsymbol{I}_{\mathrm{p}} = m_{\mathrm{p}}\boldsymbol{v}_{\mathrm{p}} - m_{\mathrm{p}}\boldsymbol{V}_{\mathrm{p}}$$

so for the whole system

$$\sum \boldsymbol{I}_{\mathrm{p}} = \sum m_{\mathrm{p}}\boldsymbol{v}_{\mathrm{p}} - \sum m_{\mathrm{p}}\boldsymbol{V}_{\mathrm{p}}$$

and is the resultant external impulse action on the system. Now

$$\boldsymbol{v}_{\mathrm{m}} \sum m_{\mathrm{p}} = \sum m_{\mathrm{p}} \boldsymbol{v}_{\mathrm{p}}$$

from equation (2) and

$$\boldsymbol{V}_{\mathrm{m}} \sum m_{\mathrm{p}} = \sum m_{\mathrm{p}} \boldsymbol{V}_{\mathrm{p}}$$

so $\sum \boldsymbol{I}_{\mathrm{p}} = \boldsymbol{v}_{\mathrm{m}} \sum m_{\mathrm{p}} - \boldsymbol{V}_{\mathrm{m}} \sum m_{\mathrm{p}}$

or the change in the resultant momentum of a system is the same as that which would be produced by the resultant impulse acting on a particle of the same mass as the total system, placed at the centre of mass.

Example 18.1

Three particles of masses 6, 2 and 2 kg, initially at rest, are at position vectors $\boldsymbol{i}+\boldsymbol{j}+\boldsymbol{k}$, $2\boldsymbol{i}+\boldsymbol{j}+\boldsymbol{k}$ and $\boldsymbol{j}+\boldsymbol{k}$ at time $t=0$. Find the position vector of the centre of mass. The particles are acted upon by forces $\boldsymbol{F}_1$, $\boldsymbol{F}_2$ and $\boldsymbol{F}_3$ respectively, where $\boldsymbol{F}_1 = 3\boldsymbol{i}-3\boldsymbol{j}+\boldsymbol{k}$, $\boldsymbol{F}_2 = \boldsymbol{i}+4\boldsymbol{j}-\boldsymbol{k}$ and $\boldsymbol{F}_3 = -2\boldsymbol{i}+\boldsymbol{j}$, all measured in newtons. Find the acceleration they impart to the centre of mass. Find also the resultant momentum of the system after two seconds and the impulse of each force.

The position of the centre of mass is defined as

$$\boldsymbol{R}_{\mathrm{m}} = \frac{\sum m_{\mathrm{p}} \boldsymbol{R}_{\mathrm{p}}}{\sum m_{\mathrm{p}}} \text{ at } t=0$$

Hence

$$10\boldsymbol{R}_{\mathrm{m}} = 6(\boldsymbol{i}+\boldsymbol{j}+\boldsymbol{k}) + 2(2\boldsymbol{i}+\boldsymbol{j}+\boldsymbol{k}) + 2(\boldsymbol{j}+\boldsymbol{k})$$

so the position vector of the centre of mass is

$$\underline{\boldsymbol{R}_{\mathrm{m}} = \boldsymbol{i}+\boldsymbol{j}+\boldsymbol{k}}$$

The acceleration of the centre of mass $\boldsymbol{a}_{\mathrm{m}}$ is given by

$$\boldsymbol{a}_{\mathrm{m}} = \frac{\sum \boldsymbol{F}_{\mathrm{p}}}{\sum m_{\mathrm{p}}} = \frac{2}{10}\boldsymbol{i} + \frac{2}{10}\boldsymbol{j} = \underline{\frac{1}{5}\boldsymbol{i} + \frac{1}{5}\boldsymbol{j}}$$

The resultant linear momentum is given by integrating with respect to time for the equation

$$\boldsymbol{a}_{\mathrm{m}} \sum m_{\mathrm{p}} = \sum \boldsymbol{F}_{\mathrm{p}}$$

then

$10\boldsymbol{a}_{\mathrm{m}} = 2\boldsymbol{i}+2\boldsymbol{j}$, integrating with respect to time gives

$$10\boldsymbol{v}_{\mathrm{m}} + \boldsymbol{V} = (2\boldsymbol{i}+2\boldsymbol{j})t,$$

At $t=0$, $\boldsymbol{v}_{\mathrm{m}}=0$. Therefore $\boldsymbol{V}=0$ and

$$\boldsymbol{v}_{\mathrm{m}} = \tfrac{2}{5}\boldsymbol{i} + \tfrac{2}{5}\boldsymbol{j} \text{ at } t = 2 \text{ s}$$

The resultant momentum of the system is equal to the momentum of a particle of mass 10 units at the centre of mass, i.e. $10\boldsymbol{v}_{\mathrm{m}}$, so

$$\text{resultant momentum} = \underline{4\boldsymbol{i}+4\boldsymbol{j}}$$

Using $\boldsymbol{I}_p = \int \boldsymbol{F}_p \, dt$ for each particle we have

$$\boldsymbol{I}_1 = \int_0^2 (3\boldsymbol{i} - 3\boldsymbol{j} + \boldsymbol{k}) \, dt = \underline{6\boldsymbol{i} - 6\boldsymbol{j} + 2\boldsymbol{k}}$$

$$\boldsymbol{I}_2 = \int_0^2 (\boldsymbol{i} + 4\boldsymbol{j} - \boldsymbol{k}) \, dt = \underline{2\boldsymbol{i} + 8\boldsymbol{j} - 2\boldsymbol{k}}$$

and $$\boldsymbol{I}_3 = \int_0^2 (-2\boldsymbol{i} + \boldsymbol{j}) \, dt = \underline{-4\boldsymbol{i} + 2\boldsymbol{j}}$$

We can see from this that

$$\boldsymbol{I}_1 + \boldsymbol{I}_2 + \boldsymbol{I}_3 = \sum \boldsymbol{I}_p = 4\boldsymbol{i} + 4\boldsymbol{j}$$

and equals the previous answer.

Work done and change in kinetic energy

Consider a set of particles moving under the action of a set of constant forces where a force $\boldsymbol{F}_p$ is applied to one particle P of mass m_p to move it from its initial position vector $\boldsymbol{R}_p$ to a general position $\boldsymbol{r}_p$ in a time t. The work done in time t on the particle P is given by

$$\boldsymbol{F}_p \cdot (\boldsymbol{r}_p - \boldsymbol{R}_p)$$

Summing for the system the total work done is therefore

$$\sum \boldsymbol{F}_p \cdot (\boldsymbol{r}_p - \boldsymbol{R}_p) = \sum \boldsymbol{F}_p \cdot \boldsymbol{r}_p - \sum \boldsymbol{F}_p \cdot \boldsymbol{R}_p \qquad (1)$$

The work done by a force $\sum \boldsymbol{F}_p$ on a particle of mass $\sum m_p$, placed at the centre of mass, in moving it from $\boldsymbol{R}_m$ to $\boldsymbol{r}_m$ is

$$\sum \boldsymbol{F}_p \cdot (\boldsymbol{r}_m - \boldsymbol{R}_m) = \sum \boldsymbol{F}_p \cdot \boldsymbol{r}_m - \sum \boldsymbol{F}_p \cdot \boldsymbol{R}_m \qquad (2)$$

In general, the right-hand sides of equations (1) and (2) are *not* equal so the total work done by the individual forces in displacing the individual particles is *not* equal to the work done by the resultant force displacing a particle of mass Σm_p at the centre of mass of the system. It follows that the change in kinetic energy of all the particles is *not*, in general, equal to the change in kinetic energy of a particle of mass Σm_p at the centre of mass of the system.

However, if the only forces acting on the particles are the weights of the particles in a *uniform* gravitational field then equation (1) becomes

$$\sum \boldsymbol{F}_p \cdot (\boldsymbol{r}_p - \boldsymbol{R}_p) = \sum m_p \boldsymbol{g} \cdot (\boldsymbol{r}_p - \boldsymbol{R}_p) = \boldsymbol{g} \cdot (\sum m_p \boldsymbol{r}_p - \sum m_p \boldsymbol{R}_p)$$

and equation (2) becomes

$$\sum \boldsymbol{F}_p \cdot (\boldsymbol{r}_m - \boldsymbol{R}_m) = \sum m_p \boldsymbol{g} \cdot \frac{(\Sigma m_p \boldsymbol{r}_p - \Sigma m_p \boldsymbol{R}_p)}{\Sigma m_p}$$

$$= \boldsymbol{g} \cdot (\sum m_p \boldsymbol{r}_p - \sum m_p \boldsymbol{R}_p)$$

so in this case the total work done by the individual forces is equal to the work done by the resultant force applied to the total mass positioned at the centre of mass. In this case also the total change in kinetic energy of all the particles *is* equal to the change in kinetic energy of a particle of mass $\Sigma\, m_p$ at the centre of mass of the system.

Problem 18.1

Particles of mass 3 and 2 kg are initially at rest. Forces $\boldsymbol{F}_1 = -3\boldsymbol{i}+2\boldsymbol{j}$ and $\boldsymbol{F}_2 = 6\boldsymbol{i}+2\boldsymbol{j}+2\boldsymbol{k}$ act on the masses for 2 s Find the impulse of the forces and the change in kinetic energy of the two masses during the 2 s for which the forces are applied.

(1) Use $\boldsymbol{a} = \boldsymbol{F}/m$ to show that $\boldsymbol{a}_1 = -\boldsymbol{i}+\frac{2}{3}\boldsymbol{j}$ and $\boldsymbol{a}_2 = 3\boldsymbol{i}+\boldsymbol{j}+\boldsymbol{k}$.
(2) Now $\boldsymbol{v} = \int \boldsymbol{a}\,dt$ and $\boldsymbol{V}_1 = \boldsymbol{V}_2 = 0$ at $t=0$. Show that at $t = 2$ s, $\boldsymbol{v}_1 = -2\boldsymbol{i}+\frac{4}{3}\boldsymbol{j}$ and $\boldsymbol{v}_2 = 6\boldsymbol{i}+2\boldsymbol{j}+2\boldsymbol{k}$.
(3) Show that $\boldsymbol{I}_1 = m\boldsymbol{v}_1 = -6\boldsymbol{i}+4\boldsymbol{j}$ and $\boldsymbol{I}_2 = m\boldsymbol{v}_2 = 12\boldsymbol{i}+4\boldsymbol{j}+4\boldsymbol{k}$.
(4) The change in KE $= \frac{1}{2}m_p|\boldsymbol{v}_p|^2$. Hence show that change in KE of the 3 kg mass = 8.7 units and the change in KE of the 2 kg mass = 4.4 units.

Note A particle of mass 5 kg acted upon by $\boldsymbol{F}_1+\boldsymbol{F}_2 = 3\boldsymbol{i}+4\boldsymbol{j}+2\boldsymbol{k}$ for 2 s will gain a velocity vector $\boldsymbol{V} = \int_0^2 \boldsymbol{a}\,dt = \frac{6}{5}\boldsymbol{i}+\frac{8}{5}\boldsymbol{j}+\frac{4}{5}\boldsymbol{k}$ if initially at rest. Its increase in KE will be $\frac{1}{2}m|\boldsymbol{V}|^2 = 11.6$ units and is *not* the same as the previous answer.

Stability of equilibrium

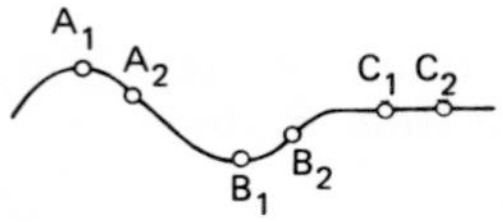

Figure 18.1

A system may be in stable, unstable or neutral equilibrium.

Consider a bead threaded on a smooth wire as shown in Fig. 18.1. If the bead is placed at A_1, B_1 or C_1 it will rest in equilibrium. If it is moved from B_1 to B_2 it will tend to return to B_1 so is in a position of stable equilibrium at B_1. When it is moved from A_1 to A_2 it will tend to move further from A_1 so is in unstable equilibrium at A_1. If the ring is moved from C_1 to C_2, where this section of the wire is horizontal, it will remain at C_2 so is in neutral equilibrium.

Conservative system of forces

In a conservative system of forces, where the total mechanical energy remains constant, then if a body is disturbed from a position of unstable equilibrium and continues to move it must gain kinetic energy.

As

$$\text{PE}+\text{KE} = \lambda$$

where λ is a constant and KE is gained then PE is lost in a conservative system.

$$\text{KE} = \tfrac{1}{2}mv^2$$

so $\quad \text{PE} = \lambda - \tfrac{1}{2}mv^2$

Differentiating with respect to time gives

$$\frac{d}{dt}(\text{PE}) = 0 - mv\frac{dv}{dt}$$

In a position of equilibrium

$$\frac{\mathrm{d}v}{\mathrm{d}t}=0$$

since the resultant force is zero so for equilibrium

$$\frac{\mathrm{d}}{\mathrm{d}t}(\mathrm{PE})=0$$

Often it is more convenient to express PE in terms of another variable, θ say, then

$$\frac{\mathrm{d}}{\mathrm{d}t}(\mathrm{PE})=\frac{\mathrm{d}\theta}{\mathrm{d}t}\frac{\mathrm{d}}{\mathrm{d}\theta}(\mathrm{PE})$$

so if

$$\frac{\mathrm{d}}{\mathrm{d}\theta}(\mathrm{PE})=0$$

then

$$\frac{\mathrm{d}}{\mathrm{d}t}(\mathrm{PE})=0$$

As Fig. 18.1 illustrates, in a position of stable equilibrium the PE is a minimum, therefore

$$\frac{\mathrm{d}}{\mathrm{d}\theta}(\mathrm{PE})=0 \quad \text{and} \quad \frac{\mathrm{d}^2}{\mathrm{d}\theta^2}(\mathrm{PE})>0$$

In a position of unstable equilibrium the PE is a maximum, therefore

$$\frac{\mathrm{d}}{\mathrm{d}\theta}(\mathrm{PE})=0 \quad \text{and} \quad \frac{\mathrm{d}^2}{\mathrm{d}\theta^2}(\mathrm{PE})<0$$

Example 18.2

A uniform rod AB of length $2a$ and mass 2.8 m is smoothly hinged at A to a fixed point A. A light elastic string of length a and modulus of elasticity mg connects the end B to a point C, a distance $2a$ horizontally from A. If the angle CAB is θ show that for a value of θ of 45° the rod is in a position of stable equilibrium.

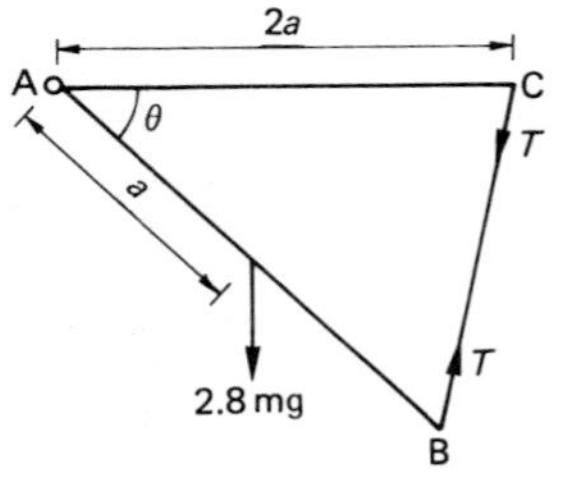

Figure 18.2

Draw a diagram (Fig. 18.2). The system of forces is conservative.

Take the PE as zero at the horizontal level through AC as this does not vary. From the cosine rule

$$\mathrm{BC}^2=4a^2+4a^2-2\times 2a\times 2a\cos\theta=8a^2(1-\cos\theta)$$

Therefore

$$\mathrm{BC}=4a\sin(\theta/2)$$

so the extension x of the elastic string BC is given by

$$x=4a\sin(\theta/2)-a$$

and the elastic PE of BC is given by

$$\text{elastic PE} = \frac{\lambda x^2}{2a} = \frac{mg}{2a} a^2[4 \sin(\theta/2) - 1]^2$$

Hence

$$\text{total PE} = \frac{mg}{2} a[4 \sin(\theta/2) - 1]^2 - 2.8ga \sin \theta$$

$$= \frac{mga}{2}[16 \sin^2(\theta/2) - 8 \sin(\theta/2) - 2.8 \sin \theta + 1]$$

$$\frac{d}{d\theta}(\text{PE}) = \frac{mga}{2}[16 \sin(\theta/2) \cos(\theta/2)$$

$$- 4 \cos(\theta/2) - 2.8 \cos \theta]$$

$$= \frac{mga}{2}[8 \sin \theta - 4 \cos(\theta/2) - 2.8 \cos \theta]$$

Substituting θ for 45°,

$$\frac{d}{d\theta}(\text{PE}) = 0.0$$

so is in equilibrium for conservative forces and

$$\frac{d^2}{d\theta^2}(\text{PE}) = 8 \cos \theta + \frac{4}{2} \sin\left(\frac{\theta}{2}\right) + 2.8 \cos \theta$$

and is positive so the rod is in a position of stable equilibrium for $\theta = 45°$.

Example 18.3

A smooth circular hoop of radius a is fixed in a vertical plane. A small ring of mass m is threaded onto the hoop and is connected by a light inextensible string of length $3a$ to a particle of mass $mg/2$. The string passes over a smooth ring fixed at the highest point of the hoop. Find the potential energy of the system and the positions of equilibrium for the ring. Are these postions stable?

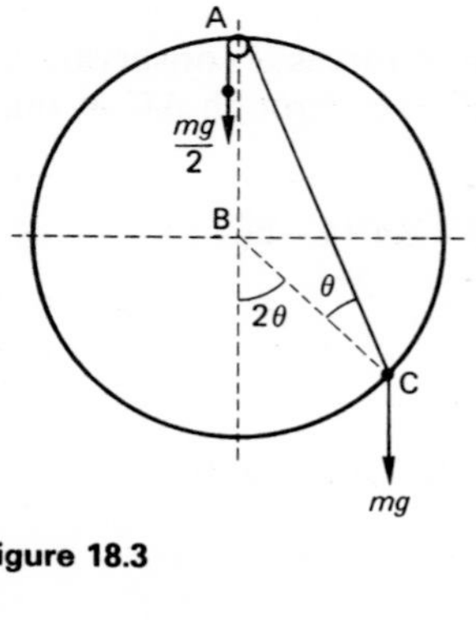

Figure 18.3

Draw a diagram. The system of forces is conservative so again the condition

$$\frac{d}{d\theta}(\text{PE}) = 0$$

may be applied to find a position of stable equilibrium. The external force in this system is the reaction of the hoop on the ring and as it is always perpendicular to the displacement of the ring it can do no work.

Take the PE as zero at the horizontal level through B.

$$\text{PE of the ring} = -mga \cos 2\theta$$

where $\widehat{ACB} = \widehat{CAB} = \theta$.

$$\text{PE of the mass} = \frac{mg}{2}[a-(3a-\text{AC})]$$

$$= \frac{mg}{2}[a-(3a-2a\cos\theta)]$$

$$= mg(a\cos\theta - a)$$

Hence

$$\text{total PE} = \underline{mg(a\cos\theta - a - a\cos 2\theta)}$$

$$\frac{\text{d(PE)}}{\text{d}\theta} = mg(-a\sin\theta + 2a\sin 2\theta)$$

When this is zero

$$0 = -\sin\theta + 2\sin 2\theta$$

so $0 = -\sin\theta + 4\sin\theta\cos\theta$

either

$$\sin\theta = 0$$

$$\theta = 0°$$

or $\cos\theta = \frac{1}{4}$

$$\theta = 75.52°$$

Hence equilibrium occurs for $\underline{\theta = 0° \text{ or } \theta = 75.52°}$.

$$\frac{\text{d}^2}{\text{d}\theta^2}(\text{PE}) = mga[-\cos\theta + 4\cos 2\theta]$$

When $\theta = 0°$

$$\frac{\text{d}^2}{\text{d}\theta^2}(\text{PE}) = mga[-1+4] > 0 \quad \text{so is stable}$$

When $\theta = 75.52°$

$$\frac{\text{d}^2}{\text{d}\theta^2}(\text{PE}) = mga[-\tfrac{1}{4}+(-3.5)] < 0 \quad \text{so is unstable}$$

Summary

(1) The centre of mass of a system of n particles, whose masses $m_1, m_2, \ldots, m_p, \ldots, m_n$, at points with position vectors $\boldsymbol{r}_1, \boldsymbol{r}_2, \ldots, \boldsymbol{r}_p, \ldots, \boldsymbol{r}_n$, is at the point whose position vector is

$$\boldsymbol{r}_{\text{m}} = \frac{\sum_{p=1}^{p=n} m_p \boldsymbol{r}_p}{\sum_{p=1}^{p=n} m_p}$$

(2) The acceleration of the centre of mass of a system of particles is the same as that of a particle whose mass is the total mass of the system acted upon the the sum of external forces exerted on the system.

(3) The change in resultant momentum of a system of particles is the same as that which would be produced by the resultant

impulse acting upon a particle of the same mass as the total system, placed at the centre of mass.

(4) The work done and so the change in kinetic energy of all the individual particles in a system when acted upon by a set of individual forces is not in general equal to the change in kinetic energy of a particle of mass equal to the total mass of the system, at the centre of mass of the system, when acted upon by the resultant force.

(5) When a system is given a small displacement from an equilibrium position, it is in stable equilibrium if it tends to return to the equilibrium position. It is in unstable equilibrium if motion continues away from the equilibrium position. If the system remains in the position to which it was displaced then it is in neutral equilibrium.

(6) A system in which the total mechanical energy remains constant is conservative. For such a system positions of equilibrium occur when

$$\frac{d}{d\theta}(PE) = 0$$

where θ is a single variable. The equilibrium is stable if

$$\frac{d^2}{d\theta^2}(PE) > 0$$

and unstable if

$$\frac{d^2}{d\theta^2}(PE) < 0$$

19
Rotation: moments of inertia

Objectives

The student should be able to:

(1) define the moment of inertia of a body,
(2) use Newton's second law for rotational motion to relate torque to moment of inertia,
(3) state and calculate the kinetic energy of rotation of a body of moment of inertia I,
(4) define and calculate the angular momentum of a body rotating about a fixed axis,
(5) calculate the moment of inertia of some standard figures and give the results in terms of radius of gyration,
(6) state and use the parallel and perpendicular axes theorems,
(7) state and use the principle of conservation of angular momentum,
(8) define and calculate the impulse of a torque,
(9) apply the conservation of mechanical energy to rigid bodies,
(10) calculate the work done by a couple,
(11) define a compound pendulum, show that its motion is simple harmonic for small oscillations and calculate the length of the equivalent simple pendulum,
(12) calculate the reaction at the axis of a rotating body,
(13) set up the equations of two-dimensional motion for a rigid body and consider separately the translational and rotational motion using

$$\mathrm{KE} = \tfrac{1}{2}m2I\omega^2 + \tfrac{1}{2}Mv^2$$

Properties of a body rotating about a fixed axis

A body can have both translational and rotational motion. When a torque is applied to a rigid body rotating about a fixed axis its rotation changes because it experiences a rotational acceleration just as the linear motion (translation) of a body changes when it experiences a force. Experiment shows that the rotational acceleration is proportional to the applied torque for a given body.

Consider a rigid body freely rotating about a fixed axis. Let P be a particle of mass m in the rigid body a distance r from the axis. Figure 19.1 shows a cross-section through P perpendicular to the axis of rotation and cutting it at O.

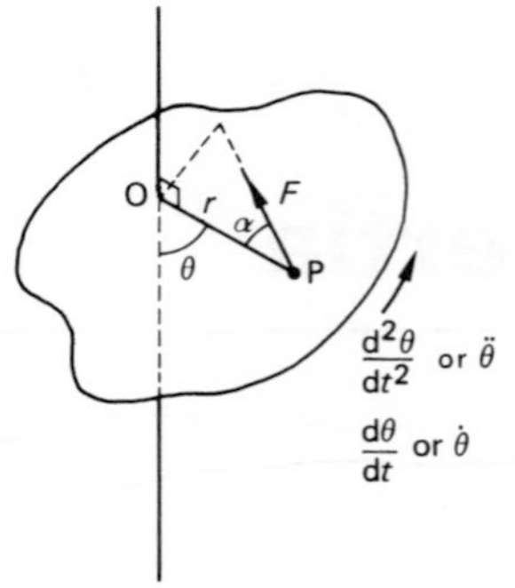

Figure 19.1

Let $d^2\theta/dt^2$ be the angular acceleration and $d\theta/dt$ the angular velocity of the body and of every particle in it. Since the relative position of each particle in the body is fixed then each particle will be moving in a circular path with O as centre and the resultant force unit, F, must act in this plane making an angle α, say, with OP. Applying Newton's law perpendicular to OP,

$$F \sin \alpha = mr\frac{d^2\theta}{dt^2}$$

or $$rF \sin \alpha = mr^2\frac{d^2\theta}{dt^2}$$

where $rF \sin \alpha$ is the moment of F about 0.

Summing for the whole body consisting of n particles

$$\sum_{i=1}^{i=n} r_i F_i \sin \alpha_i = \sum_{i=1}^{i=n} m_i r_i^2 \frac{d^2\theta}{dt^2}$$

or $$C = I\frac{d^2\theta}{dt^2}$$

since $d^2\theta/dt^2$ is the same for each particle.

$$C = \Sigma\, rF \sin \alpha$$

is the sum of the moments of the external forces about the axis of rotation. Any internal forces must occur in equal and opposite pairs and will not affect the sum.

$$I = \sum mr^2$$

is called the **moment of inertia** of the body about the given axis. It depends on the mass of the body and the distribution of the mass about the given axis. Just as mass is a measure of the translational inertia of a body so the moment of inertia is a measure of the rotational inertia of a body about a given axis. We can compare the equations

$$F = m\frac{d^2x}{dt^2}$$

and $$C = I\frac{d^2\theta}{dt^2}$$

where F is the resultant force acting on a mass m necessary to produce a resulting linear acceleration of d^2x/dt^2 and C is the resultant torque acting on a body of moment of inertia I necessary to produce a resultant angular acceleration of $d^2\theta/dt^2$ or $\ddot{\theta}$.

The moment of inertia has units of kg m^2.

Kinetic energy of rotation

Consider a rigid body rotating with angular velocity $\omega = d\theta/dt$ about a fixed smooth axis OA. Figure 19.2 shows a cross section of the body perpendicular to the axis of rotation of the body,

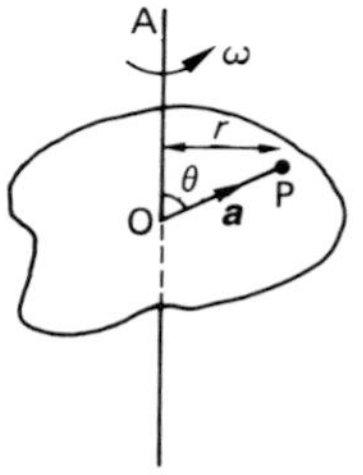

Figure 19.2

passing through O. P is a constituent particle, located a distance a from O, where $\boldsymbol{a}$ is its position vector with respect to the origin O.

The kinetic energy of the particle KE_P is given by

$$KE_P = \tfrac{1}{2}mv^2 = \tfrac{1}{2}m|(\boldsymbol{\omega} \times \boldsymbol{a})|^2 = \tfrac{1}{2}m\omega^2(\text{OP} \sin \theta)^2 = \tfrac{1}{2}m\omega^2 r^2$$

where r is the perpendicular from P to the axis OA.

The kinetic energy of the whole body is given by

$$\text{total KE} = \sum (\tfrac{1}{2}mr^2\omega^2)$$

but ω^2 is common to all constituent particles so

$$\text{total KE} = \tfrac{1}{2}\omega^2 \sum mr^2 = \tfrac{1}{2}I\omega^2$$

Again a comparison with translation motion when $KE = \tfrac{1}{2}mv^2$ gives a parallel with linear motion.

Angular momentum

The angular momentum or moment of momentum of a particle P, mass m, a distance r from a fixed axis and moving with a velocity $v = r\omega$ as shown in Fig. 19.2 is given by

$$\text{angular momentum} = mrv = mr^2\omega$$

Again ω is common to all particles so the total angular momentum of the body about the axis OA is given by

$$\text{total angular momentum } \Sigma mr^2\omega = \omega\Sigma mr^2 = I\omega$$

where I is the moment of inertia of the body about OA.

Again a comparison with translational motion occurs where linear momentum $= mv$.

Angular momentum has units of kg m^2 s^{-1}.

Example 19.1

A uniform circular wheel of moment of inertia 1 kg m^2 rotates about a fixed axis under the action of a constant retarding torque. In 10 seconds the speed of rotation decreases from 30 revolutions per minute to 15 revolutions per minute. Find the torque (or moment of the couple) on the wheel and the decrease in kinetic energy of the wheel.

$$I = 1 \text{ kg m}^2$$

(as given) and

$$C = I\ddot{\theta}$$

therefore

$$\ddot{\theta} = C$$

The torque is constant so

$$\omega = \omega_0 + \ddot{\theta}t$$

where ω is the angular velocity at a time t and ω_0 its initial value. Hence

$$\frac{15 \times 2\pi}{60} = \frac{30 \times 2\pi}{60} - 10C$$

as $\ddot{\theta}$ is negative, so the retarding torque

$$C = \pi/20 \text{ N m}$$

$$\text{Loss in kinetic energy} = \tfrac{1}{2}I(\omega_0^2 - \omega_1^2)$$

$$= \frac{1}{2}\left[\left(\frac{30\times 2\pi}{60}\right)^2 - \left(\frac{15\times 2\pi}{60}\right)^2\right]$$

$$= \frac{3\pi^2}{8} \text{ joules}$$

Problem 19.1

A string is wound around a pulley of radius 0.5 m and moment of inertia 25 kg m^2. The pulley is free to rotate about a smooth horizontal axis through its centre. The string is pulled vertically downwards with a constant force of 30 N. If the pulley starts from rest find the angular acceleration of the pulley and the angular velocity after the pulley has turned through $\pi/2$ radians.

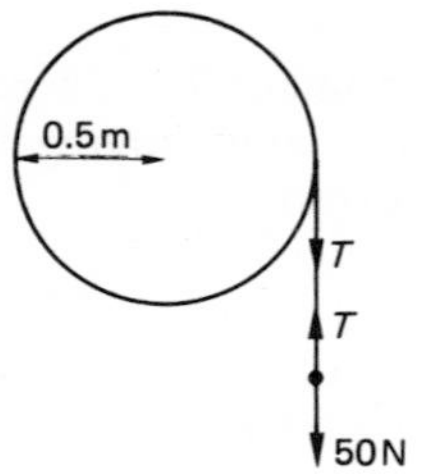

Figure 19.3

(1) Draw a diagram (Fig. 19.3).
(2) The moment of the tension in the string about the axis of the pulley $= 30\times 0.5 = 15$ N m. Use $C = I\ddot{\theta}$ to show that $\ddot{\theta} = 0.6$ rad s^{-2}.
(3) Now use $\omega^2 = \omega_0^2 + 2\ddot{\theta}\theta$ to find $\omega = \sqrt{(0.6\pi)}$. The angular velocity of the pulley $= 1.4$ rad s^{-1} after it has turned through $\pi/2$ radians.

Calculation of the moment of inertia

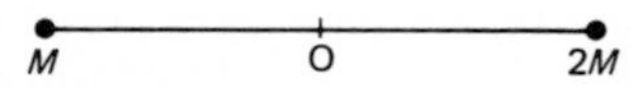

Figure 19.4

Consider two particles of masses M and $2M$ fixed at the ends of a light rod of length $2r$. Let O be the centre of the rod as shown in Fig. 19.4.

The moment of inertia of the rod about an axis through O perpendicular to the page is given by

$$I = \sum mr^2$$

So for the system

$$I = Mr^2 + 2Mr^2$$

i.e. $I = 3Mr^2$

This evaluation can be made easily by a straight summation. If the body is solid we consider it as a continuous distribution of matter with an infinite number of particles so we carry out the summation by integration

$$I = \lim_{\delta m\to 0} \sum r^2\,\delta m$$

i.e. $I = \displaystyle\int r^2\,\mathrm{d}m$

The evaluation of the moment of inertia of some standard bodies follows.

Thin uniform rod of mass M and length $2a$

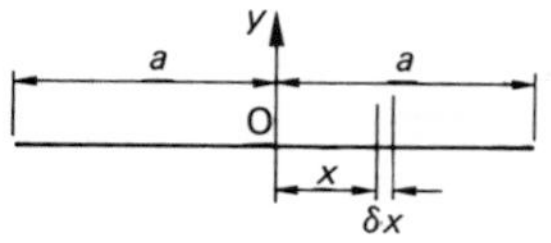

Figure 19.5

I about an axis through its centre perpendicular to its length
See Fig. 19.5. Let m = mass per unit length of the rod. Take the centre of the rod as the origin O, with Ox along the rod and Oy perpendicular to the rod. The moment of inertia of an element of the rod, of length δx, and a distance x from O is $m\,\delta x\,x^2$. Therefore the moment of inertia of the rod about Oy is given by

$$I = \int_{-a}^{a} mx^2\,dx = \frac{1}{3}m[x^3]_{-a}^{a} = \frac{2}{3}ma^3$$

but $2am = M$ therefore

$$I = \tfrac{1}{3}Ma^2$$

In general, moments of inertia can be written Mk^2, where k is the **radius of gyration** of a body and gives the same moment of inertia as if the whole of its mass had been concentrated at a distance k from the axis of rotation. In this case $k = a/\sqrt{3}$.

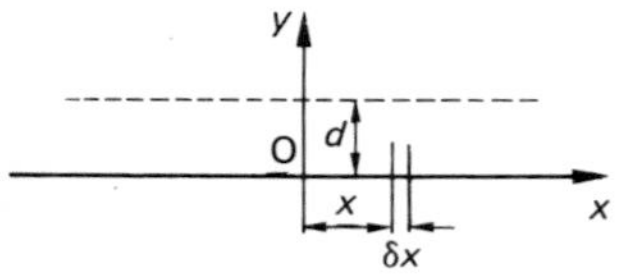

Figure 19.6

I about an axis parallel to its length a distance d away
See Fig. 19.6. Every element of the rod is at a distance d from the axis so

$$\sum m\,\delta x\,d^2 = Md^2$$

so $\quad k = d$

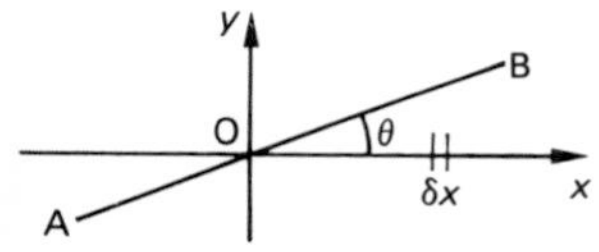

Figure 19.7

I about an axis through its centre at an angle θ with its length
See Fig. 19.7. The moment of inertia of the elemental piece δx about the axis AB is $m\,\delta x\,x\sin\theta$. Therefore the moment of inertia of the rod about the axis AB is given by

$$I = \int_{-a}^{a} mx^2\sin^2\theta\,\mathrm{d}x = \frac{2}{3}ma^3\sin^2\theta = \frac{1}{3}Ma^2\sin^2\theta$$

so $\quad k = (a\sin\alpha)/\sqrt{3}$

Circular hoop of mass M and radius a about an axis through its centre and perpendicular to its plane

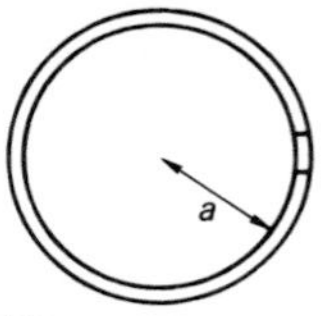

Figure 19.8

Consider an element of mass m a distance a from the axis (Fig. 19.8). The moment of inertia of the elemental piece = ma^2. Therefore the moment of inertia of the hoop is given by

$$I = \sum ma^2 = Ma^2$$

and $k = a$

Thin uniform circular lamina of mass M and radius a about an axis through its centre and perpendicular to its plane

Let m = mass per unit area = $M/\pi a^2$. Consider a concentric ring of radius x and thickness δx (Fig. 19.9). The moment of inertia of the elemental ring about the given axis = $2\pi xm\,\delta x\,x^2$. Moments

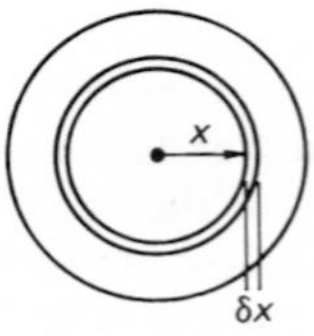

Figure 19.9

of inertia may be added provided that they are about the same axis (see compound bodies, p. 219). Therefore the moment of inertia of the lamina is given by

$$I = \int_0^a 2\pi m x^3 \, dx = \frac{m\pi a^4}{2} = \frac{1}{2} Ma^2$$

and $k = a/\sqrt{2}$

Uniform hollow sphere of mass *M* and radius *a* about a diameter

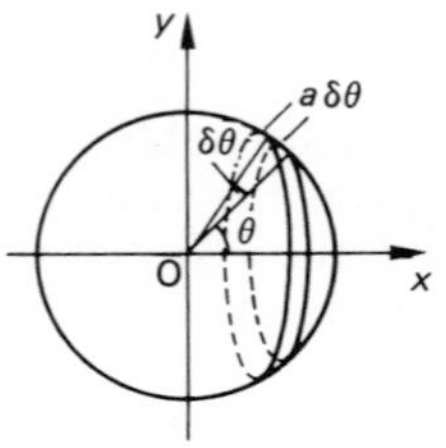

Figure 19.10

Let m = mass per unit area. Consider a ring-like element of thickness $a\,\delta\theta$ and radius $a \sin\theta$ (Fig. 19.10). The moment of inertia of the elemental ring about the given axis = $m 2\pi a \sin\theta \, a\,\delta\theta (a \sin\theta)^2$. Therefore the moment of inertia of the hollow sphere is given by

$$I = \int_0^\pi 2\pi m a^4 \sin^3\theta \, d\theta$$

$$= \int_0^\pi 2\pi m a^4 (\sin\theta - \sin\theta \cos^2\theta) \, d\theta$$

$$= 2\pi m a^4 \left[-\cos\theta + \frac{1}{3}\cos^3\theta \right]_0^\pi$$

$$= 2\pi m a^4 \left[\left(1 - \frac{1}{3}\right) - \left(-1 + \frac{1}{3}\right) \right]$$

i.e. $I = \dfrac{8 m a^4 \pi}{3} = \dfrac{2}{3} Ma^2$

and $k = a\sqrt{(2/3)}$

Uniform solid sphere of mass *M* and radius *a* about a diameter

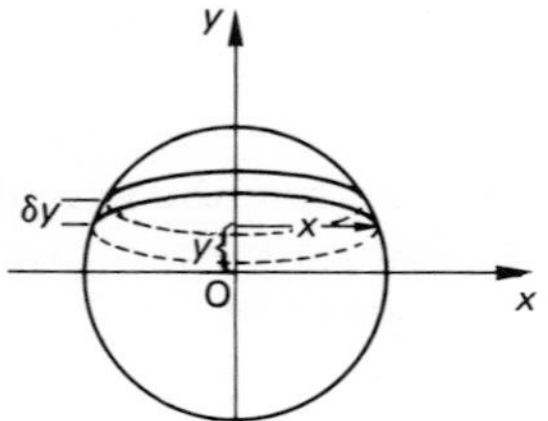

Figure 19.11

Let m = mass per unit volume. Therefore $M = 4\pi a^3 m/3$. Consider a disc-like element of thickness δy and radius x (Fig. 19.11). The moment of inertia of the elemental disc about the axis $Oy = \frac{1}{2} m\pi x^2 \, \delta y \, x^2$ (this involves an approximation for the volume of the disc but it is acceptable). Therefore the moment of inertia of the sphere about the axis Oy is given by

$$I = \int_{-a}^{a} \frac{m\pi}{2} x^4 \, dy$$

Now $x^2 + y^2 = a^2$ so

$$I = \int_{-a}^{a} \frac{m\pi}{2} (a^2 - y^2)^2 \, dy = \frac{m\pi}{2} \left[a^4 y - \frac{2}{3} a^2 y^3 + \frac{y^5}{5} \right]_{-a}^{a}$$

i.e. $I = \dfrac{8\pi m a^5}{15} = \dfrac{2}{5} Ma^2$

and $k = a\sqrt{(2/5)}$

Problem 19.2

Find the moment of inertia of a uniform rectangular lamina of sides $2a$ and $2b$ and mass M about a side of length $2b$.

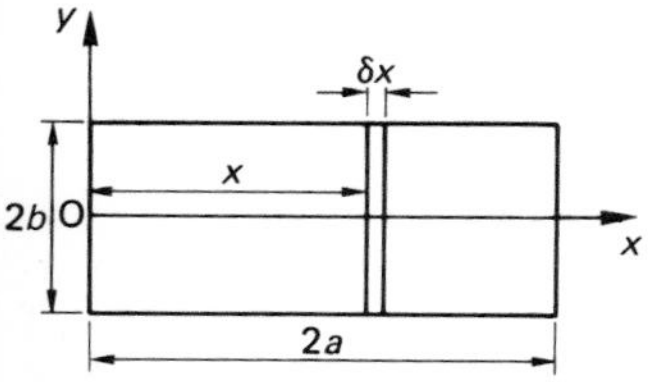

Figure 19.12

(1) Draw a diagram (Fig. 19.12) and consider an elemental section of thickness δx a distance x from the side of length $2b$.
(2) Let m = mass per unit area = $M/4ba$. Calculate the moment of inertia of the elemental strip = $2b\,\delta x\,m$.
(3) Now find the moment of inertia of the rectangle about Oy, $I = \int_0^{2a} 2bmx^2\,dx$, to show that $I = 16mba^3/3 = 4Ma^2/3$.

Compound bodies

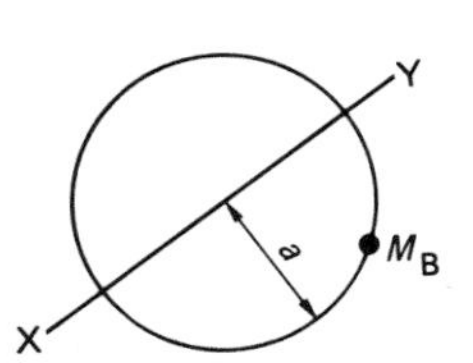

Figure 19.13

Consider a circular lamina of radius a and mass M_A with a particle of mass M_B attached to a point on its circumference (Fig. 19.13). The moment of inertia of the body about the axis XY = Σmr^2 over the whole body. Therefore

$$I = \sum_{\text{disc}} mr^2 + \sum_{\text{mass}} mr^2$$

and, in general,

$$\sum_{AB} mr^2 = \sum_{A} mr^2 + \sum_{B} mr^2$$

Now

$$I = \tfrac{1}{2}M_A a^2 + M_B a^2 = I_A + I_B$$

so the moment of inertia of a compound body about an axis is the sum of the moments of inertia of the separate objects forming the compound body about the same axis.

Parallel and perpendicular axes theorems

If we wish to calculate the moment of inertia about an axis other than that which passes through its centre of mass we use either the parallel axes theorem or the perpendicular axes theorem.

Parallel axes theorem

If the moment of inertia of a body, of mass M, about an axis through its centre of mass is Mk^2, then its moment of inertia about a parallel axis a distance a away is $M(k^2 + a^2)$.

Let XY be an axis passing through G, the centre of mass of the body and let AB be a parallel axis a distance a away (Fig. 19.14). Let P be a constituent particle of mass m a distance l from AB and r from XY. The moment of inertia of P about AB = $ml^2 = m(r^2 + a^2 - 2ra\cos\theta)$. Summing over the whole body,

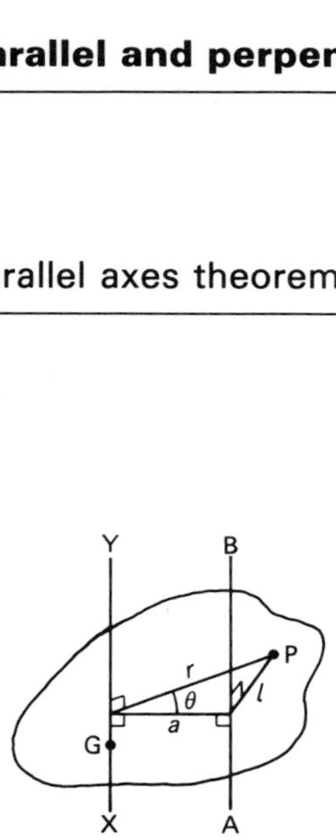

Figure 19.14

$$I_{AB} = \sum (mr^2 + ma^2 - 2mra\cos\theta)$$

i.e. $I_{AB} = Mk^2 + M\sum a^2 - 2a\sum mr\cos\theta$

Now $mr\cos\theta$ is the moment of the particle P about the axis XY so $\Sigma mr\cos\theta = 0$ as XY passes through G, the centre of mass, and the whole body has zero moment about this axis. Therefore

$$I_{AB} = Mk^2 + Ma^2 = M(k^2 + a^2)$$

Perpendicular axes theorem

Given that the moments of inertia of a lamina about two perpendicular axes in its plane are I_A and I_B, then the moment of inertia of the body about a third axis which is perpendicular to the first two and passing through their point of intersection is $I_A + I_B$.

Note The perpendicular axes theorem can be applied to laminae but not solid bodies.

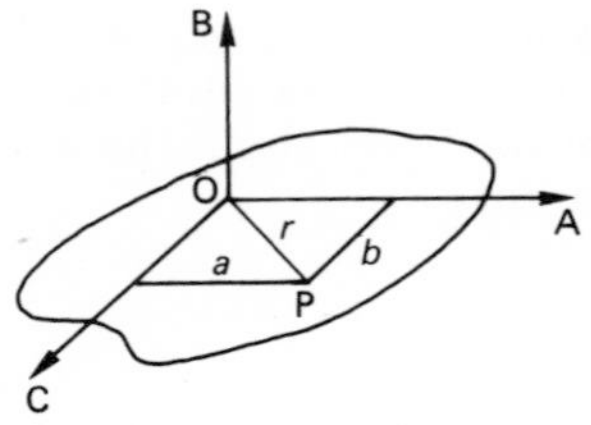

Figure 19.15

Consider a constituent particle P of the lamina of mass m a distance r from O (Fig. 19.15). The moment of inertia P about $O = mr^2 = m(a^2 + b^2)$. Therefore the moment of inertia of the lamina about O,

$$I_C = \sum mr^2 = \sum m(a^2 + b^2)$$

i.e. $I_C = I_A + I_B$

Example 19.2

Find the moment of inertia of a hollow cylinder of radius R and mass M about an axis through the centre of mass parallel to the length of the cylinder. Use the parallel axis theorem to find its moment of inertia about a generator of the cylinder.

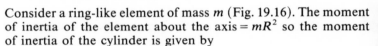

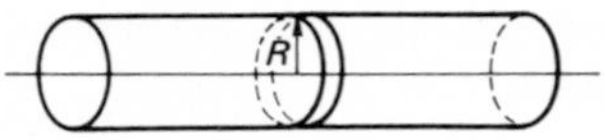

Figure 19.16

Consider a ring-like element of mass m (Fig. 19.16). The moment of inertia of the element about the axis $= mR^2$ so the moment of inertia of the cylinder is given by

$$I = \sum mR^2 = \underline{MR^2}$$

Using the parallel axis theorem, the moment of inertia about a generator parallel to the axis through the centre of gravity is given by

$$I' = M(k^2 + a^2) = MR^2 + MR^2 = \underline{2MR^2}$$

Problem 19.3

Find the moment of inertia of a solid sphere of radius a and mass M about a tangent parallel to a diameter using the parallel axis theorem.

The moment of inertia of the sphere about its centre $= 2Ma^2/5$. By applying the theorem, show that it equals $7Ma^2/5$ about a tangent to its face.

Motion of a rigid body about a fixed axis

Principle of conservation of angular momentum

We saw at the beginning of this chapter that

$$C = I\ddot{\theta}$$

where the torque C is the sum of the moments of the external forces acting on a body. This can be written

$$C = \frac{d}{dt}(I\dot{\theta})$$

hence the rate of change of angular momentum, $d(I\dot{\theta})/dt$, equals the resulting torque acting on a body so unless an external force exerts a torque on a system then the total angular momentum of that system remains constant. This latter deduction is called the **principle of conservation of angular momentum.**

A parallel can again be drawn with the principle of conservation of linear momentum and Newton's second law stating that the rate of change of momentum of a body is proportional to the applied force and takes place along the line of action of the force.

Impulse of a torque

When impulsive forces act on a rigid body we usually have a very large force for a very short period of time and can consider the body to be rotating freely about an axis. Its equation of motion is $C = I\ddot{\theta}$ with the usual notation. Suppose that a torque C acts on the body for a time t causing the angular velocity to change from ω_1 to ω_2 in that time. Integrating with respect to time,

$$\int_0^t C\,dt = \int_0^t I\ddot{\theta}\,dt = \int_{\omega_1}^{\omega_2} I\,d\omega = [I\omega]_{\omega_1}^{\omega_2} = I\omega_2 - I\omega_1$$

where $\int_0^t C\,dt$ is called the **impulse of the torque** C and equals $I\omega_2 - I\omega_1$, the change in angular momentum it produces.

As again internal impulses will occur in equal and opposite pairs, then summing over the external forces acting on the body, the total external impulsive torque which equals the sum of the moments of the external impulses about a given axis is equal to the change in angular momentum. When C is constant

$$Ct = I\omega_2 - I\omega_1$$

A comparison can be seen with impulse of force = change in linear momentum. Let $J = \int F\,dt$ be the impulse of a force F so $r\int F\,dt$ is the moment of that impulse.

Example 19.3

A disc of mass m and radius a rotates freely about its axis of symmetry perpendicular to its plane with an angular velocity of g/a rad s^{-1}. A constant torque of $2mga$ is applied. Find the angular velocity of the disc 5 seconds after the torque is applied.

The moment of inertia of the disc $= \frac{1}{2}ma^2$. In this case

$$\int_0^t C\,dt = Ct = I(\omega_2 - \omega_1)$$

Therefore

$$2mga \times 5 = \tfrac{1}{2}ma^2(\omega_2 - \omega_1)$$

$$20g/a = \omega_2 - \omega_1$$

since

$$\omega_1 = g/a,$$

$$\omega_2 = 21g/a$$

So the angular velocity of the disc 5 seconds after the torque was applied is $\underline{21g/a}$.

Example 19.4

A uniform square door ABCD of length $2l$ and mass M is free to rotate in the horizontal plane about a vertical axis through AB. It is moving with angular velocity 10 rad s^{-1} when the top end of the door strikes a fixed stop at D and is immediately brought to rest. Find the impulse exerted by the stop.

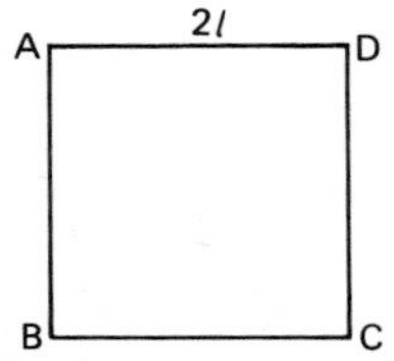

Figure 19.17

The moment of inertia of the door about the axis AB $= 4Ml^2/3$ (Fig. 19.17). Let J be the impulse exerted by the stop so the torque is $2lJ$, hence

$$2lJ = 10I = \text{change in angular momentum}$$

$$J = \frac{10I}{2l} = \frac{4Ml^2 \times 10}{3 \times 2l}$$

i.e. $$\underline{J = \frac{20Ml}{3}}$$

Conservation of mechanical energy applied to rigid bodies

We have used the principle of conservation of mechanical energy previously. It states that in a conservative system of forces (i.e. no external force other than gravity does work, and no sudden changes in motion take place) the total mechanical energy of a system remains constant.

When a body is rotating about an axis which is said to be smooth then no work is done at the axis by resistance to motion. The only external force doing work is gravity, hence the total mechanical energy of the system remains constant.

Example 19.5

A uniform rod AB of mass $2m$ and length $2l$ is free to turn in a vertical plane about a smooth horizontal axis through A. A particle of mass m is attached to B and the rod is released from rest with AB horizontal. Find the angular velocity of the mass m when AB first becomes vertical.

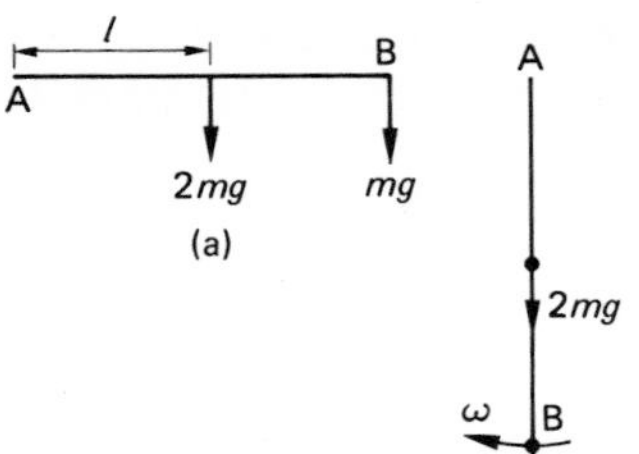

Figure 19.18

First draw a diagram (Fig. 19.18). The moment of inertia of the rod AB about the horizontal axis through A is given by

$$I_A = \tfrac{1}{3}Ml^2 + Ml^2 = \tfrac{4}{3}Ml^2$$

from the parallel axis theorem. The moment of inertia of the attached particle about the axis is given by

$$I_P = 4Ml^2$$

Therefore the moment of inertia of the rod plus attached particle is given by

$$I = I_A + I_P = \tfrac{16}{3}Ml^2$$

Initially (see Fig. 19.18(a)),

$$PE = KE = 0$$

When AB is vertical and the angular velocity is ω

$$KE = \tfrac{1}{2}I\omega^2 = \tfrac{1}{2}(\tfrac{16}{3}Ml^2)\omega^2 = \tfrac{8}{3}Ml^2\omega^2$$

$$PE = -2Mlg - 2Mlg = -4Mlg$$

Using the conservation of mechanical energy we have

$$0 + 0 = \tfrac{8}{3}Ml^2\omega^2 - 4Mlq$$

i.e. $\omega^2 = 3g/2l$

so the angular velocity of the mass m when AB first becomes vertical is given by

$$\underline{\omega = \sqrt{(3g/2l)}}$$

Work done by a couple

Consider a body rotating about an axis AB under the action of an *external* couple of resultant torque C of magnitude $2aF$, where the couple comprises two equal and opposite forces F separated by a distance $2a$. When the body rotates through a small angle $\delta\theta$ the point of application of each force moves through $a\,\delta\theta$ as shown in Fig. 19.19. The work done by each force is given approximately by $Fa\,\delta\theta$, hence the work done by the couple is given by

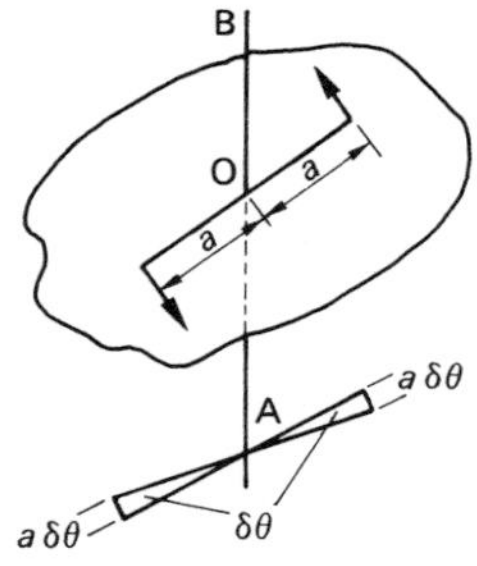

Figure 19.19

$$\delta W = 2Fa\,\delta\theta = C\,\delta\theta$$

so $$\frac{\delta W}{\delta\theta} = C$$

and in the limit as $\delta\theta \to 0$,

$$\frac{dW}{d\theta} = C$$

or $$W = \int_0^\alpha C\,d\theta$$

when the body rotates through an angle α.

If C is constant then $W = C\alpha = 2aF\alpha$ and the total mechanical energy is no longer constant.

Compound pendulum

A rigid body of mass m rotating under gravity about a fixed smooth horizontal axis is known as a **compound pendulum**. Let G be the centre of mass of the body and let it be a distance h from the axis of rotation, where I is the moment of inertia of

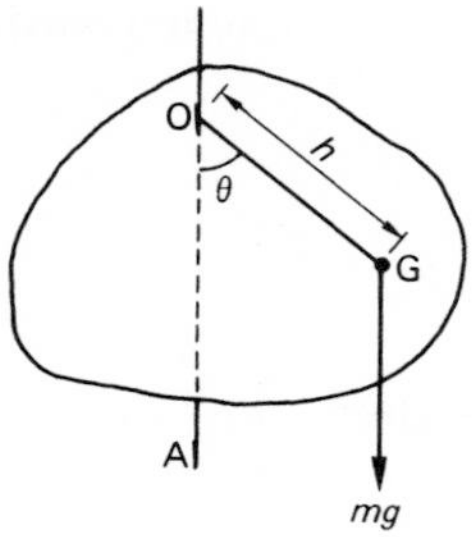

Figure 19.20

the body about the axis. Figure 19.20 shows a vertical section of such a body through the centre of mass. Let AO be the vertical through O then $\widehat{AOG} = \theta$ at some instant in time. Taking moments about the horizontal axis through O,

$$C = I\ddot{\theta}$$

Therefore

$$mgh \sin \theta = -I\ddot{\theta}$$

This is the equation of motion of the body. The negative sign is necessary since the torque exerted on the body opposes the increase of θ. It could also be obtained by differentiating an expression given by the principle of conservation of energy. Since the weight of the body is the only force with a moment about the axis then

$$\frac{\mathrm{d}}{\mathrm{d}t}\text{(initial mechanical energy)} = 0 = \frac{\mathrm{d}}{\mathrm{d}t}(\tfrac{1}{2}I\omega^2 - mgh\cos\theta)$$

For *small* oscillations $\sin\theta \doteqdot \theta$ and the equation of motion becomes

$$I\ddot{\theta} = -mgh\theta$$

or $$\ddot{\theta} = \frac{-mgh\theta}{I}$$

This is the equation of angular simple harmonic motion about the vertical through A with period

$$T = 2\pi\sqrt{\left(\frac{I}{mgh}\right)}$$

The period of small oscillations for a simple pendulum of length l is

$$T = 2\pi\sqrt{\left(\frac{l}{g}\right)}$$

so the length l of the **simple equivalent pendulum** is given by

$$l = \frac{I}{mg}$$

Note If $I = Mk^2$ about G then it equals $m(k^2 + h^2)$ about a parallel horizontal axis through O from the parallel axis theorem.

Reaction at the axis of a rotating body

In the previous chapter we saw that the acceleration of the centre of mass of a system of particles is the same as that of a single particle of the total mass of the system acted upon by the resultant of the forces acting upon the system. A rigid body is made up of a system of particles so we can apply this result to it. Figure 19.21 shows a cross-section of the body, of mass m, through the centre of mass G and perpendicular to the smooth horizontal axis through O. The body is rotating about the horizontal axis

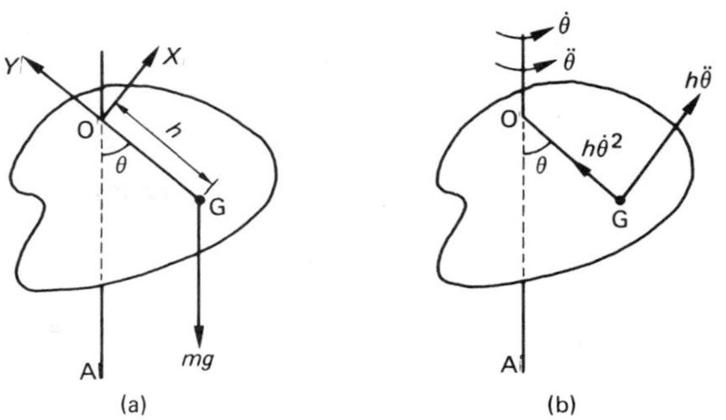

Figure 19.21

through O and the angular displacement θ is measured from the downward vertical OA. We resolve the reaction at the axis into components Y and X parallel and perpendicular to GO as shown in Fig. 19.21(a), where the corresponding components of the acceleration are $h\dot{\theta}^2$ and $h\ddot{\theta}$ for a particle of mass m placed at G (Fig. 19.21(b)).

Applying Newton's second law radially and transversely,

$$Y - mg\cos\theta = mh\dot{\theta}^2$$

and $X - mg\sin\theta = mh\ddot{\theta}$

We may find X and Y and so the reaction at the axis if we know $\dot{\theta}$ and $\ddot{\theta}$. The angular velocity $\dot{\theta}$ can be found using the conservation of mechanical energy and the angular acceleration $\ddot{\theta}$ by differentiating the energy equation or by using $C = I\ddot{\theta}$.

Example 19.6

Prove, by integration, that the moment of inertia of a uniform rod, of mass M and length $2a$, about an axis perpendicular to its length and passing through one end is $4Ma^2/3$.

A uniform rod AB of mass M and length $2a$ can rotate freely about a fixed horizontal axis through A. A particle of mass $7M/12$ is fixed to the rod at a distance x from A. Find the period of small oscillations of the system about its position of stable equilibrium.

Find the value of x for which the period is a minimum. (AEB J84)

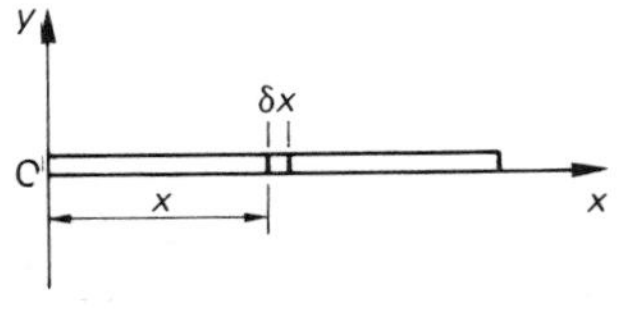

Figure 19.22

Let m = mass per unit length. Therefore $2am = M$. Consider an element of width δx a distance x from the axis Oy, perpendicular to the length of the rod and passing through one end (Fig. 19.22). The moment of inertia of the element about O$y = m\,\delta x\,x^2$. Summing over the whole body, the total moment of inertia I about Oy is given by

$$I = \int_0^{2a} mx^2\,dx = \left[\frac{mx^3}{3}\right]_0^{2a} = \frac{8a^3m}{3} = \frac{4}{3}Ma^2$$

The moment of inertia about the horizontal axis through A for the rod is

$$I_R = \tfrac{4}{3}Ma^2$$

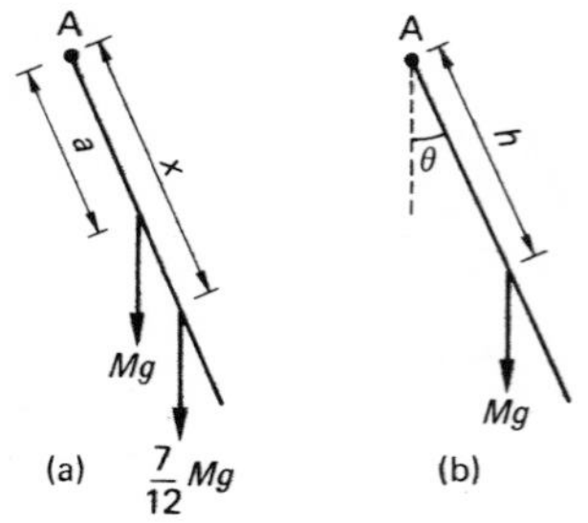

Figure 19.23

and for the particle is

$$I_P = \tfrac{7}{12}Mx^2$$

as shown in Fig. 19.23(a). Hence for the whole body

$$I = \tfrac{7}{12}Mx^2 + \tfrac{4}{3}Ma^2 = Mh^2$$

where

$$h^2 = \tfrac{7}{12}x^2 + \tfrac{4}{3}a^2$$

and M acts at h as shown in Fig. 19.23(b).

Using Newton's law for rotation, taking moments about the horizontal axis through A,

$$Mga \sin\theta + \tfrac{7}{12}Mgx \sin\theta = -I\ddot{\theta}$$

For small angles $\sin\theta \doteqdot \theta$ so

$$\theta(Mga + \tfrac{7}{12}Mgx) = -I\ddot{\theta}$$

This is the equation for simple harmonic motion for small oscillations, where the period

$$T = 2\pi\sqrt{\left(\frac{I}{Mga + \tfrac{7}{12}Mgx}\right)}$$

hence

$$T = 2\pi\sqrt{\left(\frac{\tfrac{7}{12}Mx^2 + \tfrac{4}{3}Ma^2}{Mga + \tfrac{7}{12}Mgx}\right)} = 2\pi\sqrt{\left(\frac{7x^2 + 16a^2}{12ag + 7xg}\right)}$$

The period is a minimum when

$$\frac{d}{dx}\left(\frac{7x^2 + 16a^2}{12a + 7x}\right) = 0$$

i.e. $(7x + 12a)(14x) - (7x^2 + 16a^2)(7) = 0$

Collecting terms and simplifying,

$$7x^2 + 24ax - 16a^2 = 0$$

$$(7x - 4a)(x + 4a) = 0$$

i.e. $x = -4a$ or $x = 4a/7$

Only the positive value has a meaning so the period is a minimum for $x = 4a/7$ and is given by

$$T = 2\sqrt{\left(\frac{16a^2 + 7x^2}{12ag + 7xg}\right)}$$

Example 19.7

Prove, by integration, that the moment of inertia of a uniform square lamina, of mass M and side $2l$, about one of its sides is $4Ml^2/3$.

A uniform square lamina ABCD, of mass M and side $2\sqrt{2}a$, is suspended from A and hangs in equilibrium with the diagonal AC vertical and C below A. Show that the moment of inertia of the lamina about a horizontal axis through A perpendicular to its plane is $16Ma^2/3$.

The lamina, which is free to rotate in its own plane about this horizontal axis through A, receives a horizontal impulse J applied in the plane of the lamina at the point C. Given that the lamina rotates so that C just reaches a position vertically above A, find J.

Also show that the horizontal and vertical components of the reaction at A, when AC is horizontal, are $3Mg/2$ and $Mg/4$ respectively. (AEB J84)

Method

Let m = mass per unit area. Therefore $4l^2m = M$. Consider a rectangular element of thickness δx a distance x from AB (Fig. 19.24). The moment of inertia of the element about AB = $2lm\,\delta x\, x^2$. Summing over the whole body, the total moment of inertia about AB is given by

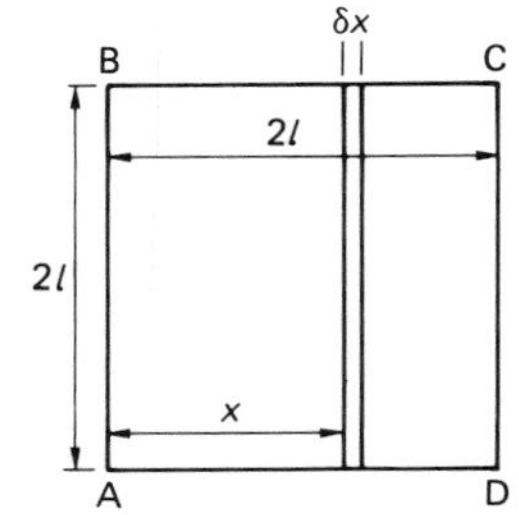

Figure 19.24

$$I_{AB} = \int_0^{2l} 2lmx^2\,dx = \left[2am\frac{x^3}{3}\right]_0^{2l} = \frac{16l^4m}{3} = \frac{4l^2M}{3}$$

By symmetry the moment of inertia about the axis AD, perpendicular to AB but also in the plane of the lamina, is

$$I_{AD} = I_{AB} = \tfrac{4}{3}Ml^2$$

For ABCD of side $2\sqrt{2}a = 2l$ then

$$I_{AD} = \tfrac{4}{3}M \times 2a^2 = \tfrac{8}{3}Ma^2$$

By the perpendicular axes theorem, the moment of inertia of the square lamina about a horizontal axis through A perpendicular to the plane is given by

$$I_A = I_{AD} + I_{AB} = \tfrac{16}{3}Ma^2$$

Using

moment of impulse = change in angular momentum

then

$$4aJ = I\omega$$

where a is the angular velocity gained by the lamina, with AC vertical (Fig. 19.25). The system of forces is conservative so using the conservation of mechanical energy,

gain in PE = loss in KE

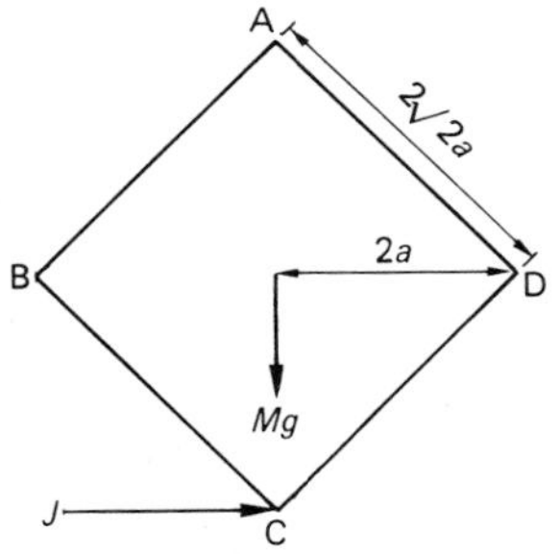

Figure 19.25

as C moves from vertically below to vertically above A. Hence

$$4aMg = \tfrac{1}{2}I\omega^2 = \tfrac{8}{3}Ma^2\omega^2$$

so $$\omega^2 = \frac{3g}{2a} \qquad (1)$$

Now

$$J = \frac{I\omega}{4a} = \frac{16Ma^2}{12a}\sqrt{\left(\frac{3g}{2a}\right)} = \underline{M\sqrt{\left(\frac{8ga}{3}\right)}}$$

The acceleration of the centre of mass of the system G is that which would be produced by the resultant force acting on the

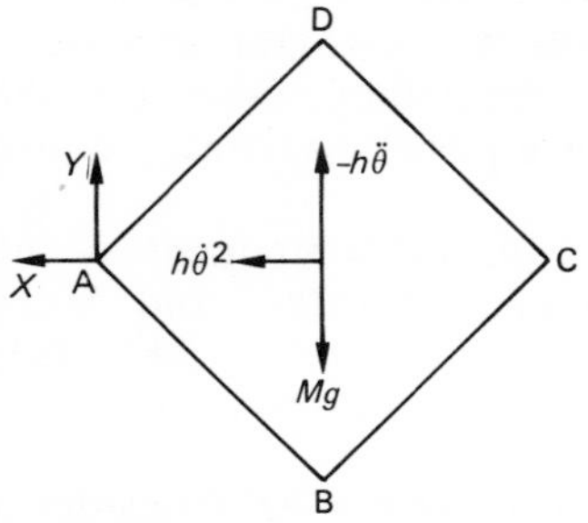

Figure 19.26

total mass of the system placed at the centre of mass. Let X and Y be the reactions at A, $h=2a$ and $\frac{1}{2}I\dot{\theta}^2=2aMg$ (Fig. 19.26) so

$$\dot{\theta}^2=4aMg/I \quad \textit{with AC horizontal} \qquad (2)$$

Hence, along AC,

$$X=Mh\dot{\theta}^2=2a\dot{\theta}^2M$$

from Newton's second law. Substituting from equation (2),

$$X=\frac{2aM\times 4aMg\times 3}{16Ma^2}=\frac{3}{2}Mg$$

Perpendicular to AC from Newton's second law,

$$Mg-Y=h\ddot{\theta}M=2a\ddot{\theta}M \qquad (3)$$

Now $\quad C=I\ddot{\theta}$

and with AC horizontal,

$$C=2aMg=I\ddot{\theta}$$

Substituting from equation (3),

$$Y=Mg-h\ddot{\theta}M$$

because the angular acceleration acts downwards. Substituting for $\ddot{\theta}$,

$$Y=Mg-2a\frac{2aMg}{I}M=Mg-\frac{4a^2M^2g\times 3}{16Ma^2}=\frac{1}{4}Mg$$

So the vertical and horizontal components of the reactions at A are $3Mg/2$ and $Mg/4$ respectively.

Equations of the two-dimensional motion of a rigid body including sliding and rolling

First consider a lamina of mass M, centre of mass G, moving under the action of a set of coplanar forces of resultant R. The acceleration of the centre of mass, $\ddot{x}$, is given by

$$R=M\ddot{x}$$

(from Chapter 18). Any constituent particle P a distance r from G as shown in Fig. 19.27 has radial and transverse components

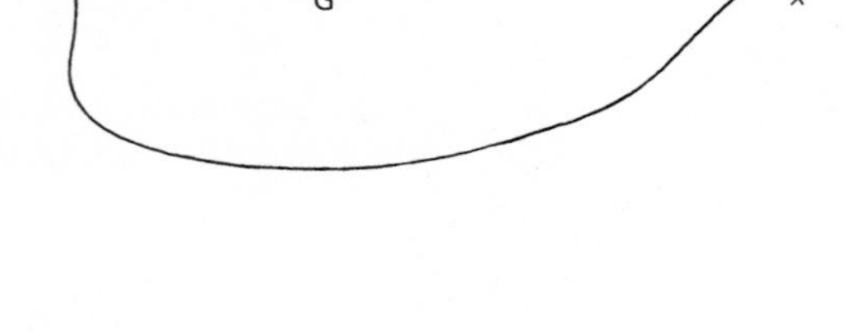

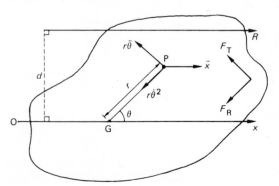

Figure 19.27

of acceleration $r\ddot{\theta}$ and $r\dot{\theta}^2$ respectively for rotational motion about G. Let F_R and F_T be the radial and transverse components respectively of the force acting on the particle P of mass m. Every particle moves along with linear acceleration $\ddot{x}$.

Applying Newton's second law to the motion of P, parallel to F_R,

$$F_T = m(r\ddot{\theta} - \ddot{x} \sin \theta)$$

so $$rF_T = mr(r\ddot{\theta} - \ddot{x} \sin \theta)$$

Summing for the whole body,

$$\sum rF_T = \sum mr^2\ddot{\theta} - \ddot{x} \sum (mr \sin \theta)$$

Using the usual notation, $C = \Sigma rF_T$, $I = \Sigma mr^2$ and $\Sigma(mr \sin \theta) = 0$ as G is the centre of mass. Therefore

$$C = I\ddot{\theta}$$

so the lamina rotates as if the resultant torque C were acting about a fixed axis through G. This means that the rotational and translational motion in its own plane of a lamina can be considered independently by considering the linear motion through the centre of mass and the rotation about an axis through the centre of mass. An equivalent system for the resultant force R is an equal force R acting through G and a couple of moment Rd.

A rigid body can be considered to be made up of a series of parallel laminate sections so the motion of such a body, of mass M, can be analysed in the same way by considering separately the linear motion of a particle of mass M at the centre of mass and the rotation of the body about an axis through the centre of mass, i.e.

$$R = M\ddot{x}$$

and $$C = I\ddot{\theta}$$

$$\text{KE of particle P} = \tfrac{1}{2}m[(\dot{x} - r\dot{\theta} \sin \theta)^2 + (r\dot{\theta} \cos \theta)^2]$$

Summing for the lamina,

$$\text{KE} = \tfrac{1}{2}\dot{x}^2 \sum m - \dot{x}\dot{\theta} \sum (mr \sin \theta) + \tfrac{1}{2}\dot{\theta}^2 \sum mr^2$$

$$\sum (mr \sin \theta) = 0$$

as before. Therefore

$$\text{KE} = \tfrac{1}{2}M\dot{x}^2 + \tfrac{1}{2}I\dot{\theta}^2$$

The result can again be extended to a rigid body.

Example 19.8

A uniform solid cylinder of mass M and radius a rolls without slipping on a horizontal surface with constant angular velocity ω. Find the kinetic energy of the sphere.

See Fig. 19.28. Let V be the velocity of the centre of mass. Since there is no slipping,

$$a\omega = V$$

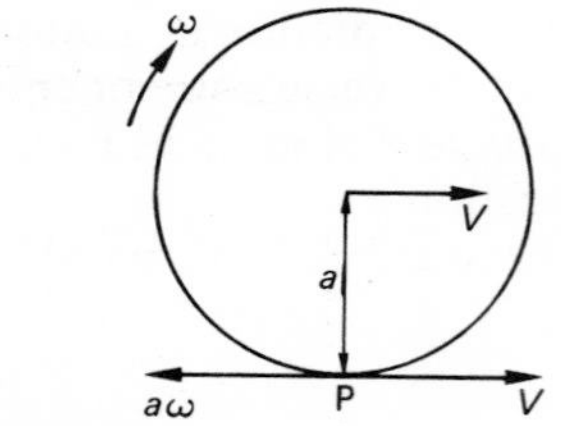

Figure 19.28

$$\dot{\theta} = \omega$$

and KE of the cylinder $= \frac{1}{2}MV^2 + \frac{1}{2}I\omega^2$

The moment of inertia about the axis is $Ma^2/2$ so

$$KE = \tfrac{1}{2}Ma^2\omega^2 + \tfrac{1}{4}Ma^2\omega^2$$

hence

$$\underline{\text{total KE} = \tfrac{3}{4}Ma^2\omega^2}$$

Example 19.9

A uniform solid sphere of mass M and radius a rolls down an inclined plane without slipping. Find the acceleration of the centre of mass and the coefficient of friction necessary to prevent sliding where the angle of the plane is 45°.

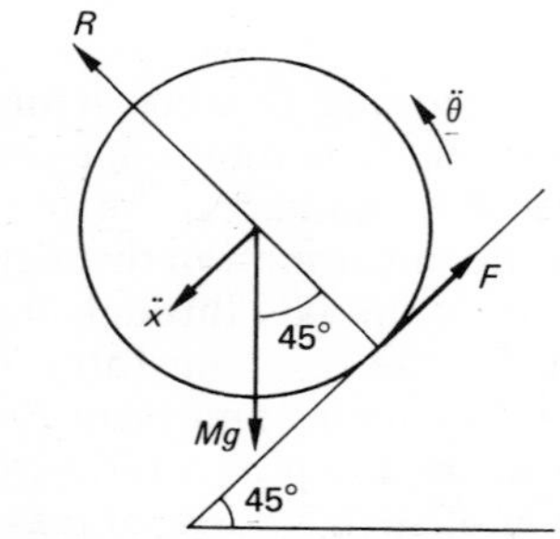

Figure 19.29

See Fig. 19.29. Let N be the point in contact with the plane and so momentarily at rest.

$$\dot{x} - a\dot{\theta} = 0$$

or $$\dot{x} = a\dot{\theta}$$

differentiating,

$$\ddot{x} = a\ddot{\theta} \tag{1}$$

Considering the motion of the centre of mass, parallel to the plane,

$$M\ddot{x} = Mg \sin 45° - F \tag{2}$$

and perpendicular to the plane,

$$0 = R - Mg \sin 45° \tag{3}$$

where R is the normal reaction, Mg the weight and F the frictional force. Taking moments about the centre of mass G,

$$aF = I\ddot{\theta}$$

For the sphere

$$I = \tfrac{2}{5}Ma^2$$

From equation (1)

$$F = \tfrac{2}{5}Ma\ddot{\theta} = \tfrac{2}{5}M\ddot{x}$$

From equation (2)

$$F = Mg \sin 45° - M\ddot{x} = \tfrac{2}{5}M\ddot{x}$$

hence

$$\ddot{x} = \tfrac{5}{7}g \sin 45° = \frac{5\sqrt{2}g}{14} \text{ m s}^{-2}$$

so $$F = \frac{\sqrt{2}Mg}{7}$$

From equation (3)

$$R = \frac{\sqrt{2}Mg}{2}$$

so $$\frac{F}{R} = \mu = \frac{2}{7}$$

Example 19.10

A uniform disc of radius r and mass m is free to rotate in a vertical plane about a fixed smooth pivot at a point O on its circumference. A particle of mass $2m$ is attached to the disc at a point P on the diameter through O. Denoting the distance of P from O by x, show that the period of small oscillations when the system is slightly disturbed from its position of stable equilibrium is

$$2\ddot{\pi}\sqrt{\left(\frac{4x^2+3r^2}{2(2x+r)g}\right)}$$

Find the greatest and least possible values of this period as x varies. (JMB J85)

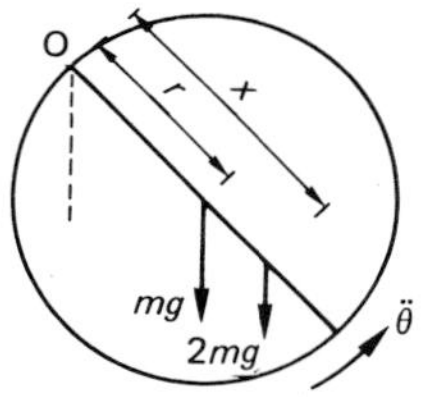

Figure 19.30

See Fig. 19.30. The moment of inertia of the disc about the axis through O is given by

$$I_D = \tfrac{1}{2}mr^2 + mr^2 = \tfrac{3}{2}mr^2$$

from the parallel axis theorem. The moment of inertia of the particle about the axis through O is given by

$$I_P = 2mgx^2$$

So the moment of inertia of the whole body about the axis through O is given by

$$I = \tfrac{3}{2}mr^2 + 2mx^2 = m(\tfrac{3}{2}r^2 + 2x^2)$$

Using Newton's law for rotation,

$$C = I\ddot{\theta}$$

then

$$mgr \sin\theta + 2mgx \sin\theta = -I\ddot{\theta}$$

For small oscillations $\sin\theta \doteqdot \theta$ so

$$\theta(mgr + 2mgx) = -I\ddot{\theta}$$

or $$\ddot{\theta} = -\left(\frac{mgr + 2mgx}{\tfrac{3}{2}mr^2 + 2mx^2}\right)\theta$$

This is the equation of angular simple harmonic motion about the vertical axis through O in which

$$2\left(\frac{gr + 2gx}{3r^2 + 4x^2}\right) = \text{constant of proportion}$$

Hence T, the period of oscillation, is given by

$$T = 2\pi\sqrt{\left(\frac{4x^2+3r^2}{2(2x+r)g}\right)} \qquad (1)$$

The period will be a minimum when

$$\frac{d}{dx}\left(\frac{4x^2+3r^2}{2x+r}\right)=0$$

i.e. $(2x+r)(8x)-(4x^2+3r^2)(2)=0$

or $$-4x^2-3r^2+8x^2+4rx=0$$

so $$-3r^2+4rx+4x^2=0$$

$$(3r+2x)(-r+2x)=0$$

i.e. $x=r/2$ or $x=-3r/2$

but the latter is impracticable. To check if it is a minimum, the second differential coefficient $4r+8x$ is positive for $r/2=x$. Then from equation (1)

$$T=2\pi\sqrt{\left(\frac{r}{g}\right)}$$

The maximum value of the period will occur at $x=2r$ when the particle has the greatest moment of inertia mx^2 about O. In this case

$$T=2\pi\sqrt{\left(\frac{19r}{10g}\right)}$$

Example 19.11

A constant force of magnitude 100 N is applied to the circumference of a stationary disc of diameter $2m$ and mass 50 kg. If the disc can rotate about a horizontal smooth axis through its centre perpendicular to the disc find the angular velocity of the disc after 10 revolutions.

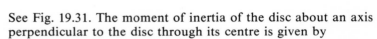

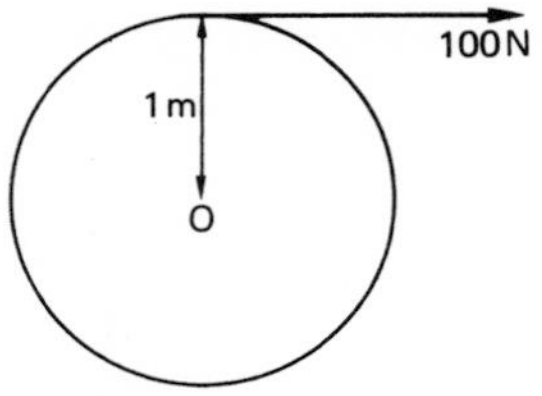

Figure 19.31

See Fig. 19.31. The moment of inertia of the disc about an axis perpendicular to the disc through its centre is given by

$$I=\tfrac{1}{2}ma^2=\tfrac{1}{2}(50\times 1)=25 \text{ kg m}^2$$

The work done by the 100 N force after 10 revolutions is given by

$$W=100\times \text{angle turned through}=100\times 20\pi=2000\pi$$

The weight and reaction at O do no work, so from the principle of work,

$$\text{final KE}-\text{initial KE}=\text{work done}$$

Therefore

$$\tfrac{1}{2}I\omega^2=2000\pi$$

and $\tfrac{1}{2}\times 25\omega^2=2000\pi$

$$\omega^2=160\pi$$

Hence the angular velocity of the disc after 10 revolutions is given by

$$\omega=\underline{12.7\sqrt{\pi}\text{ rad s}^{-1}}$$

Summary

(1) The moment of inertia I of a body about a fixed axis is a measure of the rotational inertia about that axis in a similar way to mass being a measure of translational inertia. The value of the moment of inertia is defined as $I = \Sigma mr^2$.

(2) When a torque C acts on a body with moment of inertia I producing an angular acceleration $\ddot{\theta}$ then $C = I\ddot{\theta}$.

(3) The kinetic energy of a rotating body of moment of inertia I moving with angular velocity ω is given by $\frac{1}{2}I\omega^2$, where $\omega = \dot{\theta}$.

(4) The angular momentum or moment of momentum of a body is $I\omega$.

(5) Moments of inertia can be written Mk^2, where k is the radius of gyration of a body and gives the same moment of inertia as if the whole of the mass of the body has been concentrated a distance k from the axis of rotation.

Moments of inertia of some standard figures are tabulated below.

Standard moments of inertia

Uniform body of mass *M*	Axis	*I*
Rod of length 2*a*	Perpendicular to the rod and through the centre	$\frac{1}{3}Ma^2$
Rod	Parallel to the rod and a distance *d* from it	Md^2
Rectangular lamina of length 2*a* and width 2*b*	Perpendicular to sides of length 2*b* and passing through their midpoints	$\frac{1}{3}Mb^2$
Ring of radius *a*	Perpendicular to the ring and through its centre	Ma^2
Disc of radius *a*	Perpendicular to the disc and through its centre	$\frac{1}{2}Ma^2$
Solid sphere of radius *a*	A diameter	$\frac{2}{5}Ma^2$
Hollow sphere of radius *a*	A diameter	$\frac{2}{3}Ma^2$
Solid cylinder of radius *a*	The axis	$\frac{1}{2}Ma^2$
Hollow cylinder of radius *a*	The axis	Ma^2

(6) The theorem of parallel axes states that if the moment of inertia of a body of mass M, about an axis through its centre of gravity, is Mk^2 then its moment of inertia about a parallel axis a distance a away is $M(k^2 + a^2)$.

The perpendicular axis theorem can be applied to laminae but not solid bodies. It states that given that the moments of inertia of a lamina about two perpendicular axes in the same place are I_A and I_B then the moment of inertia of the body about a third axis perpendicular to the first two and passing through their point of intersection is $I_A + I_B$.

(7) The principle of conservation of angular momentum states that unless an external force exerts a torque on a system then the total angular momentum of that system remains constant.

(8) The impulse of a torque C is given by $\int_0^t C\,dt$ and equals the change in angular momentum it produces, $I\omega_2 - I\omega_1$. The impulse of a torque equals the momentum of the resultant impulse, i.e. $r\int_0^t F\,dt$.

(9) When a body is rotating about a smooth axis then no work is done at the axis by resistance to motion. The only external force doing work is gravity so the total mechanical energy of the system remains constant.

(10) The work done by a couple C is given by $W = \int_0^\alpha C\,d\theta$.

(11) A rigid body of mass M rotating under gravity about a fixed smooth horizontal axis is known as a compound pendulum. For small oscillations the motion is approximately angular simple harmonic with the period T given by

$$T = 2\pi\sqrt{\left(\frac{I}{Mgh}\right)}$$

where I is the moment of inertia of the body about the axis and the centre of mass is a distance h from the axis. The quantity I/Mh is the length of the equivalent simple pendulum which would have the same period.

(12) The acceleration of the centre of mass of a system is the same as that of a particle whose mass is equal to the total mass of the system, acted on by the resultant of the forces acting on the system. We derive the equations of motion for such a particle at the centre of mass in the radial and transverse directions.

(13) The motion of a rigid body of mass M can be analysed by considering independently the linear motion of a particle of mass M at the centre of mass acted on by a resultant force R to produce a linear acceleration $\ddot{x} = R/M$ and the rotation of the body about the centre of mass to produce an angular acceleration $\ddot{\theta} = C/I$, where C is the torque of R about the centre of mass. The KE is thus given by

$$\text{KE} = \tfrac{1}{2}M\dot{x}^2 + \tfrac{1}{2}I\dot{\theta}^2$$

Index

NOTES

NOTES

NOTES

NOTES

NOTES

NOTES

NOTES

NOTES